The Power Thyristor and its Applications

The Power Thyristor and its Applications

David Finney

Chief Engineer, GEC Industrial Controls Ltd, Rugby

McGRAW-HILL Book Company (UK) Limited

London · New York · St Louis · San Francisco · Auckland · Bogotá
Guatemala · Hamburg · Johannesburg · Lisbon · Madrid
Mexico · Montreal · New Delhi · Panama · Paris · San Juan
São Paulo · Singapore · Sydney · Tokyo · Toronto

Published by
McGRAW-HILL Book Company (UK) Limited
MAIDENHEAD · BERKSHIRE · ENGLAND

British Library Cataloguing in Publication Data

Finney, David
  The power thyristor and its applications.
  1. Thyristors
  I. Title
  621.3815′28   TK7871.99.T5   79-40655

ISBN 0-07-084533-6

12345   JWA   83210

PRINTED IN GREAT BRITAIN BY
WILLIAM CLOWES (BECCLES) LIMITED, BECCLES AND LONDON

Contents

Notation

V_{RSM} Non-repetitive peak reverse voltage rating.
V_{DSM} Non-repetitive peak off-state voltage rating.
V_{RRM} Repetitive peak reverse voltage rating.
V_{DRM} Repetitive peak off-state voltage rating.
V_{RWM} Crest working reverse voltage rating.
V_{TM} Forward voltage drop of a thyristor.
I_{TSM} Surge on-state current capability.
t_d Delay time.
t_r Rise time.
t_{gt} Turn-on time.
t_q Turn-off time.
R_{JB} Thermal resistance junction to base.
R_{HS} Thermal resistance of heatsink.
T_j Junction temperature.
α Delay angle.
V_{dio} Open circuit d.c. voltage with $\alpha =$ zero.
V_d Mean d.c. voltage at any delay angle.
V_{ac} A.C. supply line voltage.
X_t Per unit reactance of supply and transformer.
V_{dL} D.C. voltage drop due to regulation.
I_d Mean value of d.c. current.
I_{ac} A.C. RMS current.
V_{T} Thyristor forward voltage drop at current I_d.
I_{F} D.C. short circuit mean current.
E_b Motor induced emf.
σ Load angle of a synchronous motor.
u Overlap angle.

Preface

During the past twenty years, the advances made in power thyristors and the applications to which they have been put have caused a minor revolution in the field of industrial control equipment. In the early 1960s, semiconductor-controlled rectifiers (SCRs), as they were then called, were being made and used on a minor scale. Now, the situation is completely transformed; they are now the first choice for all control and power conversion apparatus, they have caused the demise of the rotary convertor and mercury arc rectifier, and they have taken over from the motor generator set and a wide range of a.c. commutator machines. Even a new subject, 'power electronics', has come into being as a direct result of thyristors.

This transformation has been solely due to the dramatic improvement in thyristor capabilities and the very great reduction in price with which it has been accompanied. Almost without exception, all power switching and conversion requirements can now be obtained most economically using thyristors.

It is therefore surprising that there is, as yet, no authoritative technical book available covering the whole of this field.

I have tried to fill this gap with this book which I have written specifically for the benefit of: the user of thyristors; the user of thyristor equipment; and the general student of this subject.

In trying to cover such a wide field in a reasonable-sized book, I decided early on to keep to as few words as possible and to avoid long repetitive explanations to make each point. The book therefore needs to be read carefully and each statement needs to be considered to appreciate its full implications. My intention has been to make it a practical authoritative reference book for anyone involved in thyristors. I sincerely hope I have succeeded.

The present important role played by thyristors is due solely to the inventiveness of the many researchers, designers, and manufacturers of power thyristors. Over the years they have been able to pack more and more switching capability into a cheaper and cheaper device. As a result, the whole world is now benefiting from the resulting technology every time any product is manufactured and any time electricity is used.

I would therefore like to dedicate this book to the many unnamed designers and developers of thyristors who have made this all possible.

The contents of this book result from my working in this field for the past twenty years with other engineers who have given me much information, help and assistance. I would particularly like to record the debt I owe to Mr S. H. Dale, whose extensive knowledge and enthusiasm encouraged my longstanding interest in this convertor field. I am also very grateful for the willing help given to me by my friends and colleagues at GEC Industrial Controls Ltd, Rugby, during the preparation of the manuscript.

Special thanks are due to Mrs R. L. Jones who freely gave her time to convert my untidy handwriting into a neat, correct, and readable manuscript.

Many equipment manufacturers have been very helpful in allowing me to use photographs of their products to illustrate the technical principles explained in the book. The names of the appropriate manufacturers are given next to each of the photographs; I would like to thank them all for their assistance in this respect.

Acknowledgements are also given to the Management of The General Electric Company of England and GEC Industrial Controls Ltd for permission to publish this book, the contents of which having been learned while in their employ.

May I hope all readers find this book interesting, informative, and readable.

D. Finney,
Daventry, 1979

PART I

The Thyristor and its Use

This first part deals with the capabilities of thyristors and the practical ways they are used and protected. It includes details of all the circuits in which they are used, the methods used for firing and cooling them as well as explanation of the techniques used to protect them against excessive currents, voltages, and temperatures.

1. Thyristor Principles and Characteristics

The thyristor is a device of considerable complexity and its static operation means that its internal processes cannot easily be observed. Its complexity can be appreciated by the fact that it has at least twenty limiting current and voltage parameters, all of which must be fully understood if the thyristor is to be reliably and satisfactorily used.

This chapter is devoted to explaining the physical and electrical principles of the thyristor and to defining the many limiting operational parameters.

Many definitions will be introduced in this chapter and most of these originate from Publication 146 on Semiconductor Convertors, produced by the International Electrotechnical Commission (IEC); and from British Standard 9300, which covers Semiconductor Devices of Assessed Quality.

The thyristor is related to a whole family of semiconductor devices all using similar principles of electric physics including, for example, diodes and transistors. In this book the name *thyristor* is used to describe three-terminal bistable power switching devices capable of carrying current in one direction only. In precise terms this is the device defined as the reverse blocking triode thyristor.

1.1 Physical Principles

The active part of a thyristor is a solid slice of silicon taken from a single-grown crystal. The processing carried out upon it divides it into four layers having semi-conducting properties; two '*n*' layers containing excess negatively charged electrons, and two positively charged layers capable of accepting electrons or, to put it another way, containing suitable 'holes' for electrons.

If the *cathode* in Fig. 1.1 is made *positive* with respect to the anode, the excess electrons of layer N1 and 'holes' of layer P2 will be attracted to the cathode and anode respectively. This will remove the free carriers (electrons and 'holes') from the region of junctions J1 and J3 and therefore will prevent current flow through the silicon. These two junctions will be reverse-biased and together will accept the full circuit voltage across them. In practice, J3 is designed to accept almost all of the reverse voltage to avoid overstressing of the gate/cathode circuit. In this condition junction J2 will be forward-biased, i.e., able to pass current.

If the *cathode* is made *negative* with respect to the anode, the 'holes' of P1 and the electrons of N2 will be attracted to the cathode and anode respectively. Junctions J1 and J3 will be forward-biased but there will still be no free carriers in the vicinity of J2 and this will be reverse-biased. So again, no current can flow and this time the circuit voltage will appear across junction J2.

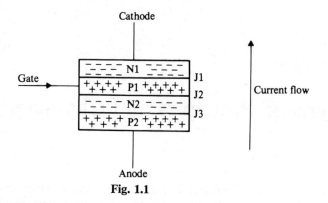

Fig. 1.1

If, under this forward blocking condition, a current is passed from gate to cathode electrons will flow from the cathode to the gate and these can be made to 'spill over' into the N2 layer and initiate current flow between anode and cathode. Once this process has commenced, electron multiplication takes place due to atomic collisions and the silicon triggers itself into a highly conducting state – the *ON-state*. Once this self-sustaining process is under way, the gate current ceases to have any influence.

This switching process results in an amplification factor (anode current to gate current) far in excess of that obtainable with a power transistor. A gate current of 0·1 A is usually sufficient to switch even the largest thyristors, and the actual level of anode current is independent of the value of gate current. Very fast switching takes place and once in the ON-state the voltage drop across the thyristor is very low.

1.2 Thyristor Construction

Thyristors are made from a circular slice of silicon initially having specific semi-conducting properties which are usually measured by its resistivity. Other materials

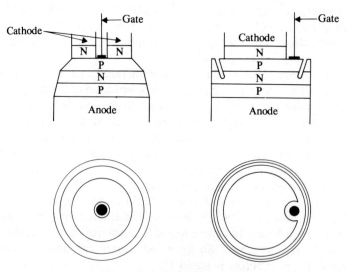

Fig. 1.2 Thyristor slices

are then diffused into its surfaces as necessary to produce the discrete layers. This process allows many possible variables to be chosen by the designer of the thyristor:

The slice diameter and thickness.

The composition of the base material.

The amount and material diffused into it.

The contact area of the gate, its shape, and position.

The profile of the slice edge.

These and other factors are controlled by the designers to obtain the optimum capabilities for the device. The fact that each of these physical factors may affect many of the thyristors' individual capabilities makes designing them more of an art than a science. The simplified cross-sections in Fig. 1.2 show two examples of the many practical arrangements possible.

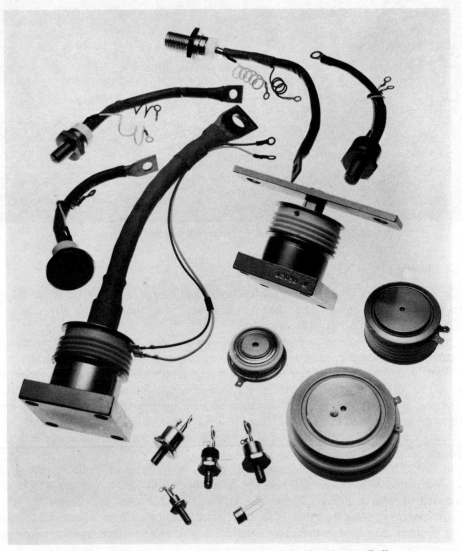

Fig. 1.3 A complete range of thyristors (AEI Semiconductors Ltd)

These slices, mounted on a supporting base of molybdenum, a material thermally compatible with silicon, are housed in hermetically sealed encapsulations to prevent moisture or dust contamination of the slice. The anode and cathode contacts are made by hard soldering or pressure-contact techniques.

The main types of encapsulation are illustrated in the photographs of Fig. 1.3; these all have their merits and are used for different sizes of thyristor. The outlines of all thyristors in common use are detailed in IEC Publication 191–2 and BS 3934. The disc type shown in Fig. 1.4 is particularly used for larger thyristors as it allows cooling from both anode and cathode surfaces, and it can be mounted in either polarity. It does, however, need special external pressure-contact clamping arrangements (see Chapter 9).

Fig. 1.4 Disc-type thyristors (ASEA Ltd)

1.3 Electrical Principles

The semiconductor *diode* is the electrical equivalent of a one-way valve: it will allow current to flow in one direction but will prevent flow in the opposite direction (see Fig. 1.5). It is a polarity-sensitive switch.

A *thyristor* also allows current to flow in one direction only, but this flow can be held up until a small current is passed between gate and cathode (see Fig. 1.6).

Switching from the OFF-state to the ON-state can take place very quickly. Once the anode to cathode current is flowing, the gate ceases to have any influence and the thyristor will continue in the ON-state until such time as the circuit in which the thyristor is connected causes the current to reduce to zero. The gate circuit can only control the turn-on point; turn-off is governed only by the external anode/cathode power circuitry.

A thyristor will only work satisfactorily within its specified capabilities: exceeding any of its many limitations will result in its maloperation, i.e., it may cease to block forward or reverse voltage, it may fire incorrectly, or it may fail completely. The main concern in using thyristors is to understand these limitations fully and to design the circuitry around the thyristors so that it will protect them against excessive conditions.

Many sizes and grades of thyristors are sold, each having different levels of capability or a differing selection of characteristics. The most suitable choice for each application always has to be made and, as a consequence, the correct choice for one application is unlikely to be the optimum choice for another.

The following sections discuss the ratings and capabilities of thyristors and useful reference can be made to BS 9300 which contains definitions and tests for these capabilities.

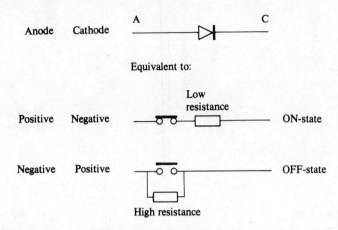

Fig. 1.5 Diode electrical principles

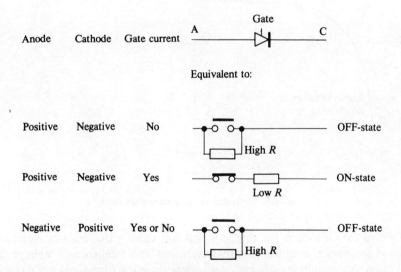

Fig. 1.6 Thyristor electrical principles

1.4 Voltage Characteristics and Ratings

All thyristors are limited in the *reverse voltage* they can withstand across their main power connections. If this voltage is exceeded, the result is either a deterioration of their capabilities or a complete failure.

7

A thyristor also has a limited *forward-voltage capability* but, in this case, exceeding this level will not in itself damage or deteriorate the thyristor; it will cause it to switch into the ON-state. However, in practical application, switching into the ON-state without gate current flowing can cause thyristor failure due to the follow-up circuit current through the thyristor. Figure 1.7 demonstrates the thyristor forward and reverse voltage–current characteristics.

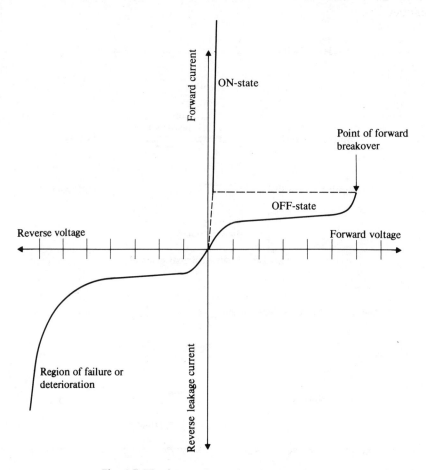

Fig. 1.7 Thyristor voltage characteristics

When in the OFF-state the thyristor will still allow a low *leakage current* to flow. Its value will vary widely between thyristors and with temperature, voltage, and gate conditions. All manufacturers assign a maximum value to the leakage current and if this is exceeded over its normal working range it will usually indicate that the thyristor has deteriorated.

The effect of leakage current is initially one of power loss, and most thyristors can accept a higher value of peak forward or reverse voltage for a short period of time.

The *non-repetitive peak reverse voltage rating*, V_{RSM}, is the highest value of reverse voltage the thyristor can withstand. It is only expected to withstand it occasionally and for short periods of time (for example, up to 100 microseconds).

The *non-repetitive peak OFF-state voltage rating*, V_{DSM}, is the highest value of forward voltage the thyristor can withstand without switching into the ON-state.

The *repetitive peak reverse voltage rating*, V_{RRM}, is the highest value of reverse voltage that the thyristor can withstand frequently for short periods of time.

The *repetitive peak OFF-state voltage rating*, V_{DRM}, is the highest value of forward voltage that the thyristor can withstand frequently for short periods of time without switching into the ON-state.

The *crest working reverse voltage rating*, V_{RWM}, is the maximum level of continuous reverse voltage which can be applied to the thyristor.

The *crest working OFF-state voltage rating*, V_{DWM}, is the maximum level of continuous forward voltage which can be applied to the thyristor without the device switching into the ON-state.

These voltage ratings are chosen by the thyristor manufacturer based on individual thyristor tests and measurements. The total production is usually divided in voltage grades or classes at particular voltage steps of, say, 100 V.

The above thyristor voltage-rating definitions should not be confused with the voltage levels which will be eventually impressed on the thyristor in service. The thyristor's capabilities should be above the peak transient and crest working voltages of the circuit in which it is to be used.

Critical rate of change of OFF-state voltage, dv/dt. Due to capacitance effects within the thyristor slice, it can be triggered into the ON-state by an excessive rate of change of OFF-state forward voltage, even though no gate current is flowing and even though the voltage is well within the V_{DRM} rating. The critical value may vary from 10 to 1000 V per microsecond between different thyristors and its value will vary both with peak operating voltage and junction temperature. The effect is similar to the application of too high a value of OFF-state voltage in that control over the thyristor is lost when it switches to the ON-state.

In itself, dv/dt breakover will not normally cause thyristor damage but it will cause circuit maloperation and the result may be a follow-up overcurrent condition which could be damaging to the thyristor.

1.5 Current Characteristics and Ratings

The passage of current through a thyristor in the ON-state results in a small voltage drop across the device which is usually between 1 and 2 V at the nominal thyristor current rating.

The shape of the voltage/current curve is as shown in Fig. 1.8 and it will vary with temperature and from device to device. The normal production of thyristors of a particular type will lie in a fairly wide band of volt drop and this will be of particular importance if thyristors are to be operated in parallel (see Chapter 7).

This *forward voltage drop*, V_{TM}, causes a power loss in the thyristor and owing to the spread of characteristics between thyristors it is necessary to use the highest value for the purposes of power-loss calculations. As the voltage/current curve is non-linear, the power losses generated will vary depending on the waveshape of the current (see Section 1.8 and Chapter 2).

Surge ON-state current capability, I_{TSM}. All thyristors have a surge or overload capacity above the normal current levels if it is accepted that control over the thyristor

9

will not be available immediately after the surge. During such a surge the temperature of the junction will reach 2 to 4 times the normal operating level without damaging the thyristor.

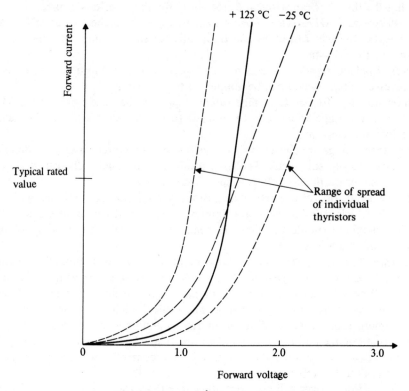

Fig. 1.8 Forward ON-state characteristic

The thyristor surge capability I_{TSM} is usually expressed as the maximum peak single half sine wave of current that it can withstand. Further information would then be given in the form of a curve of surge current capability against the number of cycles of surge current, or time. Such curves would show the thyristor's ability for times down to one half-cycle. Below this time it is more convenient to give it in the form of I^2t as this is easier to compare with fuse information when fuse protection is being considered. Figure 1.9 gives an example of such curves.

The information supplied by manufacturers will be the values which *all* thyristors can withstand and in most cases every thyristor will be tested at, say, the one half-cycle surge level before being supplied. Exceeding any of these surge current limitations will result in some of the thyristors being permanently damaged.

Critical rate of rise of ON-state current, di/dt. Once a thyristor has been switched into the ON-state by a gate current pulse, the rise of anode current will be decided by the external circuitry. The thyristor does not, however, turn on instantly; it will take some microseconds to do so. If the anode current is allowed to rise too quickly during this initial switching-on period, high losses will be caused and these will overheat small areas of the silicon slice and cause complete failure. The critical rate of rise of ON-state current capability of a thyristor is the level which will cause damage to

10

occur. Its value will depend on the level of gate current used to fire the thyristor; within limits the higher the gate current, the higher the di/dt capability. The need for high di/dt switching levels has led to the development of the amplifying gate thyristor referred to in Section 1.9.

A thyristor will have its lowest di/dt capability if no gate current is flowing, and this is the case if it is switched into the ON-state by an excessive forward voltage or dv/dt, or by an overtemperature condition. In these cases, the follow-up fault current may increase at a rate above the critical di/dt value, causing permanent damage to the thyristor.

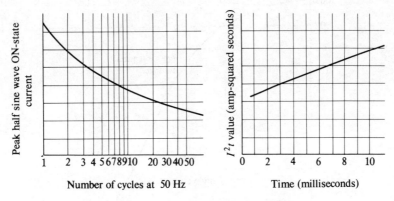

Fig. 1.9 Surge ON-state current capability

1.6 Switching Characteristics

This section will deal with the anode and cathode aspects of the switching process. To *turn on* a thyristor it is only necessary to apply an appropriate gate current pulse when a forward voltage is being applied to the thyristor (anode positive). Turn-on does not happen instantly but takes a finite time made up of a *delay time*, t_d (when little appears to happen) and a *rise time*, t_r (during which the anode/cathode voltage falls). The *turn-on time* t_{gt}, is usually defined as the time from the application of the gate pulse to the time when the anode/cathode voltage is at 10 per cent of its initial level (see Fig. 1.10).

In general, turn-on times vary up to 10 microseconds and they are very dependent on the amount of gate current used and the rate at which it rises. The higher the gate current and the faster it rises, the shorter the delay time and the shorter the turn-on time.

If, once the thyristor is conducting, the gate current is removed, the thyristor will remain in this ON-state as long as the anode–cathode current is higher than the *latching current* I_L, for the thyristor. If the anode current is below this, it will switch back into the non-conducting OFF-state.

Turn-off. When the thyristor is carrying current in excess of the latching current, it will stay in the ON-state until such time as the current reduces to below the *holding current* I_H of the thyristor. It will then switch to the OFF-state as long a positive anode voltage is not applied to the device for some time.

The above process describes the operation when the anode current is changing slowly. When the current is reducing quickly (say, above 1 A per microsecond), then

11

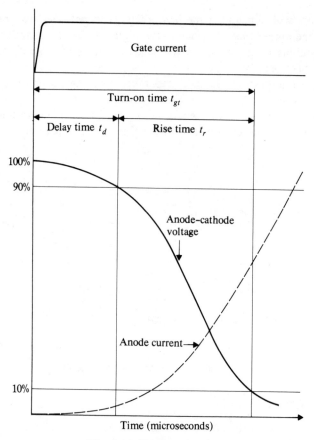

Fig. 1.10 Thyristor turn-on

the *turn-off* process becomes more complicated. The anode current reverses until the free electrons in the silicon are used up and then it collapses to zero, as in Fig. 1.11.

Even so, the thyristor will still at this point not accept forward voltage and a specific time has to be allowed before forward voltage can be applied. The time from the first current zero to when forward voltage can be safely applied is the *circuit commutated turn-off time* t_q, and this may vary from 1000 microseconds for a 'slow' thyristor to 10 microseconds for a fast one.

The temporary flow of *reverse recovery current* is usually only of significance because it ceases very quickly and this causes high circuit voltages.

The length of turn-on and turn-off times of a thyristor will directly decide the frequency of switching at which the thyristor can be used. The higher this switching frequency, the more importance has to be attached to these factors.

1.7 Gate Characteristics

The gate-to-cathode circuit of a thyristor is a *p–n* junction and looks like a diode from the external point of view. It is only able to carry current in one direction but its reverse voltage must be kept to a low value between 5 and 20 V. The value of gate

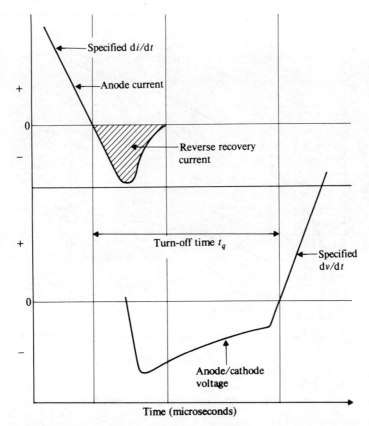

Fig. 1.11 Thyristor turn-off

current necessary to fire a thyristor will vary with temperature and will vary significantly between thyristors.

Gate characteristics are expressed in curve form as in Fig. 1.12, showing the voltage/current relationship of the gate circuit of all thyristors. The minimum gate current to fire all thyristors and the peak gate power curves can be superimposed on these in order to decide the most satisfactory level of firing supply; too little gate current may not fire all thyristors and too much may overheat and damage some. As indicated in Section 1.5, the rate of increase of anode current is limited by the finite time taken for the junction area to switch to the ON-state. In most thyristors, the level of di/dt capability will be increased if more gate current is used than that just necessary to fire the thyristor. Often peak gate currents of 10 times the nominal figure are used to obtain the most satisfactory di/dt performance.

1.8 Thermal Characteristics

A thyristor's ability to block forward voltage applied to it can only be maintained within a specific junction-temperature limit. If this *critical junction temperature* is exceeded the thyristor will switch into the ON-state even though no gate current may be flowing. This will usually be the deciding factor which controls the maximum current that can be carried by the thyristor for any significant period of time. In the

13

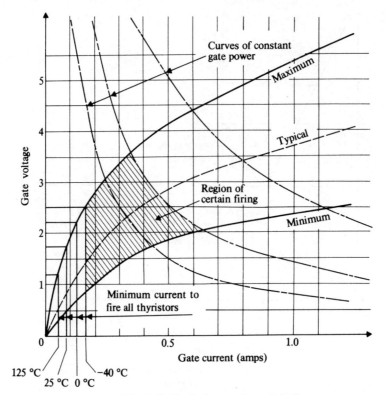

Fig. 1.12 Typical gate characteristics

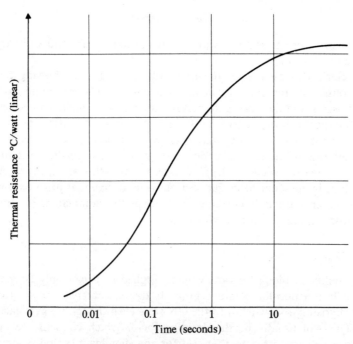

Fig. 1.13 Transient thermal resistance

14

same way as dv/dt breakdown or the application of excessive forward voltage, loss of control due to temperature is not in itself damaging but the follow-up fault will often destroy or deteriorate the thyristor.

The significant characteristic of the thyristor from this point of view is the *thermal resistance* between the junction of the thyristor and its cooling surfaces. It is invariably expressed as degree Centigrade temperature difference per watt of energy dissipated. The larger the thyristor the smaller will be its thermal resistance value.

During significant temperature changes, it is not only the steady-state thermal resistance which is important. A certain amount of energy is required to heat up the thyristor itself. The most satisfactory practical way to quantify this effect for each thyristor is to give different values for the thermal resistance for different time periods. A *transient thermal resistance curve* (Fig. 1.13) is produced for each thyristor.

In general, the thermal mass of the thyristor is only of significance for periods below 10 seconds. This subject is considered further in Section 2.6.

1.9 Special Switching Devices

Thyristors are a continuing field for invention and each new principle used may well result in another name to confuse the user. A few of these are explained below with specific reference to their importance and use.

The *amplifying gate thyristor* has been developed as a result of the need for fast turn-off thyristors with high di/dt capability. High di/dt capability can, as already explained, be obtained by high gate drive. In the amplifying gate thyristor, a high gate drive is obtained by including an auxiliary thyristor within the device. This effectively amplifies the gate drive so as to achieve high switching performance with only a modest input current to the gate (see Fig. 1.14).

Many of the thyristors now available with high di/dt capability are of this type.

The *gate turn-off thyristor* (GTO), as its name implies, is capable of being switched from the ON-state to the OFF-state by passing a current through the gate circuit. At the time of writing, these devices have not gained much importance due to the high gate current required to turn them off (approximately 20 per cent of anode current), and the difficulty in achieving satisfactory overall characteristics, i.e., voltage capability, forward voltage drop, dv/dt, etc.

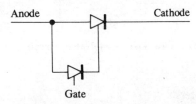

Fig. 1.14 Amplifying gate thyristor – equivalent circuit

If further developments result in more usable GTO thyristors, most of the applications requiring forced commutation will be significantly affected.

The *light-activated thyristor* is a device which can be switched into the ON-state by a light source. The thyristor contains a gating system within it including a photo-transistor which can be triggered from a fibre-optic light guide. The necessity to trigger from such a low energy level imposes severe restrictions on the capabilities of such thyristors but they will no doubt find use where very high insulation level is required between the gate and anode circuits.

The *reverse conducting thyristor* is a thyristor with a reverse-connected diode within the same encapsulation so that the unit cannot withstand reverse voltages. This can produce more satisfactory capabilities for some forced commutated circuits but thermal limitations will normally reduce the current-carrying capacity of such a device (see Fig. 1.15).

The *triac* is a related device equivalent to two thyristors in opposite polarity in the same encapsulation. It is therefore an a.c. switch capable of being triggered into the ON-state with either direction of current flow (see Fig. 1.16). The two thyristors are integrated into the same silicon slice and this affects the level of capability obtainable from them. The most significant limitation is caused by the fact that both directions of current flow through the same silicon. In use, when the current flow stops, the triac must immediately accept a high voltage applied at a high dv/dt. As the silicon has only just been carrying current, its capability to accept this is low. For significant power applications, two thyristors in opposite polarity have superior performance to that of a triac.

Thyristor

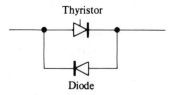

Diode

Fig. 1.15 Reverse conducting thyristor – equivalent circuit

Gate

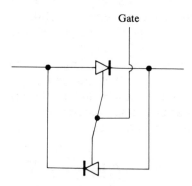

Fig. 1.16 Triac – equivalent circuit

1.10 Variability of Parameters

During the course of this chapter, the many and various capabilities of thyristors have been discussed. Almost all of these parameters vary from one thyristor to another, i.e., every thyristor will have a different limit value of each parameter to all other thyristors.

Fortunately, this is not how thyristors are presented to users. In the case of important parameters, selection by measurement is made by the manufacturers. This may take two forms:

(a) Selection into narrow bands, e.g., forward and reverse voltage capability.

(b) Choosing a value which all thyristors of the specific type will come within.

Some of these parameters may be checked on every device, e.g., forward voltage drop or surge current capability. Others may be confirmed by checking all units initially and then only samples from the production.

This variability of parameters is very important to both the thyristor and equipment user. All design has to be done based on limiting values, whereas in practice all thyristors will have different values of the same parameter.

This subject is referred to in more detail in Chapter 18. Suffice to say here that measurements on individual thyristors are no guide at all; reference must be made to the manufacturer's data sheet information to establish the limit capabilities of all the thyristors of that specific type.

1.11 References

1. IEC Publication 146, *Semiconductor Convertors*, Appendix B, 'Thyristors and thyristor stacks', 1973, amended 1975.
2. British Standard 9300: 1969, *Semiconductor Devices of Assessed Quality. Generic Data and Methods of Test.*
3. 'Power applications of controllable semiconductor devices', *IEE Conference Publication 17*, 1965.
4. R. Bradley and C. B. Lewis, 'High power thyristor design for performance and reliability', *IEE Conference Publication 53*, 22–31, May 1969.
5. Lehmann and Martin, 'Disk type power semiconductor devices and their possible applications', *Siemens Review*, 1975, No. 4
6. D. E. Crees, N. S. Nicholls, and F. Wood, 'High power pulse modulated thyristors', *IEE Conference Publication 123*, 13–19, Dec. 1974.
7. Kishi, Kurata, Imai, and Seki, 'High power gate turn-off thyristors', *USA PESC 77. Record*, 268–274.
8. C. V. Miles, J. M. Garrett, and W. T. P. Watson, 'High frequency power thyristors', *IEE Conference Publication 154*, 5–9, Sept. 1977.
9. D. Silber, M. Füllmann, and W. Lukanz, 'Recent developments in light activated thyristors', *IEE Publication 154*, 14–17, Sept. 1977.

2. Rating and Selection of Thyristors

This chapter is designed to assist engineers to choose the most suitable thyristor for a particular application, or alternatively to help them to understand how the equipment designer will have decided on a particular choice. It may also be helpful when selecting a suitable thyristor to replace a type now unobtainable.

After an initial brief survey of the different thyristor types available, the many technical factors and decisions which have to be considered in choosing the most suitable type will be discussed.

2.1 The Range of Available Thyristors

Although while reading technical papers and articles one can obtain the impression that almost any requirements can be achieved in thyristors, the intention here is to consider those thyristors which are readily available from a wide variety of suppliers, and therefore can be purchased at an economic price.

In general, thyristors are not normally made smaller than 1 A mean current rating, while ratings of individual thyristors well over 1000 A mean current are available. The smaller thyristors can usually be supplied at up to 1000 V (V_{RRM}), whereas the larger ones can often be obtained with ratings in excess of 2000 V.

Many of the thyristor characteristics and capabilities discussed in the previous chapter are interdependent, in that to obtain a good capability in one respect may adversely affect the achievable capabilities in another. Hence the thyristors made and marketed widely tend to be those devices having the most suitable balance of characteristics to meet a reasonably wide variety of applications. Two of the most important parameters from this point of view are high-voltage capability and short turn-off time.

A high-voltage thyristor will usually have less current-carrying capacity than a lower-voltage one due to the need to modify the periphery of the silicon slice to make the voltage stress acceptable, and this reduces the area available for conduction.

Turn-off time reduction is achieved by the correct choice of silicon material and doping characteristics as well as special physical design; the result is a lower voltage capability and a reduction in current rating.

These interdependent factors have led to two basic classes of thyristor being available: those suitable for lower-speed mains frequency, naturally commutated applications – *convertor grade thyristors*; and those suitable for high-speed switching – *inverter grade thyristors*.

Convertor-grade thyristors. A typical manufacturer's range will include devices having the capabilities of those given in Table 2.1.

Inverter-grade thyristors will cover a more limited range typically as in Table 2.2.

Table 2.1 Range of convertor-grade thyristors

Nominal current rating I_T (amps mean at 85 °C base)	V_{RSM} and V_{DSM} (peak volts × 10^3)	V_{RRM} and V_{DRM} (peak volts × 10^3)	ON-state voltage V_T (volts at $3 \times I_T$)	I_{TSM} (10 ms, peak amps × 10^3)	I^2t (10 ms, 125 °C amp² sec × 10^3)	Thermal resistance junction/base (°C/watt)	Type of encapsulation	$\frac{dv}{dt}$ max (volts/μs)	$\frac{di}{dt}$ max (amps/μs)	t_q max (μs)	I_{GT} to fire (mA)	$\frac{I_L}{I_H}$ (typical) (mA)
1–10	0–1·5	0–1·4	1·5–2·5	0·01–0·2	0·0005–0·2	50–2	Screwed base	100	100	100	5–60	25
10–50	0–1·5	0–1·4	1·5–2·5	0·1–1·0	0·05–5	2–0.5	Screwed base	200	100	100	100	100
50–100	0–1·5	0–1·4	1·5–2·0	1–2	5–20	0·5–0·2	Flat or screw base	200	100	150	150	100
100–270	0–1·8	0–1·6	1·5–2·0	2–4	20–80	0·2–0·11	Flat base or disc	300 –1000	100	200	200	150
270–500	0–4·0	0–3·0	1·5–2·0	4–7	80–245	0·11–0·05	Flat base or disc	300 –1000	100	300	200	200
500–650	0–4·0	0–3·0	1·5–2·0	6–11	180–605	0·07–0·035	Flat base or disc	300 –1000	100	350	150–250	200
650–850	0–2·5	0–2·0	1·5–2·0	10–16	500–1280	0·04–0·03	Disc	300 –1000	100	400	150–250	300
850–1100	0–1·5	0–1·4	1·5–2·0	15–20	1125–2000	0·035–0·03	Disc	300 –1000	100	400	150–250	300

Table 2.2 Range of inverter-grade thyristors

Nominal current rating I_T (amps mean at 85 °C base)	V_{RSM} and V_{DSM} (peak volts × 10³)	V_{RRM} and V_{DRM} (peak volts × 10³)	ON-state voltage V_T (volts at 3 × I_T)	I_{TSM} (10 ms, peak amps × 10³)	I^2t (10 ms, 125 °C amp² sec × 10³)	Thermal resistance junction/base (°C/watt)	Type of encapsulation	$\frac{dv}{dt}$ max (volts/ μs)	$\frac{di}{dt}$ max (amps/ μs)	t_q max (μs)	I_{GT} to fire (mA)	$\frac{I_L}{I_H}$ (typical) (mA)
0–10	0–1·1	0–1·0	2–2·8	0·05–0·1	0·0125–0·05	50–2	Screwed base	200	100	5–25	5–60	100
10–50	0–1·2	0–1·1	2–2·8	0·1–1·0	0·05–5·0	2–0·5	Screwed base	200	100	10–20	100	250
50–100	0–1·2	0–1·1	2–2·5	1·0–2·0	5–20	0·5–0·2	Screwed base	200	100	15–50	100	250
100–200	0–0·6	0–0·5	2–2·5	2·0–4·0	20–80	0·2–0·1	Screw or flat base	200	300	10–20	150	250
100–200	0·6–1·4	0·5–1·3	2–2·5	1·5–3·0	11·25–45	0·2–0·1	Screw or flat base	200	300	20–40	150	250
200–300	0–0·9	0–0·8	2–3	4–9	80–405	0·1–0·05	Disc	500	400	10–20	250	200
200–300	0·8–1·4	0·7–1·3	2–3	4–8	80–320	0·1–0·05	Disc	500	400	20–40	250	200
300–400	0–0·6	0–0·5	2–3	8–12	320–720	0·08–0·04	Disc	500	400	10–15	300	200
300–400	0·6–1·2	0·5–1·1	2–3	6–10	180–500	0·08–0·04	Disc	500	400	25–40	300	200
300–400	1·2–2·0	1·1–1·9	2–3	5–8	125–320	0·08–0·04	Disc	500	400	40–60	300	200

Manufacturer's type numbers. Within each basic size of thyristor, the manufacturer will test many parameters and select out different grades of thyristor which will then be sold with different type numbers. Voltage grades are the most obvious ones but other selections for dv/dt and di/dt may be made, as well as forward voltage drop and turn-off time. Type numbers can therefore by very long and complicated to cover all these selections. It is essential to refer to the manufacturer's catalogue to ensure the correct thyristor is being specified.

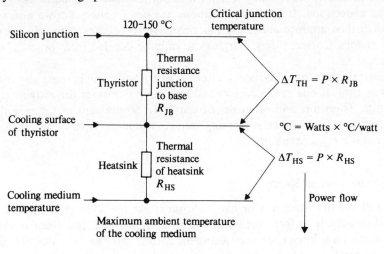

Fig. 2.1 Thyristor thermal analogue

Fig. 2.2 A flatbase thyristor on its heatsink (Westinghouse Brake and Signal Co. Ltd)

2.2 Rating Philosophy

All semiconductor devices have definite limits to their capability, and exceeding these even for short times will result in failure, loss of control, or irreversible deterioration.

All thyristors therefore have to be used within their capability at all times; this must include extreme conditions such as may exist during circuit faults and it must take into account load, supply system, temperature, and environmental variations.

To use thyristors successfully it is most important that all conditions of operation are fully understood. If extreme conditions are not precisely known and cannot be calculated, then appropriate safety margins have to be chosen to allow for the unknown factors. Correct safety margins can only be decided from practical operating experience.

In general, therefore, thyristors often seem to have much more capability than needed and this is due to the correct and necessary allowance for extreme conditions and faults. Thyristors will often be used at 30 to 50 per cent of the manufacturer's stated current rating, and crest working voltages will in many cases be less than half of the thyristor's V_{DSM} capability.

2.3 Thyristor Current Rating

The size of the thyristor may be chosen from either the level of continuous current required through it or from the level of fault current which can occur in the circuit. The principle most often used in choosing the correct thyristor is to study both of these conditions carefully; when a size of thyristor is chosen then the cooling arrangements to be made are based on the continuous power dissipation occurring in the thyristor. In some cases, fault conditions cause a much larger thyristor to be used than that needed for the normal load currents; a simpler cooling system with, say, less air or water flow may then be used satisfactorily.

2.4 Normal Operating Conditions

The size of thyristor necessary to withstand the normal continuous current flow is chosen by assessing the total power losses generated in the thyristor and the effectiveness of the cooling system to be employed.

As already stated, thyristors can lose their blocking ability if the junction temperature is allowed to exceed the critical value of between 120 and 150 °C. This cannot be permitted to happen during normal operation.

The overall thermal conditions can best be assessed by constructing a thermal analogue of the thyristor and its cooling structure as shown in Fig. 2.1.

The size of the thyristor will control the value of its thermal resistance. The correct choice will be made by selecting an appropriate thyristor cooling surface temperature to allow for practical cooling systems to be used.

The choice will also depend on the power loss generated in the thyristor; the temperature difference between the junction and the cooling surface will be equal to:

Power loss × thyristor thermal resistance

For example, with a cooling surface temperature of 85 °C and a critical junction temperature of 125 °C, a power loss of 40 W will require a thyristor with a thermal

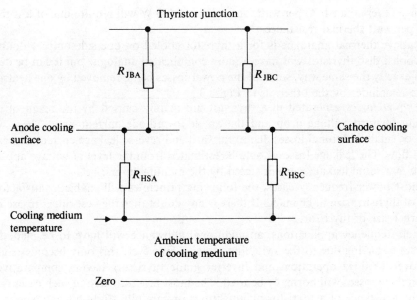

Fig. 2.3 Double-sided cooling thermal analogue

Fig. 2.4 Double-sided cooled disc thyristor (Brown Boveri Ltd)

resistance of less than 1 °C per watt, and a loss of 400 W will require one of less than 0·1 °C per watt thermal resistance.

The above thermal analogue is for a thyristor cooled on one side only; a double-sided cooled disc thyristor will have a more complicated analogue but it can be dealt with in exactly the same way, some of the power losses being removed by one heatsink and the remainder by the other, as in Fig. 2.3.

The *power losses* generated in a thyristor are mainly caused by the result of the ON-state forward voltage drop and the anode-to-cathode current flow. There will always be small additional losses due to forward and reverse leakage current and gate current flow. The leakage losses should be estimated from the level of voltage applied and the maximum leakage current stated by the manufacturers.

In most power-frequency cases, the following principles will enable a satisfactory choice of thyristor size to be made. If there is any doubt then the best rule is to use the next larger size of thyristor.

In high-frequency applications, an additional allowance will have to be made for the losses occurring due to the switching process. However, this only becomes significant over 1000 Hz operation, and inverter grade thyristors having comparatively low switching losses will normally be used. The most practical step in such cases is to enlist the assistance of a thyristor manufacturer or carefully study his data sheets.

2.5 Power Loss Due to Anode Current

The ON-state forward voltage drop of a thyristor (see Fig. 1.8) is a non-linear function of the current, therefore the unusual current waveshapes occurring in thyristor circuits make the losses difficult to establish precisely. Fortunately, most manufacturers produce rating and power loss curves for the most common operating conditions and these allow a first estimate of the thyristor size to be made. Figure 2.5 gives an example of such curves, in this case drawn for the rectangular current pulses which occur in naturally commutated rectifier circuits.

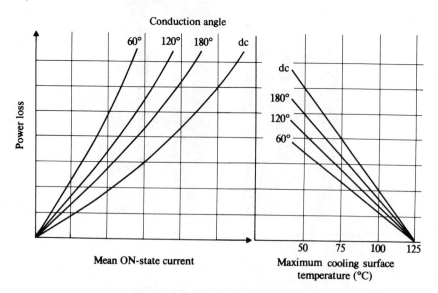

Fig. 2.5 Temperature/power loss curves

24

In using such curves it must be remembered that the current to be used is the maximum level to be experienced for a significant time; this may well be under overload or current-limit operating conditions.

If the operating conditions do not fit into the most common conditions specified by manufacturers, a more precise method of calculation is required. This involves an instantaneous calculation of voltage times current as shown in Fig. 2.6.

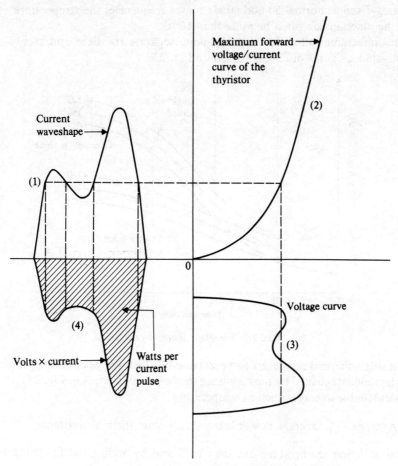

Fig. 2.6 Construction to obtain the thyristor power loss

This method, which can be used for any waveshape of current, involves drawing the current waveshape (1) and the limit forward voltage drop curve (2) to scale. Then:

1. Draw the voltage/time curve (3) using curves (1) and (2).
2. Carry out an instantaneous multiplication of curves (1) and (3) to obtain the power pulse waveshape (4).
3. The power per pulse can be found by estimating the area under the curve (4).
4. Multiply this by the number of pulses per second to obtain the average power loss in watts.

Clearly, the assistance of a computer can greatly help the speed and accuracy of such calculations, particularly where a large number of current waveshapes are involved.

2.6 Junction Temperature

Once the total power losses have been assessed, the junction temperature can be estimated as in Section 2.4 by multiplying the average power loss by the appropriate thermal resistance values.

However, it is, in most cases, also necessary to allow for the cyclic variation of junction temperature which will be caused by the pulsed nature of the current and power losses. Even at normal 50 and 60 Hz power frequencies the temperature oscillation of the junction can often be more than 10 °C.

Some manufacturers allow for this by giving separate transient and steady-state thermal resistance figures or curves similar to Fig. 2.7.

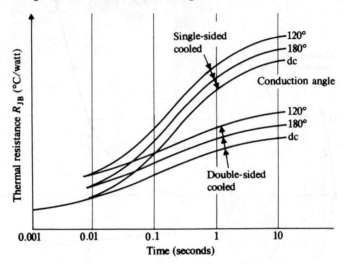

Fig. 2.7 Transient thermal resistance

If only a single thermal resistance curve is available, then the peak temperature can be approximately established by the following method, which refers to Fig. 2.8.

First calculate the average junction temperature:

$$\text{Average } T_j = \text{average power loss} \times \text{steady-state thermal resistance}$$

The peak junction temperature can then be found by adding the following temperature to the average T_j, i.e.,

$$\Delta T_J = T_{J\,\text{peak}} - T_{J\,\text{average}} = \left\{ \left(1 - \frac{t_1}{t_2}\right) R_{t_1+t_2} - R_{t_2} + R_{t_1} \right\} P \frac{t_2}{t_1}$$

where

$$P = \text{average power loss}$$
$$R_{t_1} = \text{thermal resistance for time } t_1$$
$$R_{t_2} = \text{thermal resistance for time } t_2$$
$$R_{t_1+t_2} = \text{thermal resistance for time } t_1 + t_2$$

are obtained from a curve similar to Fig. 1.13.

26

When applied to power-frequency applications, this equation becomes:

for 180° conduction, 50 Hz,

$$\Delta T_j = 2P\{\tfrac{1}{2}R_{.03} - R_{.02} + R_{.01}\};$$

for 180° conduction, 60 Hz,

$$\Delta T_j = 2P\{\tfrac{1}{2}R_{.025} - R_{.017} + R_{.0083}\};$$

for 120° conduction, 50 Hz,

$$\Delta T_j = 3P\{\tfrac{1}{3}R_{.027} - R_{.02} + R_{.0067}\};$$

for 120° conduction, 60 Hz,

$$\Delta T_j = 3P\{\tfrac{1}{3}R_{.022} - R_{.017} + R_{.0056}\}.$$

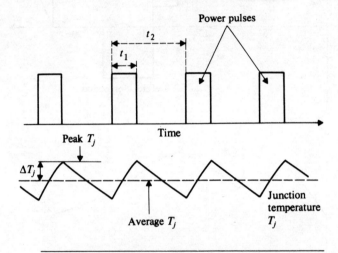

Fig. 2.8 Junction temperature oscillations

2.7 Cyclic Loads

In many applications, the load current is not constant and continuous: it will vary in a repetitive pattern due to the load process. This means the thyristor power losses will also follow this cyclic pattern and the junction temperature calculations will need to allow for this.

To take account of this, it is necessary to calculate the power loss at each stage of the load cycle and use appropriate values of the thermal resistance to obtain the junction temperature levels.

If the load is a repeated pattern of constant-magnitude pulses then the methods detailed in Section 2.6 can be used, i.e., calculate the average junction temperature and then find the peak by using

$$\Delta T_j = P\frac{t_2}{t_1}\left\{\left(1 - \frac{t_1}{t_2}\right)R_{t_1+t_2} - R_{t_2} + R_{t_1}\right\}$$

but obviously the values of thermal resistance will be different to those used in Section 2.6.

If the load has a more complicated pattern, a step-by-step calculation is required at each level of power loss. Figure 2.9 shows such a condition for a variable-speed motor drive. A computer is an ideal tool to assist in such a calculation.

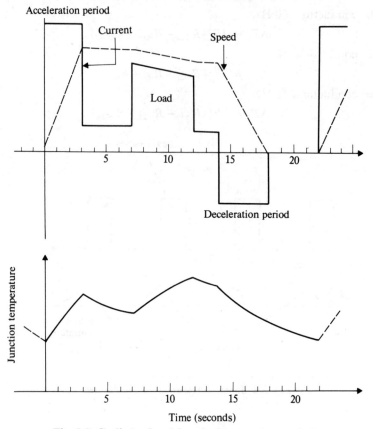

Fig. 2.9 Cyclic load and junction temperature variations

2.8 Overloads and Fault Currents

All power circuits will be exposed to temporary overcurrent conditions during faulty operation. It may be inadvertent short-circuiting of the output terminals, loss of control of a thyristor due to excessive dv/dt or misfiring, or it could be a semiconductor device failing into a short-circuited condition. These conditions are discussed in more detail in Chapter 6.

It is a principle of most designs to ensure that under such fault conditions the thyristors are not damaged; in some cases one may wish for the equipment to continue in operation after such a fault, in which case the critical junction temperature must not be exceeded during the fault.

The fault conditions are very likely to be the decisive factors in the choice of a particular thyristor, and then it is not sufficient to get only a rough idea of the fault current unless large margins are to be left above the necessary ratings. Precise calculation is needed if the most suitable choice is to be made.

The fault condition will need to be measured or calculated and then compared to the thyristor capability. If the fault will result in the equipment being switched off then the thyristor capability is its surge current capability (see Section 1.5). If it is necessary to maintain control of the thyristor during and after the fault then the fault has to be treated like a short pulse of normal current, the power loss will need to be estimated, and the appropriate transient thermal resistance figure used to ensure the junction temperature at the end of the fault does not exceed the critical value.

2.9 Voltage Ratings

It is essential that the voltage capability of a thyristor is not exceeded during operation even for a very short period of time. All circuits will exhibit a maximum thyristor operating voltage and Chapters 3, 4, and 5 contain such information for all the circuits in common use. For example, a thyristor in a naturally commutated bridge-connected convertor operating on a 380 V RMS, 50 Hz supply will have to accept $380 \times \sqrt{2} = 537$ V every cycle of operation. This value is known as the *crest working voltage* of the circuit.

This will not, however, be the highest voltage occurring across any thyristor during each cycle of operation. The switching process itself, whether it be a natural or forced commutation system, will result in transient overvoltages and oscillations occurring at regular points in the cycle (see Chapter 6). These levels must not exceed the *repetitive peak reverse voltage* (V_{RRM}) of the thyristor or the *repetitive OFF-state voltage* (V_{DRM}) as appropriate.

Very occasionally, say, during fault conditions or switching conditions on the input power supply, a thyristor circuit will have to accept an even higher level of voltage for a short period of time, e.g., during lightning strikes. Although these transients may well be attenuated by surge-absorbing circuits or surge arresters, the level eventually applied to the thyristors must be within their *non-repetitive peak OFF-state and reverse voltage ratings*, V_{DSM} and V_{RSM}.

Figures 2.10 and 2.11 show the comparison between circuit condition and thyristor voltage ratings for a naturally commutated and forced commutated practical application respectively.

Voltage safety margins are a frequent source of discussion and, maybe, disagreement. In fact, if the above voltage levels produced in the circuit are precisely known then no safety margin at all is required. In practice, however, even if normal conditions are known the peak voltages during maloperation or fault may be more difficult to estimate. A safety margin is the answer but its level will depend on:

  (a) how safe the engineer wishes to be; and
  (b) what level of surge voltage absorbing circuits are included to attenuate the overvoltages.

A safety margin is particularly required when thyristors are to be directly exposed to the power frequency mains supply at 50 or 60 Hz. Switching and lightning strikes will cause transient voltages many times the normal level for short periods of time. Some means of surge absorption is essential but even then a thyristor having a V_{DRM} at least twice the crest working voltage of the circuit will be needed.

Thyristors used in forced-commutated circuits are usually working under more predictable conditions, and lower safety margins can then be used. Refer to Chapter 6 for more detailed information.

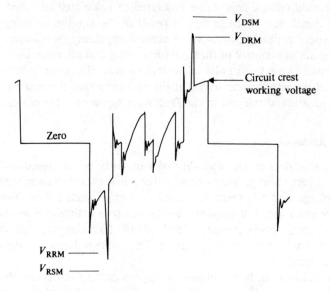

Fig. 2.10 Anode-to-cathode voltage of a thyristor in a naturally commutated three-phase bridge circuit

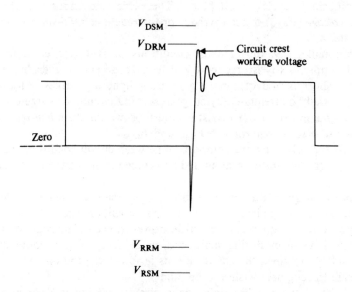

Fig. 2.11 Anode-to-cathode voltage of a thyristor in a forced-commutated inverter circuit

2.10 Transient Ratings dv/dt, di/dt

All that can be done in the case of these transient parameters is to ensure that the capabilities of the thyristor are in excess of the conditions during normal and fault operation. If the circuit produces conditions in excess of the economic dv/dt and di/dt limits of the thyristor then methods must be used to reduce them. These methods are described in detail in Chapter 6. Information on circuit dv/dt and di/dt conditions is included in Chapters 3, 4, and 5.

2.11 References

1. A. J. Blundell, 'The effect of on-state temperature coefficient on thyristor junction temperature calculations', *IEE Conference Publication 53*, 53–60, May 1969.
2. N. Yamada and Y. Ikeda, 'Determination of ratings for semiconductor assemblies for variable load with periodicity', *IEE Conference Publication 53*, 101–107, May 1969.
3. B. U. Newsam, 'Transient thermal resistance – its measurement and use in rating of thyristors', *IEE Conference Publication 53*, 85–93, May 1969.

3. A.C. Thyristor Controllers

In the next three chapters, the circuits in which thyristors are used to achieve control in a.c. and d.c. systems will be explained and discussed. In this chapter, the use of thyristors in a.c. power-frequency circuits will be examined and this use is chosen first because thyristor turn-off occurs simply at the circuit current zeros. In the rectifier and inverter circuits explained in Chapters 4 and 5, the methods of turn-off are more complex.

Although thyristors are unidirectional switching devices, they can be used in pairs to allow current to flow in either direction. They can therefore be used in a.c. circuits where the currents will be alternating and reversing in every cycle of operation. This means that the thyristors will turn off each cycle of operation naturally when the circuit currents reach zero.

3.1 The Single-phase A.C. Thyristor Controller

The principle of a.c. control can be understood from study of the single-phase power-frequency circuit shown in Fig. 3.1.

If the thyristors are not fired at all, then no current will flow and no voltage will appear across the load resistance; the supply voltage will in fact appear across the thyristor switches.

If the thyristors are fired all the time, then one or other of them will maintain current flow at all times and the maximum a.c. current will flow in the load. Only the forward voltage drop will appear across the thyristors.

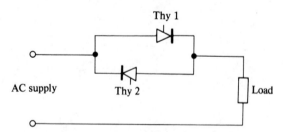

Fig. 3.1 Single-phase a.c. thyristor controller

If the thyristors are fired once every cycle and the point of firing is delayed past the voltage zero, then a part of the a.c. voltage waveform will appear across the load. The load current will cease every half-cycle, the thyristors turning off at the current zeros.

Figure 3.2 shows the waveforms occurring under these three operating conditions.

Therefore, if cyclic firing is adopted and the point in the cycle when the thyristors are fired can be controlled, the effective voltage occurring across the load can be varied at will. If the two thyristors are always fired 180 electrical degrees apart, then the load voltage waveform will contain no d.c. component; it will be a.c.

With a resistance load, the current waveform will exactly follow the voltage wave and the current will come to zero every half-cycle and remain there until the next thyristor is fired.

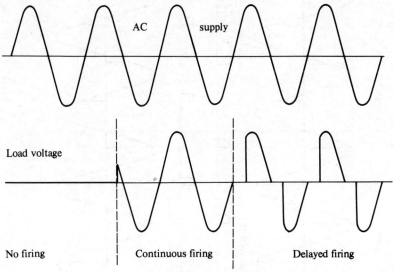

Fig. 3.2 A.C. controller modes of operation

Figure 3.3 shows the whole range of load conditions which can exist in this circuit with various values of delay angle α. The overall results of phase control of this single-phase a.c. controller on resistance load are expressed in graphical form in Fig. 3.4 which shows the total RMS load voltage expressed as a percentage of the supply voltage.

The graph also shows the mean value which would occur if the load voltage were measured by a rectifier-type a.c. voltmeter which would rectify the waveshape and take the mean value of the result (it is assumed the meter is calibrated to read sinusoidal values).

The Effect of Load Inductance

As with other thyristor circuits, the operation depends on the type of load supplied. In the resistive case explained above, the current ceases at the voltage zero.

If the load is inductive, the current zero will be delayed with respect to the voltage zero and the circuit will operate differently (see Fig. 3.5).

The operation will now be dominated by the following facts:

1. Whenever the complete a.c. supply waveform is connected to the load, then the load current will be sinusoidal and will have a value equal to:

$$\frac{V_{\text{RMS supply}}}{\sqrt{(R^2 + wL^2)}}$$

2. The supply voltage will be connected to the load whenever current is flowing in the circuit, i.e., one thyristor will always be in the ON-state whenever current is flowing.

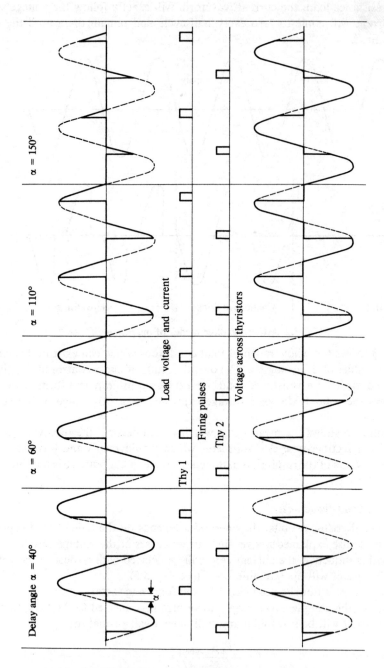

Fig. 3.3 Single-phase a.c. controller – resistance load

34

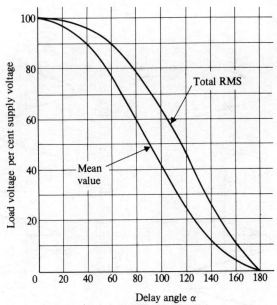

Fig. 3.4 Single-phase a.c. controller – resistance load

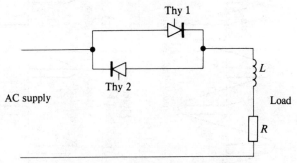

Fig. 3.5 A.C. controller – inductive load

The result of these facts is that increase in delay angle does not initially cause a reduction in the load current. While it is less than the power factor angle of the load, full sinusoidal current flows. Increase in α above this point will, however, reduce the load current and enable it to be controlled down to zero.

It should be noted from these waveforms that there is a sudden rise in the voltage across the thyristors when each current pulse ceases. This rise appears as a high forward dv/dt on the thyristor previously in the OFF-state. Additional circuit components are needed to control the rate of rise to be within the capability of the thyristors, or else breakover and loss of control will occur.

Figure 3.6 shows the waveforms of this cirucit with an inductive/resistance load at various delay angles, and Fig. 3.7 shows the effect of load power factor on the total RMS load voltage over the full range of delay angle.

Control Methods

In addition to phase control, as explained above, the a.c. controller can be used as a switch. It can be used only in either the fully ON or fully OFF conditions and in some

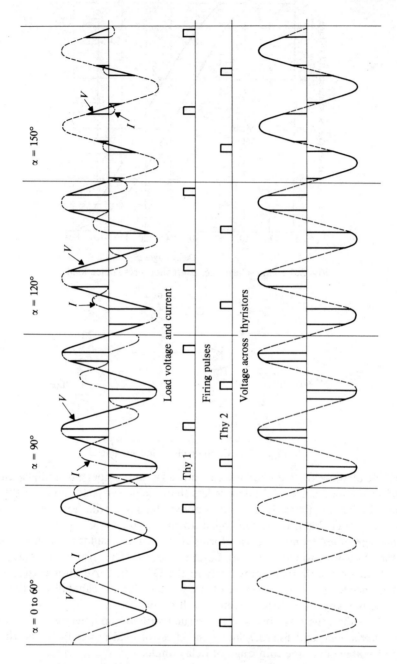

Fig. 3.6 Single-phase a.c. controller – inductive load

36

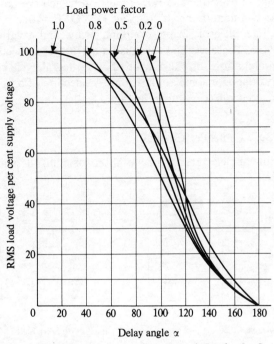

Load power factor

Fig. 3.7 Single-phase a.c. controller – inductive load

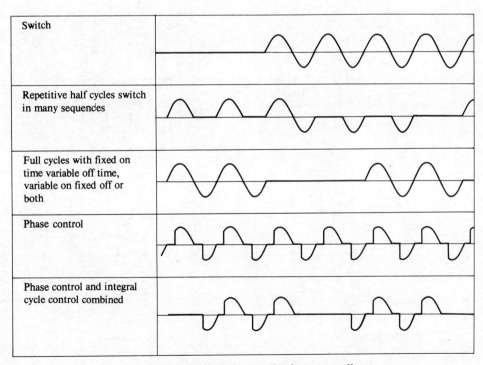

Switch	
Repetitive half cycles switch in many sequences	
Full cycles with fixed on time variable off time, variable on fixed off or both	
Phase control	
Phase control and integral cycle control combined	

Fig. 3.8 Control methods for a.c. thyristor controllers

circumstances, control over the load power can still be achieved by sequential switching between these two conditions. If frequent ON–OFF switching is employed, it is known as either 'integral cycle firing' or 'burst firing' and a variety of load voltage patterns are possible. These methods are discussed further in Section 3.6.

In addition, combinations of phase control and integral cycle control can be used together, with advantage for some applications. A selection of output voltage patterns possible from a.c. controllers is shown in Fig. 3.8.

3.2 Three-phase A.C. Controller Circuits

There are many three-phase versions of a.c. thyristor controllers and Fig. 3.9. shows a selection of them.

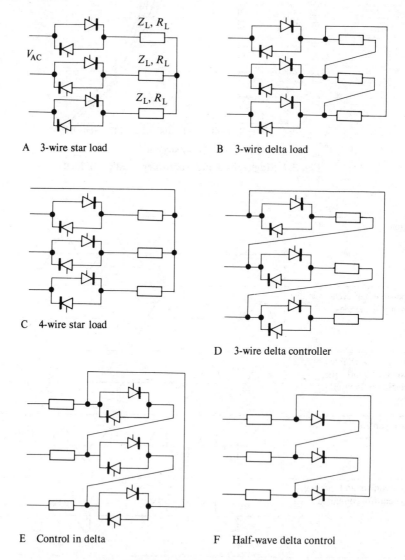

A   3-wire star load

B   3-wire delta load

C   4-wire star load

D   3-wire delta controller

E   Control in delta

F   Half-wave delta control

Fig. 3.9 Three-phase a.c. controllers

They all operate in slightly different ways and in this section the characteristics and performance of these circuits will be compared. In Section 3.4 the detailed operation of circuit A will be explained to show the principles of how to analyse three-phase a.c. controller circuits.

The following are the important points of comparison between the circuits of Fig. 3.9:

1. In circuits C and D, the individual phase controllers control their own loads independently of the others. They can therefore be studied as three single-phase controllers.
2. In the other circuits, the individual phase controllers affect the other phase loads also and they have to be studied as complete three-phase circuits.
3. The peak voltages occur across thyristors at or near to the fully OFF state. In the case of circuits D, E, and F the maximum thyristor voltage is the peak of the line voltage, whereas in circuit C it is the peak of the phase voltage; in circuits A and B the maximum thyristor voltage will be somewhere between the peak of the phase and line voltages depending on the leakage current of the thyristors, the method of firing, and the presence of voltage-sharing resistors across the thyristors.

Table 3.1 Rating parameters of three-phase a.c. controllers*

Circuit (Figs 3.9 and 3.10)	Delay angle α for full control (degrees)	Maximum input line current I_{ac} (RMS)	Maximum load power dissipation	Thyristor CWV $\dfrac{}{V_{ac}}$	Thyristor currents		
					Peak $\dfrac{}{I_{ac}}$	Mean $\dfrac{}{I_{ac}}$	RMS $\dfrac{}{I_{ac}}$
A	150	$\dfrac{V_{ac}}{\sqrt{(3)} \times Z_L}$	$3I_{ac}^2 R_L$	1·225	1·414	0·450	0·707
B	150	$\dfrac{\sqrt{(3)}V_{ac}}{Z_L}$	$I_{ac}^2 R_L$	1·225	1·414	0·450	0·707
C	180	$\dfrac{V_{ac}}{\sqrt{(3)} \times Z_L}$	$3I_{ac}^2 R_L$	0·816	1·414	0·450	0·707
D	180	$\dfrac{\sqrt{(3)}V_{ac}}{Z_L}$	$I_{ac}^2 R_L$	1·414	0·816	0·260	0·408
E	150	$\dfrac{V_{ac}}{\sqrt{(3)} \times Z_L}$	$3I_{ac}^2 R_L$	1·414	0·816	0·260	0·408
F	210	$\dfrac{V_{ac}}{\sqrt{(3)} \times Z_L}$	$3I_{ac}^2 R_L$	1·414	1·414	0·675	0·766
G	210	$\dfrac{V_{ac}}{\sqrt{(3)} \times Z_L}$	$3I_{ac}^2 R_L$	1·225	0·414	0·450	0·707
H	210	$\dfrac{\sqrt{(3)}V_{ac}}{Z_L}$	$I_{ac}^2 R_L$	1·225	1·414	0·450	0·707

* In the table, V_{ac} = RMS line voltage; I_{ac} = RMS line current; Z_L = load impedance per phase; R_L = load resistance per phase.

4. All these circuits can be used under either phase control or integral cycle control.
5. The range of phase angle required to achieve full output range from zero to maximum varies between the circuits and these are given in Table 3.1.
6. The maximum current flow in the thyristors is decided from the fully ON condition and the size of thyristors to be used should be chosen from this condition. The peak, mean, and RMS thyristor currents given in Table 3.1 are related to the RMS a.c. input current which should be found by applying the full supply voltage to the load-circuit impedances.
7. Although only three thyristors are required in circuit F, they each have to carry a higher current than the other circuits. Under full conduction conditions, the current flows in each thyristor for 240 degrees in every cycle.

Thyristor/Diode Circuits

Some of the above circuits can work satisfactorily with only half as many thyristors, replacing the other half by diodes, i.e., having one thyristor and one diode in each phase. This is only possible in those circuits where the remaining thyristors are still able to prevent the flow of power current completely. In fact, circuits A and B of Fig. 3.9 can be arranged this way but not circuits C, D, or E as current would continue to flow through the diodes even when the thyristors were fully off.

The thyristor/diode versions of circuits A and B are shown in Fig. 3.10. These circuits are most useful when integral cycle firing is adopted as they only then work in either the fully ON or fully OFF conditions.

When they are used with phase control, as only three points per cycle are controllable, the load current and voltage will contain additional second and fourth harmonics and the higher even harmonics (see Fig. 3.13).

Table 3.1 summarizes the current and voltage rating parameters associated with all of these three-phase a.c. controller circuits.

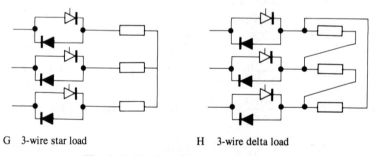

G   3-wire star load   H   3-wire delta load

Fig. 3.10 Thyristor/diode circuits

3.3 Phase Control of A.C. Controllers

The principles of phase-angle control were introduced in Section 3.1 in relation to the single-phase circuit. This principle can be applied to all a.c. controller circuits and the following are the common features associated with all phase-controlled circuits.

(a) Control is achieved by delaying the turn-on of the thyristor so that a selected part of each cycle is applied to the load.
(b) In all except the fully ON and fully OFF conditions, the circuit waveforms will contain significant harmonics.

(c) When the load is inductive, control over the load current is only possible when the delay angle α is in excess of the power-factor angle of the load.

(d) The voltage across the thyristors progressively increases as the delay angle α is increased. At and near to the fully ON condition the forward voltage at the point of firing is low.

(e) On inductive load the natural turn-off of one thyristor will cause a high forward dv/dt to be applied to the other, and the magnitude of the instantaneous voltage rise will depend on the load power factor and the control angle.

(f) The thyristor di/dt conditions at switch-on will be dictated principally by the load. A pure resistive load can result in a high di/dt level. The presence of circuit capacitors will also be important to thyristor di/dt levels.

Thyristor firing requirements are discussed in general in Chapter 8, but there are a few specific points related to a.c. controllers which need mention here:

1. Although a thyristor only needs a short pulse of gate current to switch it into the ON-state, this may not be sufficient because of circuit conditions. If, when the gate pulse occurs, a reverse voltage exists across the thyristor, it will not turn on. It will only turn on when a gate current pulse is applied while forward voltage occurs across the thyristor. If, due to circuit conditions, the current reduces to zero, the thyristor will turn off even though a further current flow period is expected soon after. Another gate pulse is required whenever forward current is anticipated.

2. When the thyristors are fired to give maximum load voltage, very low forward voltage occurs across the thyristors and the current will be slow to build up. If the gate pulse is short, the thyristors may not fully turn on and they will then revert to the OFF-state at the end of the gate pulse.

3. If the load is inductive, a long gate pulse is essential as forward voltage does not occur across the thyristor until the delay angle exceeds the power factor angle (see Fig. 3.7).

4. Reference to Section 3.4 will show that circuits A and B require either a long gate pulse in excess of 60 electrical degrees or twin pulses 60 degrees apart if delay angles above 90 degrees are to be used.

5. Circuit F requires two gate pulses 120 degrees apart, at least, to cater for delay angles between 90 and 120 degrees.

6. If a long gate pulse or a train of pulses is used, care must be taken to ensure that the increased thyristor leakage current when the thyristor is reverse-biased is acceptable to the circuit. If series operation of thyristors is being used it will seriously upset the sharing of the total voltage.

Distortion and harmonics in the load voltage and currents will depend on the nature of the load, i.e., whether it is resistive, inductive, or even capacitive, and so an exhaustive study is not possible here. The use of resistive load is, however, fairly regularly the case and so Figs 3.11 to 3.13 have been included to show the conditions in some of the circuits over the full control range.

Figure 3.11 shows the harmonics existing in the load voltage and circuit current of the single-phase thyristor circuit of Fig. 3.1 and these graphs can also be used for the load voltage of any of the circuits in which the phases are controlled independently, i.e., circuits C and D of Fig. 3.9. The input currents of circuit C also contain these harmonics but in circuit D the third harmonic remains in the delta loop and does not appear in the input current.

41

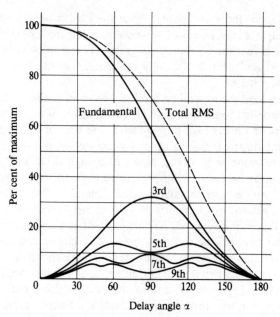

Fig. 3.11 Harmonic content of load voltage and current – single-phase a.c. controller and three-phase circuits C and D of Fig. 3.9

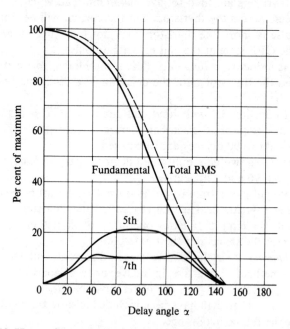

Fig. 3.12 Harmonic content of load voltage and current – three-phase a.c. controller circuits A and B of Fig. 3.9

Figure 3.12 shows the harmonics existing in the load currents and voltages of circuits A and B of Fig. 3.9 and in these cases the third harmonic is not present. Figure 3.13 shows the harmonics occurring in the thyristor/diode circuits of Fig. 3.10.

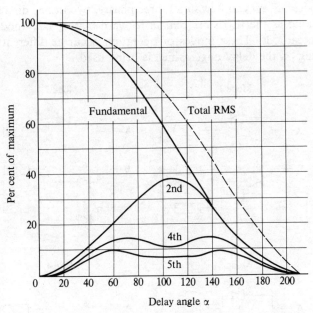

Fig. 3.13 Harmonic content of load voltage and current – three-phase thyristor/
diode a.c. controller circuits G and H of Fig. 3.10

3.4 The Three-phase, Three-wire A.C. Controller with Resistive Load and Phase Control

As an example of the method of analysing three-phase a.c. controller circuits, circuit A of Fig. 3.9 will be considered in detail. The circuit is shown more specifically in Fig. 3.14, where the three-phase supply voltages with respect to the supply neutral are V_A, V_B, and V_C displaced 120 electrical degrees from each other, and the thyristors will be fired in the sequence 1 to 6 as shown, this being the correct sequence for the phase rotation A–B–C.

Let us assume that each thyristor is fired for a period up to 180 degrees so that current can flow whenever forward voltage occurs across the thyristor. The circuit will pass through six modes of operation in every cycle of supply frequency and these modes are shown in Fig. 3.15.

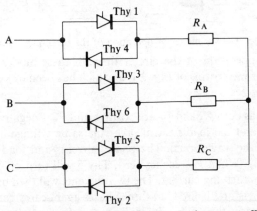

Fig. 3.14 Three-phase, three-wire a.c. thyristor controller

43

In each mode, current can flow in all three phases, two in one direction and one in the other as long as the thyristors remain forward-biased, i.e., anode positive with respect to the cathode. These modes of operation occur at different periods in the cycle depending on the delay angle which is being used.

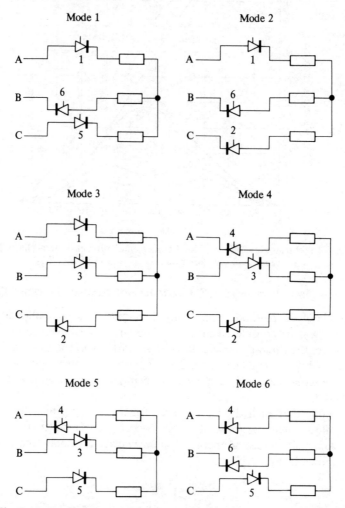

Fig. 3.15 The six modes of operation of the three-phase a.c. controller

The sequential operation of the circuit through these modes will be explained to arrive at the circuit waveforms of Fig. 3.16a, which has been drawn for a delay angle α of 30 electrical degrees.

Mode 1. Initially, as both V_A and V_C are positive and V_B is negative, all three thyristors conduct and the load neutral takes the same voltage as the supply neutral (zero on the waveforms). The phase currents and load voltages will follow the supply. When V_C reaches zero, Thy 5 will turn off and leave just Thy 1 and Thy 6 carrying current. The two currents will then be equal but opposite.

Mode 2. When thyristor 2 is fired, all three phases again carry current and the neutral is again zero, the load voltages and therefore currents revert to the three-

44

phase a.c. supply voltage. When the current in Thy 6 reaches zero it turns off and only Thy 1 and Thy 2 carry current, causing the neutral voltage to increase from zero.

Mode 3. When Thy 3 is fired, the system reverts to a balanced a.c. system until Thy 1 current reaches zero, when only Thy 2 and Thy 3 carry current.

And so on through modes 4 to 6, etc.

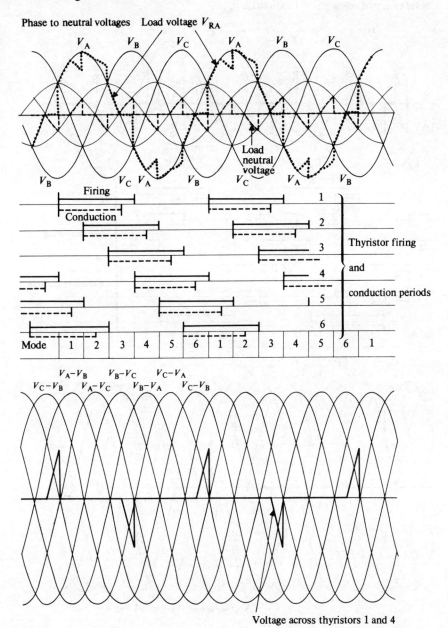

Fig. 3.16a Circuit conditions and waveforms for α = 30 degrees; three-phase, three-wire a.c. controller – resistive load

The current and voltage waveforms will then be as shown in Fig. 3.16a.

Using these same step-by-step methods, Fig. 3.16b shows the waveforms which will result when the delay angle is 120 degrees.

Figure 3.12 shows the RMS current and load voltage over the whole range of delay angle.

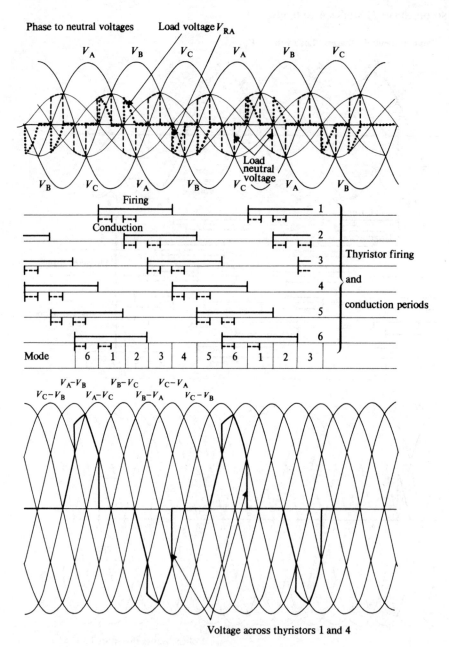

Fig. 3.16b Circuit conditions and waveforms for α = 120 degrees; three-phase, three-wire a.c. controller – resistive load

By now it will be appreciated that:
(a) Each circuit needs to be studied in detail to assess its waveforms and capabilities.
(b) It is necessary to study each of the many modes of operation in turn.
(c) The operation will depend on the pattern of firing of the thyristors: if they are fired by a single pulse the operation may be different at certain delay angles.
(d) The load waveform contains harmonics.
(e) The highest voltages across the thyristors occur at low output voltage conditions.

3.5 Integral Cycle Control

This control method, which is sometimes known as burst firing, means that full cycles of the supply voltage are applied to the load; control is effected by changing the number of full cycles applied compared with the number of cycles when the supply is not connected to the load at all. Any particular control condition results in a number of full ON cycles followed by a number of full OFF cycles. Figure 3.17 shows this generalized condition where the time period of T cycles is split up into N ON cycles and $(T-N)$ OFF cycles.

The values of N and T may vary over the control range; both N and $T-N$ may vary from zero to T cycles. In this way the effective voltage, current, and power applied to the load can be controlled.

The principal advantage of this ON–OFF method of control is that sinusoidal currents will flow during the ON periods, so avoiding the high-frequency harmonic currents which will exist with phase control in every cycle.

However, by so doing the power is applied to the load in low-frequency pulses and the load must be capable of accepting it in this form. This means it has to have a comparatively long operating time constant. Heating loads are suitable for integral cycle control but lighting and motor loads cannot, in general, operate satisfactorily in this pulsating manner. The low-frequency pulsations of current can also cause problems in the supply system. Due to its impedance, a low-frequency changing voltage drop can occur which can affect other users of electricity. This is usually referred to as 'flicker' as it is most easily detected by the flickering of tungsten lamps connected to the power supply.

In practical systems of integral cycle control, the thyristors are usually switched on and off, at, or very near to, the voltage zero points.

There are many variations on this theme:
(a) T can be kept constant over the control range with N varying to change the effective output voltage.
(b) N can be kept constant and T varied to control the voltage.
(c) Both N and T may be altered to obtain optimum control conditions.

In this latter method, the variable N and T can be computed at each control condition so that T is always the minimum number of cycles to achieve the control level; for example:

   1% output can be obtained with $N = 1, T = 100$
10% output can be obtained with $N = 1, T = 10$
25% output can be obtained with $N = 1, T = 4$
40% output can be obtained with $N = 2, T = 5$
75% output can be obtained with $N = 3, T = 4$
   etc.

The *load power* passed to a resistance load with integral cycle control can be calculated simply from the number of applied cycles during each period:

$$\text{Load power} = (N/T) \times \text{maximum load power}$$

As the resistance of most loads varies with temperature and hence power dissipation, the maximum power referred to here will be given by the supply voltage and the resistance at the dissipation being considered.

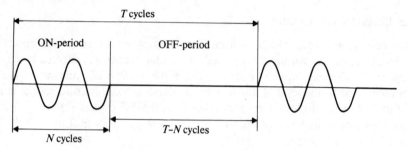

Fig. 3.17 **Generalized integral cycle control**

The *effective current* at any control level has no real meaning unless it is measured by a method having a very long time constant. The effect of the current will depend on the time constant of the item to be considered. The overall long time RMS value will be:

$$I_{\text{RMS}} = I_{\text{max}} \times \sqrt{(N/T)}$$

where I_{max} is the current during the ON pulses.

The *power factor* of the supplied current can also be confusing due to the low-frequency current pulsations. If it can be measured, say by normal wattmeter methods, it will be found that even with a resistive load the power factor will be below unity. In fact the power factor would be $\sqrt{(N/T)}$ times its value when the power is switched fully into the load.

The *flicker frequency* produced by integral cycle control will depend directly on the time period of switching, T, so that if mains frequency is F cycles per second the flicker frequency will be:

$$F/T \text{ cycles per second}$$

Hence the highest flicker frequency will be when T is the smallest number of cycles. This is the fact which leads to the optimizing method of control referred to in (c) above.

The flicker frequency and magnitude can be improved if multiple controllers are used. They can all be programmed to interact with each other so that they each perform their own functions but at the same time produce the minimum instantaneous step in supply current at the maximum flicker frequency.

3.6 A.C. Controllers to Feed Transformers

Where high or low voltages are required to be controlled it is sometimes convenient to control the voltage applied to the primary winding of a step-up or step-down transformer. Some a.c. controllers can be used for this purpose as long as their design is considered carefully.

The following factors are important when this principle is being used:

1. The supply to a transformer must be a balanced a.c. waveform with no d.c. component. The total area under the positive half-cycle of the voltage wave must be equal to the area under the negative half-cycle.

   This means that phase-controlled thyristor/diode circuits cannot be used and even when double thyristors are used the firing circuits must be carefully designed so that the thyristors are fired exactly 180 electrical degrees apart.

2. Transformer loads will not usually be at unity power factor and this means that control at low delay angles may be variable (see Fig. 3.7). It also means that high dv/dt conditions may be applied to the thyristors.

3. When switched on, transformers initially take a high inrush current for a few cycles while the correct core flux is being established. This means that integral cycle control will not be acceptable in its normal form. Phase-controlled a.c. thyristor controllers, however, do provide a means of gradually increasing the applied voltage, so removing the high inrush currents.

4. If misfiring occurs in the controller, the transformer may saturate and take large currents sufficient to cause overheating (if prolonged), or operation of the protective fuses or switches.

5. The a.c. controller will normally incorporate voltage-transient 'snubber circuits' or their equivalent in parallel with the thyristors. These may provide a sufficient path for transformer magnetization and so voltage will be measured even when the thyristors are fully off.

Single and multiphase controllers are in use for transformer loads, and circuits A, B, and C of Fig. 3.9 can be employed. It is not possible to include thyristors within a three-phase primary delta winding as they will suppress the required flow of third harmonic currents.

3.7 References

1. W. Shepherd, *Thyristor Control of AC Circuits*, Bradford University Press and Crosby Lockwood, 1976.
2. Application Report AR3, *Trinistor Single Phase AC Power Regulator*, Westinghouse Brake and Signal Company, England.
3. Application Report AR9, *Trinistor Three Phase AC Regulators*, Westinghouse Brake and Signal Company, England.
4. E. P. McCarthy and J. Danesh, 'A novel method of direct digital integral cycle power control', *IEEE*, **IECI-25**, 2, May 1978.

4. Natural Commutation Circuits

Commutation in an electrical sense means the transfer of current from one path to another; in thyristor circuits the term is used to describe the process of transferring current from one thyristor to another. As explained previously, it is not possible for a thyristor to turn itself off; the circuit in which it is connected must reduce the thyristor current to zero to enable it to turn off. Commutation is the term to describe the methods of achieving this.

Commutation is one of the most fundamental principles in the use of thyristors for control purposes. A thyristor can only operate in two modes: it is either in the OFF-state, i.e., open-circuit, or in the ON-state, i.e., short-circuit. In itself it cannot control the level of current or voltage in a circuit. Control can only be achieved by variation of the time thyristors are switched ON and OFF, and commutation is central to this switching process. All thyristor circuits therefore involve the cyclic or sequential switching of thyristors.

Natural Commutation

The simplest and most widely used method of commutation makes use of the alternating, reversing nature of a.c. voltages to effect the current transfer. This method will be referred to as natural commutation, although in other literature it may be called line commutation. This method may use a.c. mains supply voltages or the a.c. voltages generated by local rotating machines or resonant circuits.

Forced Commutation

This other method uses specially generated current sources as a means of forcing the current in a thyristor to zero and holding it there long enough for it to turn off. This method, which may in other places be referred to as self commutation, is dealt with in Chapter 5.

4.1 The Principles of Natural Commutation in Rectifying Circuits

The current in a thyristor can be reduced to zero by switching on another thyristor connected to a higher-voltage supply source without interrupting the current in the load circuit.

If, in Fig. 4.1, Thy 2 is gated on when V_2 is greater than V_1, all the current in Thy 1 will immediately transfer into Thy 2 and Thy 1 will turn off. If the two voltages V_1 and V_2 are alternating sine waves, then when V_1 becomes greater than V_2 then Thy 1 could be switched on again and the current would transfer back into it.

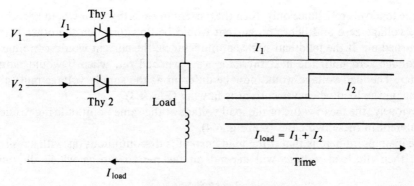

Fig. 4.1 Natural commutation

Let us consider the single-phase circuits of Fig. 4.2 in detail to establish the fundamentals. If, during the positive half-cycle of V_1, Thy 1 is gated on, current will commence flowing through the load as I_1, and the load voltage will be almost equal to V_1. This is allowed to continue until V_2 becomes greater than V_1; switching on of Thy 2 will then cause current flow through Thy 2 and if there was any current remaining in Thy 1 it would transfer to Thy 2. The load voltage would now be almost equal to V_2. The total load voltage has therefore become unidirectional and its mean level is controlled by altering the point in the waveform when the thyristors are switched on.

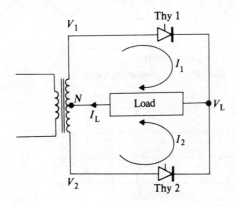

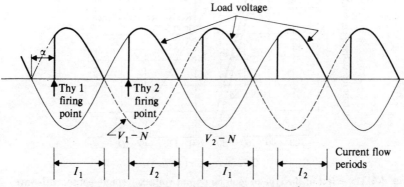

Fig. 4.2 Rectifying with natural commutation

51

If the load was resistance only, then the current in each thyristor would become zero at the voltage zero and hence no current would be flowing when the other thyristor was turned on. If the load had sufficient inductance, the current would continue after the voltage zero until the next thyristor was switched on, when it would naturally transfer. The load voltage would now be different as the supply voltage must always appear on the load whenever current is flowing (Fig. 4.3).

Obviously, the mean value of the load voltage at the same point of firing would also be different in these two cases (see Fig. 4.4).

The main point here is that if the load current is discontinuous (as with a resistance load), then the load voltage will depend on the period during which the current

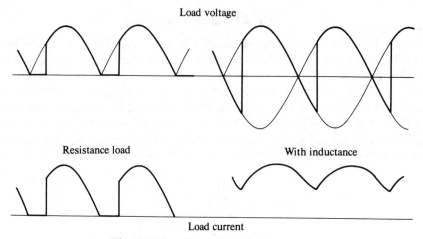

Fig. 4.3 The effect of load inductance

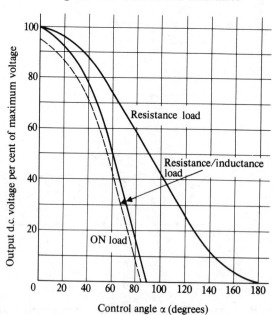

Fig. 4.4 The effect of the type of load on output voltage – single-phase, half-wave
rectifying circuit

flows; once the current becomes continuous then the voltage will remain constant. This point is also important if the load consists of a capacitor; current would then only flow when the rectified voltage was in excess of the capacitor charge voltage and eventually the capacitor would charge to the peak voltage and no current would flow at all. Similarly, with a back-e.m.f. load, i.e., a battery or a d.c. machine, current will again only flow when the rectified voltage is above the load voltage and discontinuous current will occur. However, the presence of series inductance in all of these cases will extend the current flow periods and eventually lead to continuous current and commutation current transfer from one thyristor to the other.

This process of natural commutation occurs also with diodes, but in this case the point of commutation is fixed and decided only by the applied voltage sinusoidal waveforms. Some of the circuits described in the remainder of this chapter use both diodes and thyristors in the same circuit, and these are referred to as half-controlled circuits.

Overlap and Overlap Angle

In Fig. 4.2 let us now assume a resistive/inductive load such that continuous current flows. We have up to now ignored leakage reactance in the transformer; let us now include it as a small series inductance in each winding, L_1 and L_2. The complete circuit now becomes that shown in Fig. 4.5.

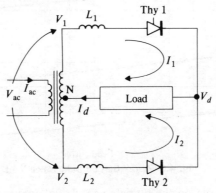

Fig. 4.5 Circuit including the commutating reactance

In this case, if Thy 2 is switched on while Thy 1 is carrying the load current, the I_1 will not be able to decrease to zero instantly due to the presence of L_1. What will happen is that I_1 will decrease slowly, causing an additive voltage across L_1, and I_2 will increase, causing a subtractive voltage across L_2. While both thyristors are conducting,

$$V_1 + L_1 \frac{dI_1}{dt} = V_2 - L_2 \frac{dI_2}{dt} = \text{load voltage, } V_d$$

This condition will continue until I_1 drops to zero.

This period while both thyristors are conducting is called the *overlap angle (u)* and it varies dependent on the level of current flowing, the magnitude of the transformer leakage resistance, and the point in the waveform when the thyristors are switched.

53

The point of firing in the waveform is usually denoted by the *delay angle* (α), this being the angle measured from the point of maximum output voltage firing (see Fig. 4.4).

Regulation is the reduction in output voltage which occurs as load current is increased. Voltage drop in thyristors and diodes and circuit resistance will contribute to the regulation but the largest single effect is usually due to the presence of transformer leakage inductance. During overlap the output voltage reduces by the inductance voltage equal to $L(dI/dt)$, and this increases with load current. This regulation caused by circuit inductance is usually shown in curve form, as in Fig. 4.6.

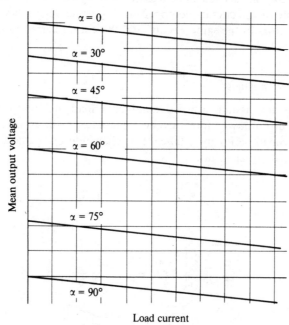

Fig. 4.6 Regulation on inductance load

The effect of regulation on the thyristor anode voltages is significant. The voltage after L_1 will be equal to V_1 during most of the cycle, but during overlap it will be equal to $V_1 - L_1(dI_1/dt)$ and as previously discussed, this will equal zero, so the anode voltage of Thy 1 becomes as shown in Fig. 4.7.

Inversion

We have already established that the value and character of the load current are decided by the load. We have also shown that the mean d.c. voltage with continuous load current will be zero at a delay angle of 90 degrees (Fig. 4.4). As long as the load is capable of maintaining the same direction of continuous current flow, there is no reason why delay angles greater than 90 degrees cannot be used and then the load voltage would be negative (see Fig. 4.8).

This condition is most easily achieved when the load is a d.c. rotating machine but it can be maintained for a short period of time with a highly inductive load.

54

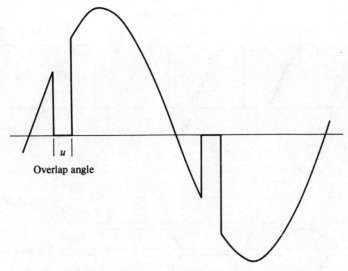

Overlap angle

Fig. 4.7 Notches in the a.c. voltage waveform due to overlap

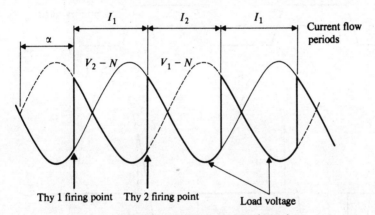

Fig. 4.8 Power reversal by inversion

With a negative load voltage and the same direction of current flow, the power is now flowing from the load into the transformer and supply system, i.e., the load power is being fed back into the supply.

This condition is known as inversion and all the natural commutation principles apply under these inversion conditions also. The complete conditions of the single-phase half-wave circuit are shown as current and voltage waveforms in Figs 4.9a and b.

4.2 Rectifying-circuit Characteristics

Each different circuit will have a number of important characteristics which need to be understood to use them correctly and to select thyristors correctly for use with them. These characteristics will be defined and explained in this section and specific details given for the single-phase half-wave circuit of Fig. 4.5 and detailed in Fig. 4.9. The particular characteristics of other circuits will be given in the succeeding sections.

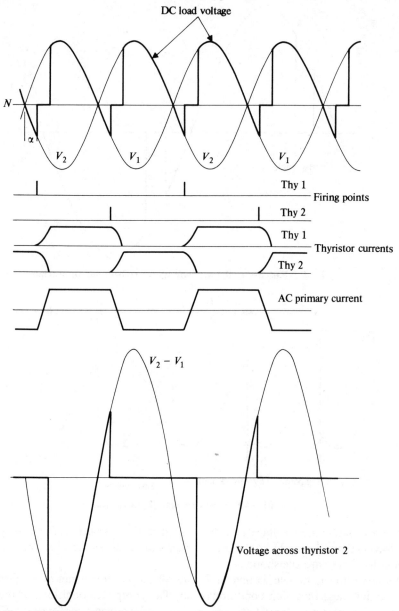

Fig. 4.9a Single-phase, half-wave circuit – delay angle α = 30 degrees

D.C. Voltage and Regulation

The d.c. voltage output always consists of sections of the a.c. voltage waveforms; it is never smooth d.c. It is normally considered in two parts, the mean d.c. value (the average value over the cycle) and its ripple components (see later in this section, d.c. voltage harmonics).

The mean d.c. level will depend on the a.c. supply voltage, the angle of delay α, and the voltage drops due to reactance, resistance, and the semiconductors.

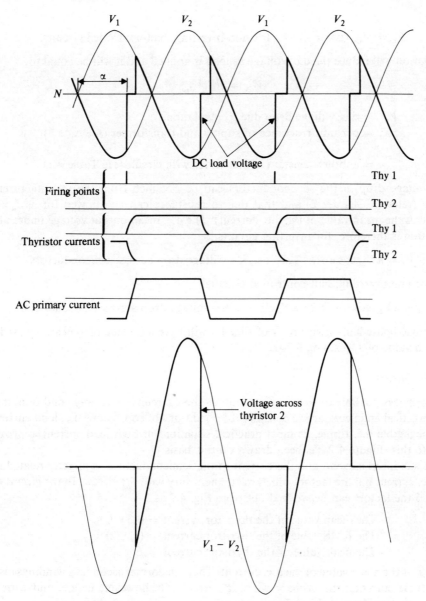

Fig. 4.9b Single-phase, half-wave circuit – delay angle α = 120 degrees

The open-circuit voltage with $\alpha = 0$ (V_{dio}) will depend directly on the circuit being used and the a.c. supply voltages.

In this chapter assume

$$V_{dio} = k \times V_{ac}$$

where V_{ac} is the RMS value of the a.c. supply line voltage and k is a constant which varies between circuits as given in Table 4.1. The mean d.c. voltage at any delay angle (α), assuming a continuous load current of small value will be:

$$V_d = V_{dio} \cos \alpha \quad \text{for inverting circuits}$$

and

$$V_d = V_{\text{dio}} (\cos \alpha + 1)/2 \quad \text{for non-inverting, half-controlled circuits.}$$

Regulation will reduce the d.c. voltage as load is applied and it will be equal to:

$$V_{\text{dL}} = dX_t V_{\text{dio}}$$

where

$V_{\text{dL}} = $ d.c. voltage drop due to regulation

$X_t = $ per unit reactance of supply and transformer (see note *)

and

$d = $ another constant which varies with circuit (see Table 4.1)

The voltage drop in the semiconductors can be obtained from the manufacturer's curves (refer to Chapter 2) and that due to resistance can be allowed for as $I_d \times R$ (I_d equals the mean value of the d.c. current). The d.c. mean output voltage under any condition is therefore, for inverting circuits,

$$V_d = kV_{\text{ac}} \cos \alpha - kV_{\text{ac}} dX_t - I_d R - \text{voltage drop across semiconductors}$$

and for non-inverting, half-controlled circuits,

$$V_d = kV_{\text{ac}}(\cos \alpha + 1)/2 - kV_{\text{ac}} dX_t - I_d R - \text{voltage drop across semiconductors}$$

The single-phase half-wave circuit of Fig. 4.5 will have a k value of $\sqrt{(2)}/\pi$, i.e., 0·45, and a d value of $1/\sqrt{2}$, i.e., 0·707.

Circuit Currents

Although it is possible to work out currents in these circuits under any condition, it is only practical and necessary to consider the conditions of continuous d.c. load current with negligible d.c. ripple, as most practical situations at high load current approximate to this. Figure 4.9 has been drawn on this basis.

The a.c. input current, and the current in the semiconductors, is directly related to the d.c. current but the factors which relate them vary with the circuit. In the circuit of Fig. 4.5 the factors can be worked out from Fig. 4.9 as:

The mean value of the thyristor current $= 0·5 \times I_d$

The RMS value of the thyristor current $= (1/\sqrt{2}) \times I_d$

The peak value of the thyristor current $= I_d$

where I_d is the mean value of the d.c. current. The transformer secondary windings also carry these currents; the primary winding current will, however, be a.c. and with a one-to-one transformer, $I_{\text{ac}} = I_d$.

These factors assume only small angles of overlap. The factors for all the circuits are given in Table 4.1.

Rate of Change of Current

In all naturally commutated circuits, the maximum rate of change of thyristor current di/dt always occurs during overlap when the current is commutating from one

* The per unit reactance of the supply, X_t, is measured by circulating full d.c. mean current through a d.c. side short-circuit, the circuit then operating in a sinusoidal condition. X_t is the value of a.c. supply voltage necessary to circulate the rated mean current, I_{dN} through the short-circuit, expressed as a proportion of the maximum d.c. voltage at no load, V_{dio}.

thyristor to another. The current rises to the d.c. level during the overlap angle and so the highest value will occur with the smallest overlap angle. In most circuits this occurs with $\alpha = 90$ degrees. The curves of Fig. 4.10 can be used to assess this condition.

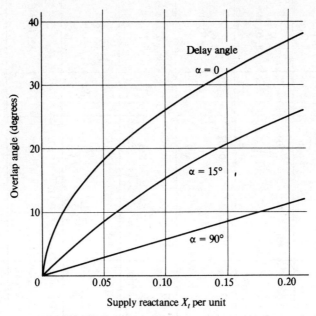

Fig. 4.10 Overlap angle in rectifying circuits

Thyristor Circuit Voltages

The correct selection of thyristors for a circuit will depend on the voltage levels impressed on the thyristors. Hence all the circuit waveform conditions include a waveform of the voltages across the thyristors. From the thyristor selection point of view, the crest working voltages (CWV) in the forward and reverse directions are of major importance and Table 4.1 includes the level of these voltages for all circuits. The CWV is usually directly related to the peak of the a.c. supply voltage but it is often most convenient to relate it to the open-circuit voltage from the circuit; hence two figures are given in Table 4.1.

In the single-phase half-wave circuit both the forward and reverse CWV values are equal to the peak of the total secondary voltage, i.e.,

$$\text{CWV} = 2\sqrt{(2)}V_{ac} = 2\sqrt{2}\,\frac{V_{dio}}{k}$$
$$= \pi \times V_{dio}$$
$$= 3\cdot142 \times \text{the maximum open-circuit d.c. voltage}$$

Rate of Change of Forward Voltage (dv/dt)

It is always necessary to study the thyristor voltage waveform to assess the maximum dv/dt likely to occur in the circuit. In general the voltage will always follow a sinusoidal form but during commutation sudden changes occur.

Table 4.1 Relationships in naturally commutated rectifying circuits

Circuit	Circuit Figure	Characteristic curves Figure	k $\dfrac{V_{dio}}{V_{ac}}$	$\dfrac{CWV}{V_{ac}}$	$\dfrac{CWV}{V_{dio}}$	Regulation d $\dfrac{Reg^N}{X_r}$	A.C. current RMS $\dfrac{I_{ac}}{I_d}$	Thyristor currents Peak $\dfrac{}{I_d}$	Mean $\dfrac{}{I_d}$	RMS $\dfrac{}{I_d}$	Pulse number	Harmonics In d.c. voltage	In a.c. current
Single-phase half-wave	4.2	4.4	0·45 $\dfrac{\sqrt{2}}{\pi}$	1·414 $\sqrt{2}$	3·142 π	0·707 $\dfrac{1}{\sqrt{2}}$	1·000 See note*	1·0	0·5	0·707 $\dfrac{1}{\sqrt{2}}$	2	2, 4, 6, 8, 10, etc.	3, 5, 7, 9, 11, etc.
Single-phase fully-controlled bridge	4.15	4.17	0·9 $\dfrac{2\sqrt{2}}{\pi}$	1·414 $\sqrt{2}$	1·571 $\dfrac{\pi}{2}$	0·707 $\dfrac{1}{\sqrt{2}}$	1·0	1·0	0·5	0·707 $\dfrac{1}{\sqrt{2}}$	2	2, 4, 6, 8, 10, etc.	3, 5, 7, 9, 11, etc.
Single-phase half-controlled bridge	4.18	4.20	0·9 $\dfrac{2\sqrt{2}}{\pi}$	1·414 $\sqrt{2}$	1·571 $\dfrac{\pi}{2}$	0·707 $\dfrac{1}{\sqrt{2}}$	1·0 See curves	1·0	0·5 See curves	0·707 See curves	2	2, 4, 6, 8, 10, etc.	3, 5, 7, 9, 11, etc.
Three-phase fully-controlled bridge	4.21	4.23	1·35 $\dfrac{3\sqrt{2}}{\pi}$	1·414 $\sqrt{2}$	1·05 $\dfrac{\pi}{3}$	0·5	0·816 $\dfrac{\sqrt{2}}{\sqrt{3}}$	1·0	0·333 $\dfrac{1}{3}$	0·577 $\dfrac{1}{\sqrt{3}}$	6	6, 12, 18, 24, etc.	5, 7, 11, 13, 17, 19, etc.
Three-phase half-controlled bridge	4.25	4.27	1·35 $\dfrac{3\sqrt{2}}{\pi}$	1·414 $\sqrt{2}$	1·05 $\dfrac{\pi}{3}$	0·5	0·816 See curves	1·0	0·333 See curves	0·577 See curves	3	3, 6, 9, 12, 15, etc.	2, 4, 5, 7, 8, 10, 11, etc.
Six-phase half-wave	4.29	4.31	0·675 $\dfrac{3}{\pi\sqrt{2}}$	1·414 $\sqrt{2}$	2·095 $\dfrac{2\pi}{3}$	0·5	0·408 See note*	0·5	0·167 $\dfrac{1}{6}$	0·289 $\dfrac{1}{2\sqrt{3}}$	6	6, 12, 18, 24, etc.	5, 7, 11, 13, 17, 19, etc.

* I_{ac} is transformer primary winding current assuming all windings have the same numbers of turns.

In the single-phase half-wave case, Fig. 4.9 shows no sudden rises of forward voltage occurring and the maximum dv/dt will be that obtained from the a.c. voltage wave.

Gating Requirements

With natural commutation, once a thyristor has been switched on the gate plays no further part in the action until the current reduces to zero, and then it needs restarting again – usually a cycle later. A gate current pulse sufficient to fire the thyristor once per cycle is all that is required. However, it will be seen later that in bridge circuits current has to flow through two thyristors and these will need to be fired together to establish current flow initially (see Chapter 8).

The range of phase shift, i.e., delay angle α, required for the gate pulses to achieve maximum voltage control range in all the circuits being considered here, is 180 degrees assuming continuous d.c. current flow. If a pure resistance load is in use then a smaller range of delay angle α may be sufficient.

The firing circuit will normally be isolated from the power circuit by a pulse transformer but whether it is or not, it must be appreciated that the cathode/gate connections to the thyristors will change in voltage to earth, during the cycle, following the thyristor cathode voltage waveform. The maximum voltage to earth will normally be the same as the thyristor CWV.

D.C. Output Harmonics

The d.c. voltage waveform in all circuits is predictable and further analysis of this will give the magnitude of the various harmonics present. Which harmonics are present in any particular circuit is related to the number of commutations per cycle, i.e., the pulse number, and these are given in Table 4.1.

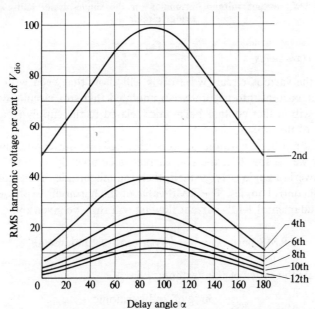

Fig. 4.11 D.C. output voltage harmonics for the single-phase, half-wave and single-phase, fully controlled bridge circuits

Reference to Figs 4.11 to 4.14 will give the magnitudes of the d.c. voltage harmonics as a proportion of the maximum output d.c. voltage, V_{dio}, assuming continuous d.c. load current for all of the circuits included in this chapter.

Assessment of load-circuit inductance with the d.c. voltage harmonics can be used to arrive at the level of harmonics in the d.c. current. This may well be of importance, particularly in two- and three-pulse circuits; if a d.c. motor load is to be used, a high current ripple adversely affects brush commutation.

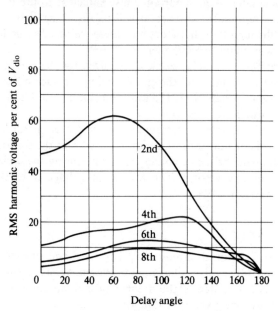

Fig. 4.12 D.C. output voltage harmonics for the single-phase, half-controlled bridge circuit

A.C. Current Harmonics

Reference to the various circuit waveforms will show that even with a smooth d.c. current the a.c. current into naturally commutated thyristor circuits will be far from sinusoidal. It will in fact contain harmonics related to the supply frequency and the pulse number of the circuit.

The magnitude of these harmonics can be obtained by Fourier analysis of the current waveforms. If we assume that the d.c. current is completely smooth with no ripple, and that the overlap angle is very small, then the magnitude of the harmonic will be the same at all control angles. The RMS value of the harmonic expressed as a percentage of the fundamental RMS current flowing will then be given by:

$$\text{RMS harmonic} = \frac{100}{m} \text{ per cent of fundamental}$$

(where m equals the order of the harmonic), i.e.,

50% of 2nd harmonic
20% of 5th harmonic
etc.

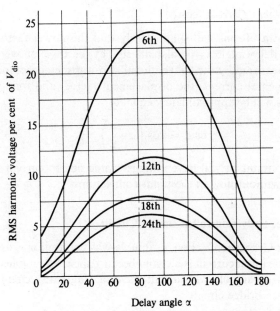

Fig. 4.13 D.C. output voltage harmonics for the three-phase, fully controlled
bridge and the six-phase, half-wave circuits

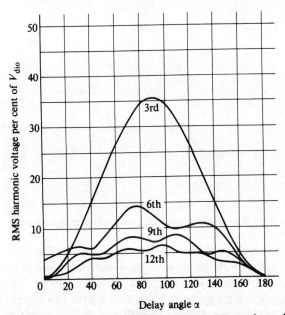

Fig. 4.14 D.C. output voltage harmonics from the three-phase, half-controlled
bridge circuit

In practice, the magnitudes vary with the angle of overlap and the d.c. current
ripple which is present. Hence different d.c. and commutating inductances and different delay angles will all vary the level of percentage harmonics present in the a.c.
line current.

Power Factor of the Input Current (cos ϕ)

Study of the circuit waveforms will show clearly that the power factor of the input current changes with delay angle α; it is also affected by the angle of overlap. The value that is likely to be measured by the conventional two-wattmeter method is the power factor of the fundamental current (the displacement factor) and for fully controlled inverting circuits this will be approximately equal to:

$$\cos \phi = \cos \left(\alpha + \frac{u}{2} \right)$$

In half-controlled circuits it will have a higher value due to current flywheeling in the thyristor circuit without flow in the input connections.

4.3 The Single-phase, Fully Controlled Bridge Circuit

The bridge circuit, or Graetz connection, or double-way connection is used in thyristor equipment because the input current is a.c. and because the CWV applied to the thyristors is lower than is obtainable with a half-wave or single-way circuit. Figure 4.15 shows the single-phase bridge circuit.

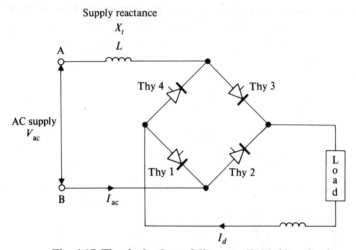

Fig. 4.15 The single-phase, fully controlled bridge circuit

The current flows through thyristors 1 and 3 during one half-cycle and in thyristors 2 and 4 during the next. With continuous load current, commutation takes place between thyristors 2 and 3 and thyristors 1 and 4 simultaneously. Thyristors 1 and 3 are fired at the same point in the cycle, and 2 and 4 are fired 180 degrees later.

Figures 4.16a and b show the detailed waveforms of this circuit at two representative delay-angle conditions, and Fig. 4.17 shows the way in which the circuit relationships change with delay angle. From these it can be seen that:

1. Voltages from full positive to full negative can be achieved as long as current flow can be maintained. As with other single-phase circuits being considered,

$$V_{\text{dio}} = \frac{2\sqrt{2}}{\pi} \times V_{\text{ac}}$$

and over the operating range

$$V_d = \frac{2\sqrt{2}}{\pi} V_{ac} \cos \alpha - \frac{2\sqrt{2}}{\pi} V_{ac} \frac{1}{\sqrt{2}} X_t - I_d R - 2V_T$$

where

V_{ac} = RMS value of the supply voltage
X_t = per unit reactance of the supply system including transformer
I_d = load current (mean value)
R = circuit resistance
V_T = Thyristor ON-state forward voltage drop at current I_d

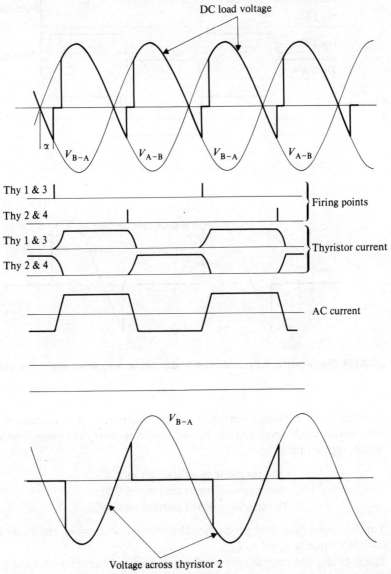

Fig. 4.16a Single-phase, fully controlled bridge circuit with delay angle α = 30 degrees

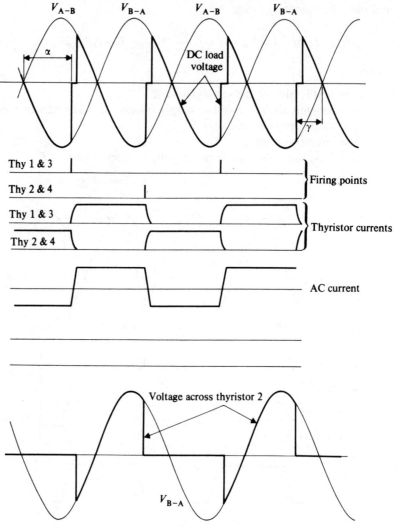

Fig. 4.16b Single-phase, fully controlled bridge circuit with delay angle α = 120 degrees

2. The period of thyristor current flow on continuous d.c. current is just over 180 degrees at all delay angles. All the thyristors carry the same level of current which approximates to:

$$\text{the thyristor peak current} = I_d$$
$$\text{the thyristor mean current} = 0 \cdot 5 I_d$$
$$\text{the thyristor RMS current} = 0 \cdot 707 I_d$$

The a.c. input current is proportional to the d.c. current at any delay angle and its RMS value is equal to I_d.

3. The forward and reverse crest working voltages of the thyristors are both equal to the peak of the a.c. supply voltage, i.e.,

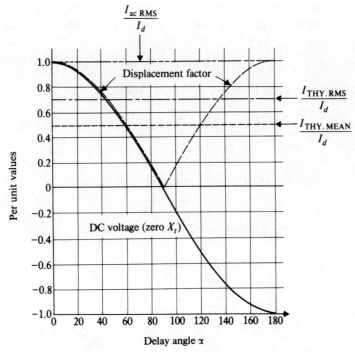

Fig. 4.17 Relationships in the single-phase, fully controlled bridge circuit

$$CVW = \sqrt{(2)}V_{ac}$$
$$= V_{dio} \times \frac{\pi}{2}$$

4. No sudden rates of rise of forward voltage dv/dt occur across the thyristors.
5. Two channels of gating pulses are required displaced by 180 degrees apart, each with two outputs to feed the two thyristors which are conducting together.

4.4 The Single-phase, Half-controlled Bridge Circuit

This bridge circuit uses only two thyristors and two diodes and its normal form is shown in Fig. 4.18.

The presence of two diodes D1 and D2 across the d.c. terminals means that the d.c. voltage can never reverse and that this circuit cannot operate in inversion. Whenever the a.c. voltage transferred to the d.c. would be negative, current circulates through D1 and D2 supported by the load inductance. This circuit has three main modes of operation; when A is positive with respect to B, current flows A→L→D2→Load→ Thy1→B; as soon as the voltage reverses, the current transfers to flowing through D2→Load→D1; and when thyristor 2 is fired the current flows B→Thy2→Load→ D1→L→A. The commutation sequence is therefore Thy1 to D1, D2 to Thy2, Thy2 to D2, D1 to Thy1, and so on.

Figures 4.19a and b indicate the circuit waveforms under two delay angle conditions and Fig. 4.20 displays the current and voltage relationships graphically. From these it will be seen that:

1. Only positive output voltages can be achieved due to the presence of the diodes. The maximum voltage obtainable is the same as the fully controlled bridge, i.e.,

$$V_{dio} = \frac{2\sqrt{2}}{\pi} V_{ac}$$

Over working range, however, the output voltage will be

$$V_d = \frac{\sqrt{2}}{\pi} V_{ac}(\cos \alpha + 1) - \frac{2\sqrt{2}}{\pi} V_{ac} \frac{1}{\sqrt{2}} X_t - I_d R - (V_T + V_D)$$

where

$$V_T = \text{thyristor forward drop at current } I_d$$

and

$$V_D = \text{diode forward drop at current } I_d$$

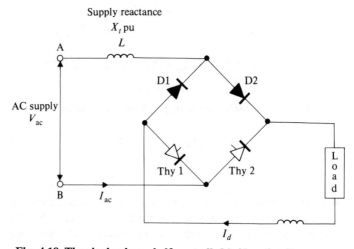

Fig. 4.18 The single-phase, half-controlled bridge circuit

2. The period of thyristor current flow reduces as the delay angle increases, whereas the period of diode current increases. The diodes may need to be higher-rated than the thyristors. The a.c. current even at constant load current reduces as the delay angle increases. The overlap angle for commutation from a thyristor to a diode is greater than that from a diode to a thyristor due to the higher circuit voltage present during the latter.
3. The CWV, both forward and reverse, is equal to the peak of the a.c. supply voltage, i.e.,

$$\text{CWV} = \sqrt{(2)}V_{ac}$$
$$= V_{dio} \times \tfrac{1}{2}\pi$$

4. There is a sudden jump up in the forward voltage across the thyristor when the other thyristor commutates out. The dv/dt occurring here will be high and will depend on other circuit components, i.e., capacitors and chokes, etc. (see Chapter 6).

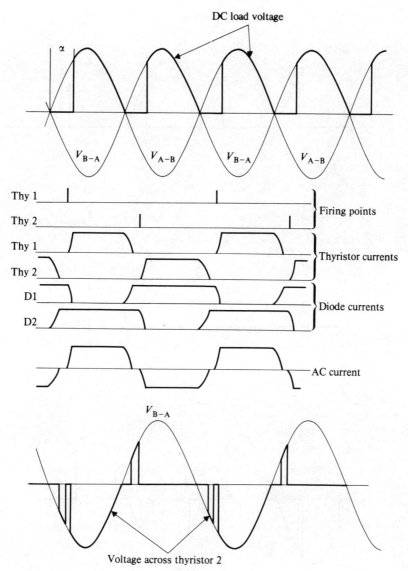

DC load voltage

V_{B-A} V_{A-B} V_{B-A} V_{A-B}

Thy 1
Thy 2 } Firing points

Thy 1
Thy 2 } Thyristor currents

D1
D2 } Diode currents

AC current

V_{B-A}

Voltage across thyristor 2

Fig. 4.19a Single-phase, half-controlled bridge circuit with delay angle $\alpha = 45$ degrees

Alternative arrangements of this circuit are possible having the two thyristors both feeding the one side of the load and the two diodes feeding the other side. In this case the periods of current flow in the diodes and thyristors are constant at all delay angles. However, the flywheel path for load current now includes both a thyristor and a diode, and if currents are induced into the load circuit forward breakover of the thyristor may be necessary to allow current flow.

4.5 The Three-phase, Fully Controlled Bridge Circuit

This three-phase bridge circuit contains six thyristors, two connected to each of the

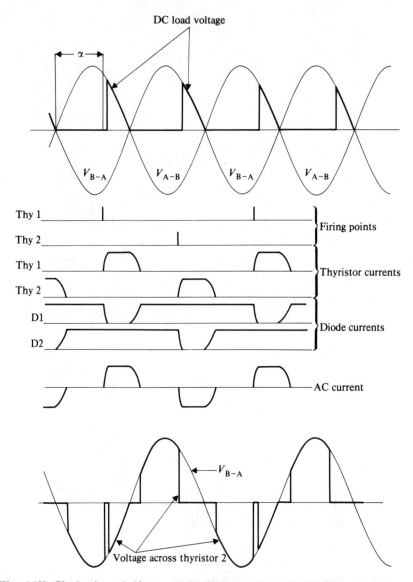

Fig. 4.19b Single-phase, half-controlled bridge circuit with delay angle α = 120 degrees

three-phase supply inputs (see Fig. 4.21). At all times current flows through at least one positive thyristor and one negative thyristor.

Each cycle is split into three equal sections by the positive thyristors and also by the three negative thyristors. The three positive thyristors fire sequentially at 120-degree (electrical) intervals, the three negative ones do likewise but always their swtiching points are 60 degrees from those of the positive arms. Hence each of the three a.c. connections are directly connected to the d.c. positive and d.c. negative for 120-degree periods of time. During one cycle the current flow is therefore

Period (degrees)	A.C. circuit	Thyristors Positive	Thyristors Negative	Load
0–60	A and C	1	2	√
60–120	B and C	3	2	√
120–180	B and A	3	4	√
180–240	C and A	5	4	√
240–300	C and B	5	6	√
300–360	A and B	1	6	√

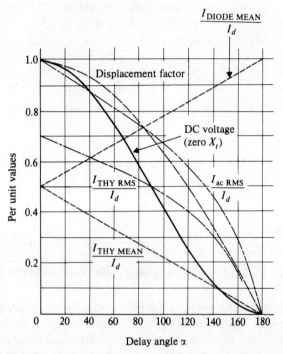

Fig. 4.20 Relationships in the single-phase, half-controlled bridge circuit

Commutation takes place separately between the positive thyristors 1 to 3, 3 to 5, 5 to 1, etc., and the negative ones, i.e., 2 to 4, 4 to 6, 6 to 2, and so on. In this circuit, commutation cannot take place when the a.c. supplies pass through zero but only when the incoming line rises above the outgoing one.

This circuit is most satisfactorily studied by considering the supply voltage with respect to a supply neutral point. The waveforms of Figs 4.22a and b are drawn on this basis and again shown for two delay angles of 30 and 120 degrees. Study of these shows:

1. Voltages from full positive to full negative can be achieved as long as current flow can be maintained by the load. As the circuit is three-phase, the open-circuit d.c. voltage becomes

$$V_{\text{dio}} = \frac{3\sqrt{2}}{\pi} V_{\text{ac}}$$

71

and over the operating range,

$$V_d = \frac{3\sqrt{2}}{\pi} V_{ac} \cos \alpha - \frac{3\sqrt{2}}{\pi} V_{ac} \frac{1}{2} X_t - I_d R - 2V_T$$

where V_{ac} now equals the RMS value of the a.c. line voltage and V_T is the thyristor forward voltage drop at current I_d.

2. Each thyristor carries current for 120 degrees plus the angle of overlap. Every thyristor carries the same level of current of approximately:

Thyristor peak current $= I_d$
Thyristor mean current $= 0.333 \, I_d$
Thyristor RMS current $= 0.577 \, I_d$

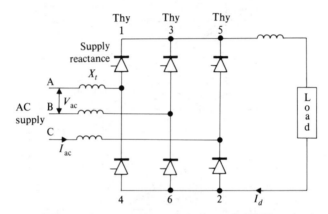

Fig. 4.21 The three-phase, fully controlled bridge circuit

The supply current is a.c. and it is independent of delay angle; it depends directly on the level of load current, its RMS value is approximately equal to $0.816I_d$.

3. The voltage across the thyristors in the OFF-state show that the CWV in the reverse direction occurs at low delay angles (rectification) and that in the forward direction it occurs at large delay angles (i.e., inversion). The maximum level in either direction is given by:

$$\text{CWV} = \sqrt{(2)}V_{ac} = \frac{\pi}{3} V_{dio}$$

i.e., CWV is only 1·05 times the maximum d.c. voltage.

4. The voltage across the thyristors shows a very sudden rate of rise of voltage in the forward direction in the $\alpha = 120$-degree condition. In fact, this is the worst case and it shows a rise to approximately 50 per cent of the CWV value in the time it takes for a thyristor to turn on (rise time) of, say, 0·5 to 1 microsecond.

5. Six separate channels of firing pulses are required, each separated by 60 electrical degrees. Working in the region of discontinuous current, when the initial starting of current is required, it is necessary to ensure that each thyristor is also gated 60 degrees after its initial pulse (see Chapter 8).

Figure 4.23 shows the relationships in this circuit in graphical form.

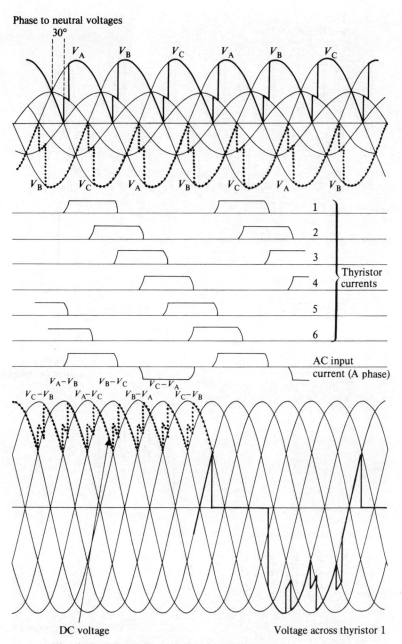

Phase to neutral voltages

V_A V_B V_C V_A V_B V_C

V_B V_C V_A V_B V_C V_A V_B

1

2

3

4

Thyristor currents

5

6

AC input current (A phase)

V_A-V_B V_B-V_C V_C-V_A

V_C-V_B V_A-V_C V_B-V_A V_C-V_B

DC voltage

Voltage across thyristor 1

Fig. 4.22a Three-phase, fully controlled bridge, $\alpha = 30$ degrees

73

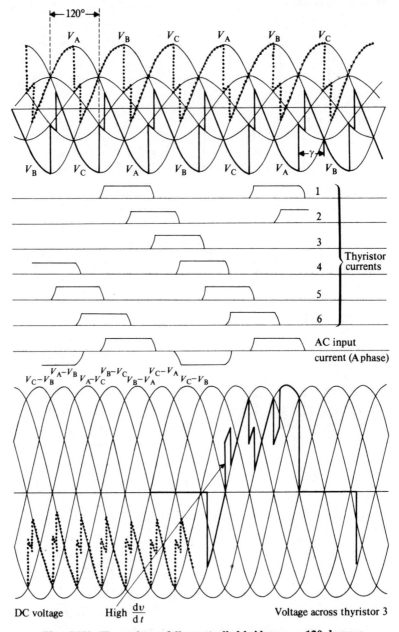

Fig. 4.22b Three-phase, fully controlled bridge, $\alpha = 120$ degrees

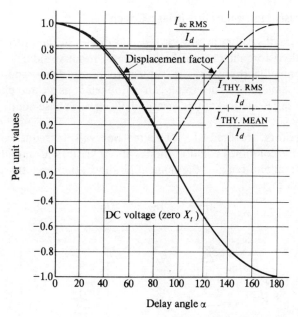

Fig. 4.23 Relationships in the three-phase, fully controlled bridge circuit

Fig. 4.24 A three-phase, fully controlled bridge thyristor assembly with the a.c. and d.c. connections shown on the left-hand side. The picture shows the heatsinks, the series reactors, and the fuses clearly (ASEA Ltd)

4.6 The Three-phase, Half-controlled Bridge Circuit

This circuit contains thyristors in three arms, and diodes in the other three (see Fig. 4.25). The three thyristors may be on the positive or negative side.

In this case, only the thyristors are subject to phase delay; the diodes always commutate at the same point. The circuit can be looked at as a three-phase, half-wave diode circuit in series with a three-phase, half-wave, phase-controlled thyristor circuit.

The three thyristors are fired at 120-degree intervals in sequence and the d.c. output voltage is the combined result of diodes and thyristors. Commutation between the diodes is constant and remains the same at all times; the three thyristors commutate between each other.

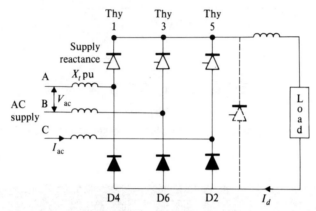

Fig. 4.25 The three-phase, half-controlled bridge circuit

Figures 4.26a and b show the circuit waveforms at two representative thyristor delay angles. These diagrams show:

1. Only unidirectional output voltage is possible and power inversion cannot be achieved.

$$V_{dio} = \frac{3\sqrt{2}}{\pi} V_{ac},$$

and over the operating range

$$V_d = \frac{3\sqrt{2}}{2\pi} V_{ac}(\cos \alpha + 1) - \frac{3\sqrt{2}}{\pi} V_{ac} \frac{1}{2} X_t - I_d R - (V_T + V_D)$$

The output voltage will contain three-pulse ripple.

2. The thyristor current over most of the working range differs from the diode current in that its overlap angle is smaller. The thyristor current also moves in phase with the delay angle whereas the diode currents remain in one phase position. The a.c. current alters in magnitude as the control angle changes because the positive and negative currents tend to overlap above $\alpha = 60$ degrees (see Fig. 4.27). The a.c. current is not symmetrical and as a result it will contain low even harmonics.

76

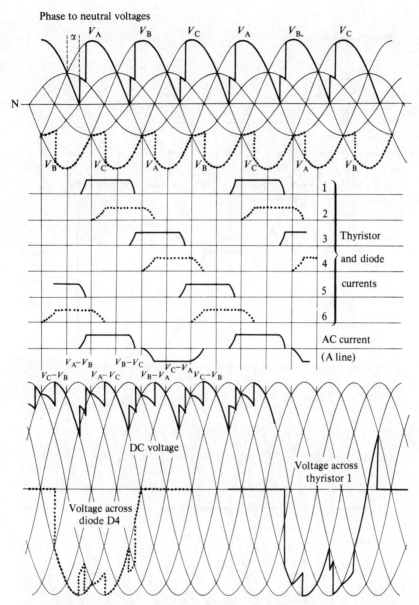

Phase to neutral voltages

Fig. 4.26a Three-phase, half-controlled bridge at delay angle of 30 degrees

77

Phase to neutral voltages

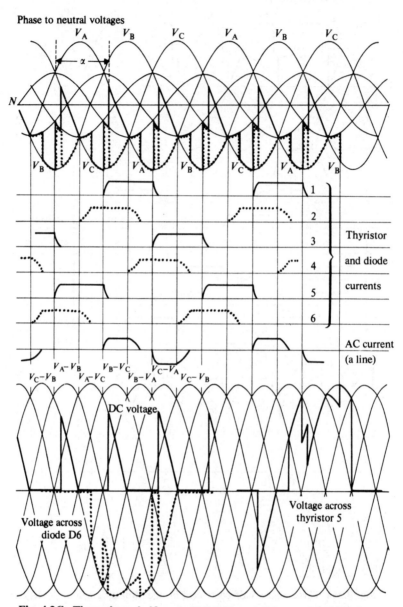

Fig. 4.26b Three-phase, half-controlled bridge at delay angle of 120 degrees

78

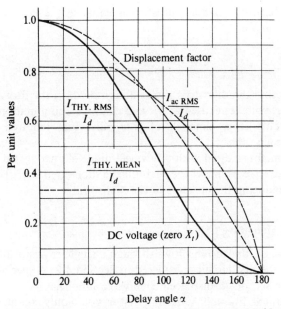

Fig. 4.27 Relationships in the three-phase, half-controlled bridge circuit

Fig. 4.28 A forced-air cooled assembly consisting of a three-phase, half-controlled
bridge with flywheel diodes (Westinghouse Brake and Signal Co. Ltd)

3. The CWV of both diodes and thyristors is equal to the peak value of the a.c. supply waveform, i.e.,

$$\mathrm{CWV} = \sqrt{(2)}V = \frac{\pi}{3}V_{\mathrm{dio}}$$

4. The voltage across the thyristors shows a high dv/dt in the forward direction at low d.c. output voltages caused at the end of diode commutation period.
5. In this case, only three channels of gate pulses are required, displaced 120 degrees from each other.

This circuit is sometimes fitted with a flywheel diode shown dotted in Fig. 4.25. If it is present it will carry current whenever both the diode and thyristor of one phase would do so, thus reducing the currents in the main bridge.

4.7 The Six-phase, Half-wave Circuit

In this six-phase circuit, the current flows through a single thyristor in the series path in a similar way to the first circuit considered in Section 4.2. A special transformer is required to produce six, phase-displaced, sine wave supplies.

In its simplest form as Fig. 4.29A, each thyristor would only conduct for a period of 60 degrees plus the overlap angle and in most power situations this is not considered satisfactory. The inter-phase transformer (IPT) shown in Fig. 4.29B enables the thyristors to conduct for periods in excess of 120 degrees. With correct transformer design, 120-degree conduction can be maintained over the majority of the load and delay-angle range. Even with circuit A, the equivalent operation can be produced with a suitable design of transformer having a five-limb core.

The circuit can best be understood by considering it as two three-phase half-wave circuits operating in parallel, the inter-phase transformer serving to ensure continuous current flow in each three-phase group. The output d.c. voltage will then be equal to the mean value between each of the two three-phase groups, the difference in voltage appearing across the inter-phase transformer.

Figures 4.30a and b show the circuit waveforms, again under two sample delay-angle conditions, and study of these diagrams shows:

1. A full range of positive and negative output voltage can be achieved and as a result both rectification and inversion operation is possible as long as current flow can be maintained. The maximum open-circuit voltage obtainable is

$$V_{\mathrm{dio}} = \frac{3}{\pi\sqrt{2}}V_{\mathrm{ac}}$$

where V_{ac} is the RMS value of the secondary line voltage. In this circuit, the output voltage on load changes significantly as the thyristor conduction period extends from an initial 60 to 120 degrees as the IPT comes into operation. A reduction of approximately 13 per cent V_{dio} occurs during this period and the d.c. voltage on load then becomes

$$V_d = \frac{3}{\pi\sqrt{2}}V_{\mathrm{ac}}\sin\frac{\pi}{3}\cos\alpha - \frac{3}{\pi\sqrt{2}}V_{\mathrm{ac}}\sin\frac{\pi}{3}\frac{1}{2}X_t - I_dR - V_{\mathrm{T}}$$

assuming 120-degree plus overlap conduction.

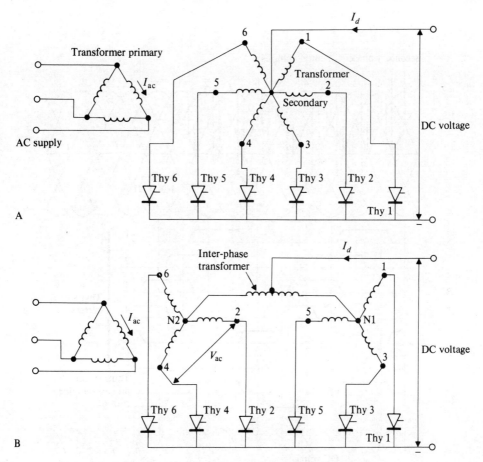

Fig. 4.29 The six-phase, half-wave rectifying circuit

2. The current in all thyristors flows for 120 degrees plus the overlap angle and the same unidirectional current flows through the transformer secondary windings. The two in-phase secondaries therefore need to be wound on the same core limb to prevent core saturation of the transformer. The circuit currents do not vary at different delay angles; they depend only on the d.c. current. For the thyristor and transformer secondary current:

$$\text{Peak value} = 0.5I_d$$
$$\text{Mean value} = 0.167I_d$$
$$\text{RMS value} = 0.289I_d$$

3. The thyristor CWV is much higher than the maximum d.c. voltage; it basically consists of the d.c. voltage plus the a.c. secondary voltage. The maximum reverse CWV occurs during rectification and the maximum forward value during inversion.

Secondary phase +. neutral voltages

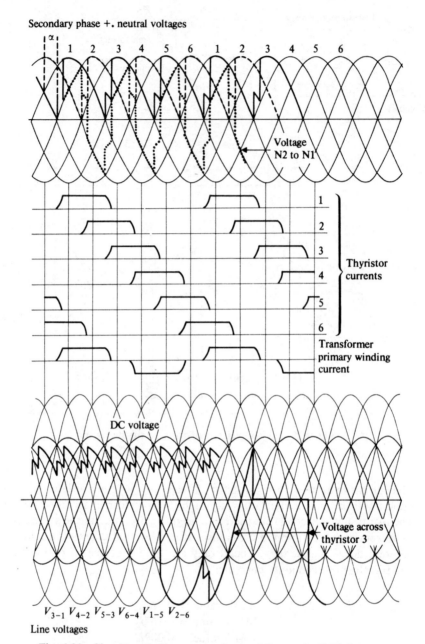

Fig. 4.30a Six-phase, half-wave circuit at a delay angle of 30 degrees

82

Secondary phase to neutral voltages

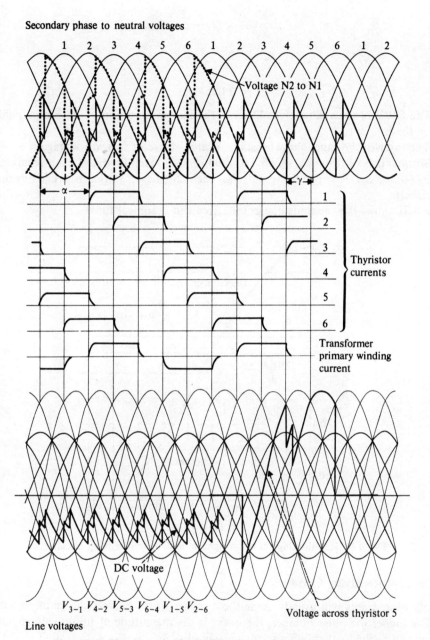

Fig. 4.30b Six-phase, half-wave circuit at a delay angle of 120 degrees

83

$$\text{CWV} = \sqrt{(2)}V_{ac}$$

$$= \sqrt{(2)}\,\frac{\sqrt{(2)}\pi}{3}\,V_{dio}$$

$$= \frac{2\pi}{3}\,V_{dio}$$

$$= 2{\cdot}095V_{dio}$$

The CWV is approximately 2·42 times the maximum output voltage obtainable on load.

4. The thyristor voltages show no sudden rates of rise of forward voltage.
5. Six channels of firing pulses are required, one for each thyristor, each separated by 60 degrees. A single firing pulse on each channel is all that is needed in this circuit.

Figure 4.31 shows the relationships in this circuit in graphical form.

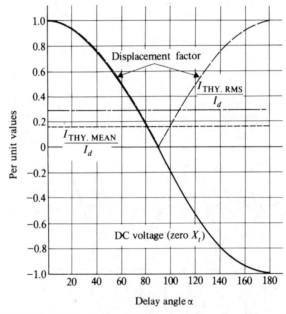

Fig. 4.31 Relationships in the six-phase, half-wave rectifying circuit

4.8 Choice of Rectifying Circuits

The following points will usually guide the designer to the correct choice of circuit:
1. The higher the pulse number, the lower is the magnitude of ripple voltage and current in the load circuit and the a.c. supply.
2. Fully controlled circuits are capable of inversion and therefore regeneration; half-controlled circuits are not.
3. Half-wave circuits require higher voltage thyristors than bridge circuits producing the same output d.c. voltage.
4. Bridge circuits require twice as many thyristors than half-wave circuits to carry the same current.

Therefore, in general, half-wave circuits tend to be used for low-voltage, high-current use and where the minimum of thyristors are required. Bridge circuits are the most widely used. The three-pulse, half-controlled bridge circuit is only used where regeneration is not required and the high harmonics are acceptable.

4.9 References

1. IEC Publication 146, *Semiconductor Convertors*, 1973 amended 1975.
2. J. C. Read, 'The calculation of rectifier and inverter performance characteristics', *IEE Proc.*, **92**, 29, 1945.
3. D. B. Corbyn and N. L. Potter, 'The characteristics and protection of semiconductor rectifiers', *IEE Proc.*, **107**, 1960.
4. R. L. Witzke, J. V. Kresser, and J. K. Dillard, 'The influences of a.c. reactance and voltage regulation of six-phase rectifiers', *IEEE*, 1952.
5. R. Feinberg and W. Y. Chen, 'Commutation reactance of the transformer in a static power convertor', *IEE Proc.*, **111**, 1, 1964.
6. L. G. Dobinson, 'Tradition changes with harmonics', *IEE Conference Publication 154*, 179–183, Sept. 1977.
7. R. A. Hammond and P. Whittaker, 'Harmonics and transients in relation to static convertors', *IEE Conference Publication 8*, Feb. 1963.
8. J. Schaefer, 'Voltage and current ripple in rectifier systems', *AIEE*, 63–196, 339–344, Nov. 1963.
9. B. R. Pelly, *Thyristor Phase Controlled Convertors and Cyclo-convertors*, John Wiley, 1971.

5. Forced Commutation Circuits

Once thyristors are operating in the ON-state, carrying forward current, they can only be turned off by reducing the current flowing in them to zero for sufficient time to allow removal of the charged carriers. When operating from a.c. supplies, the regular reversal of voltages and currents allows turn-off to be carried out naturally. When power is supplied to the circuit as direct current, there are no natural zero current or reversal periods and some other means of turn-off is needed. If additional components are included with the thyristors, it is possible to force the thyristor current to zero even in d.c. circuits. This process will be referred to as *forced commutation* and it allows the thyristor to be operated as a real switch capable of being opened and closed at will.

The use of forced commutation is not restricted to d.c.-supplied circuits; naturally commutated circuits can also benefit if thyristor turn-off is required at an unnatural point in the cycle. Early turn-off can improve the power factor of such circuits but its cost has restricted its application to very special circumstances.

Although the principles of forced commutation have been known for many years, it has been the development of the thyristor and the reduction in its turn-off time which has led to the development of practical circuits.

In this chapter it is intended to cover the general principles of forced commutation, the practical circuits used to achieve it, and the overall thyristor chopper and inverter circuits that are used in practical applications.

5.1 The Principles of Forced Commutation Switching

If a charged capacitor is switched in parallel with a thyristor which is carrying a load current, the current will temporarily transfer into the capacitor, thus reducing the thyristor current to zero. At the same time the capacitor voltage will be applied as a reverse voltage to the thyristor; as the capacitor discharges this voltage will reduce, as shown in Fig. 5.1.

This is the principle of forced commutation and it demonstrates some of the basic limitations which exist even in many of the more complex circuits used to achieve it.

    (a) The thyristor must have turned off by point B as the circuit will then apply forward voltage to the device. This point will be decided by the level of load current and the nature of the load.

    (b) The rate of change of current through the switch will be very high. This may not be a problem in the case of a mechanical switch but if it is replaced by a thyristor, di/dt will need to be limited.

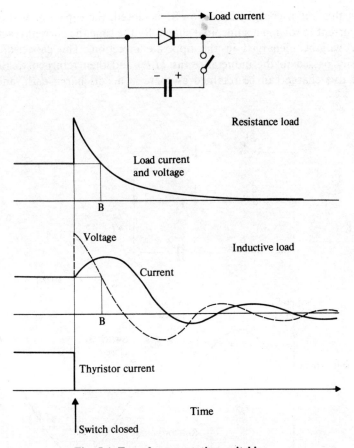

Fig. 5.1 Forced commutation switching

(c) Additional components will be needed to charge the capacitor in the correct
   direction for it to turn the main thyristor off.

In practice, most thyristor circuits need to be repetitive in operation and a cyclic
method of charging the capacitors is required. Obviously, the time taken to recharge
the capacitors will affect the frequency of switching which can be used.

The ability of such a forced-commutation capacitor method to successfully switch
off a thyristor will depend directly on the size and voltage of the capacitor and the
turn-off time of the thyristor. The capacitor will discharge at a predetermined rate
which will be related to the level of load current. The capacitor charge must be able
to maintain zero current in the thyristor for at least the turn-off time of the device,
even at the maximum circuit current.

All forced-commutation switching methods can only turn off currents up to a specific maximum level and this will be related to the capacitor charge and will be inversely
dependent on the thyristor turn-off time.

In the following sections, the practical circuits which can achieve repetitive switching
will be considered in detail. They all depend, however, on the principles of circuit
resonance and it may be useful to consider these first.

Figure 5.2 shows a charged capacitor with a series inductance, switches, and diodes.

If from this initial charged condition S1 is closed, the capacitor will discharge via D1, the current following a sinusoidal shape. By the time the current reaches zero, the capacitor will be recharged in the opposite direction. The capacitor energy has temporarily passed to the inductance (as $\frac{1}{2}LI^2$) and then returned to the capacitor. This negative charge can be retained as there is no discharge path, and S1 can be opened.

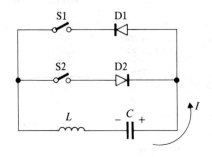

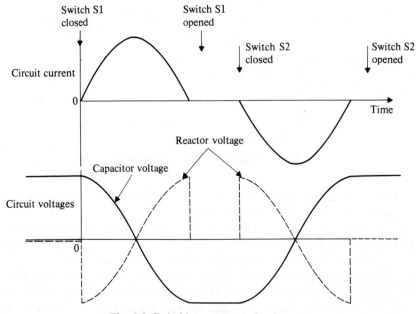

Fig. 5.2 Switching resonant circuits

If then S2 is closed, the capacitor will again discharge and recharge with a sinusoidal current waveshape, to return to its original condition.

If, as we have done, we neglect circuit resistance and diode voltage drops then:

$$\text{The half-cycle time} = \pi\sqrt{(LC)} \text{ seconds}$$

and

$$\text{the peak current} = V_C\sqrt{\left(\frac{C}{L}\right)} \text{ amperes}$$

88

The switches S1 and S2 will in practical circuits be thyristors which may be specifically included to assist commutation, or they may be the normal circuit thyristors.

Starting has always to be considered in forced-commutation circuits. The commutation capacitors need to be primed before they are called to turn off thyristors. Insufficient charge will result in failure to turn off.

5.2 Chopper Principles

The simplest application of forced commutation is the d.c. switch which is called a *chopper* when it is used for frequent switching and d.c. control. It is usually used in the form shown in Fig. 5.3, a flywheel diode being connected across the load circuit to allow circulation of load current when the main thyristor switch is opened. This allows the turn-off process to happen unhindered by the load inductance. When the main thyristor switch is turned on, the diode current will transfer into the thyristor and the d.c. supply.

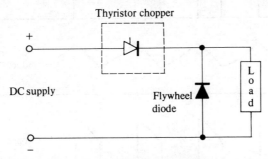

Fig. 5.3 The basic chopper circuit

A chopper can be used just to allow a d.c. circuit to be opened statically. Its more useful purpose is, however, to control the level of current and voltage in the load circuit by repetitive switching, as shown in Fig. 5.4.

Although the chopper cannot control the level of the d.c. voltage which is applied to the load, it can control the time for which it is connected. If the thyristor switch can be opened and closed frequently, the average value of the load voltage and current can be varied. Many patterns of load voltage are possible by varying the ON/OFF time ratio of the thyristor switch. If the load is inductive, the current in it can be continuous, as shown in the diagrams. If the load is resistive or capacitive, a filter may be required to smooth out the output voltage ripple.

The form of control can be any of the following:

1. A constant ON-time, varying the OFF-time to produce smooth output mean voltage variation.
2. A constant OFF-time, varying the ON-time.
3. A constant cycle time varying the ON/OFF ratio.
4. Any combination of all 1, 2, and 3.

The choice is usually made to give the minimum level of ripple current. In some cases, the chopper can be directly controlled by the load current so that as soon as the current reaches the high limit the chopper is turned OFF and when it reaches a lower limit the chopper is turned ON. The particular pattern of frequency and ON/OFF ratio is then completely dependent on the load characteristics.

Owing to the need to allow sufficient time for commutation capacitor charging and for the turn-off process, choppers often have a minimum output pulse width below which smooth control is not possible; they may also have a minimum OFF pulse width at the other extreme of the control range. The firing arrangements made must prevent the chopper firing incorrectly within these back and front stop limits (see Chapter 8).

Many designs of d.c. chopper switches of varying complexity and capability have been produced. The following two sections include three typical circuits chosen to illustrate the basic factors involved in chopper circuit design and operation.

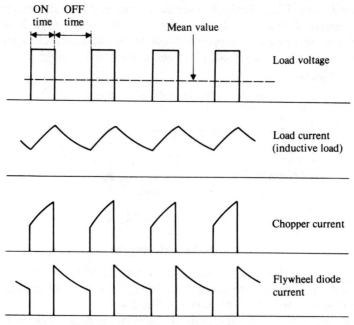

Fig. 5.4 Repetitive chopper switching

5.3 The Single-thyristor Chopper

The simplest chopper circuit possible is that using a single thyristor, as shown in Fig. 5.5. This diagram also shows the voltage and current waveforms which will occur during the switching process, these having been drawn assuming a high-inductance load, a high-capacity d.c. supply, and the initial conditions as shown in the circuit.

With this, the simplest arrangement, the only controllable feature is the point in time when the thyristor is turned ON. The process of turn-off is then completely automatic, depending only on the component values.

This circuit goes through three modes of operation as shown in Fig. 5.6. During period A, immediately following turn-on, the full supply voltage is applied to the load and the capacitor charge gradually reverses by circulating a current through the thyristor, reactor L, and capacitor C. At the end of this period the capacitor current reverses and the capacitor takes over the supply of the load current from the thyristor

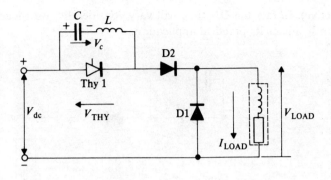

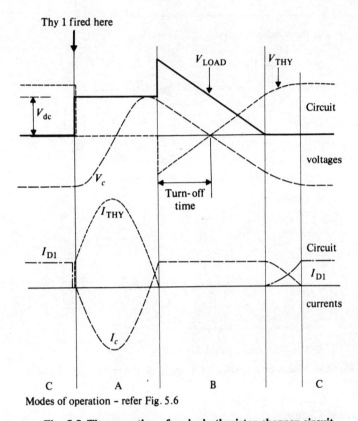

Modes of operation – refer Fig. 5.6

Fig. 5.5 The operation of a single-thyristor chopper circuit

which subsequently turns OFF (gate current having previously been removed). The load voltage therefore suddenly rises to $V_{supply} + V_{capacitor}$ at the start of period B. As the load current is assumed to be constant, the capacitor voltage will reduce linearly until the load voltage becomes zero. At the start of period C the diode gradually takes over the load current as allowed by the inductance L. The presence of diode D2 allows the capacitor to retain a higher charge than the supply voltage.

The circuit therefore has an ON-time basically fixed by the circuit components (i.e., L and C) but altered by the value of the load current and by its nature (resistive or inductive). In fact the ON-time will vary considerably with load current and this significantly affects its practical application.

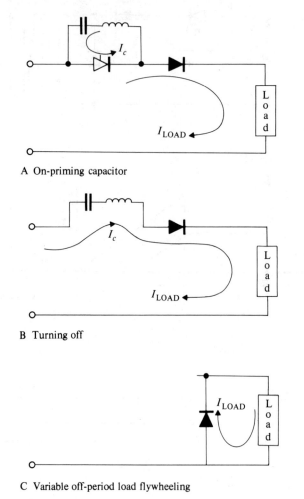

A On-priming capacitor

B Turning off

C Variable off-period load flywheeling

Fig. 5.6 Modes of operation of a single-thyristor chopper circuit

5.4 Two-thyristor Choppers

The use of two thyristors, one to control turn-on and one to turn the main thyristor off, allows a much higher degree of control and flexibility. Of the many circuit arrangements used, two examples have been chosen, one which uses a commutating capacitor/ inductive circuit connected across the main thyristor, and the other with this circuit connected across the load.

Figure 5.7 shows the circuit for the first example, the circuit voltage, and current waveforms; and the modes of operation of the circuit are shown in Fig. 5.8.

Thyristor 1 switches the supply into the load and also charges up the commutating capacitor C via D2 and L to a suitable positive value. The firing of thyristor 2 discharges C, removing the load current from the main thyristor. Explaining the modes of operation in sequence:

Assume C to be charged to V_{dc} and the load current initially circulating through D1.

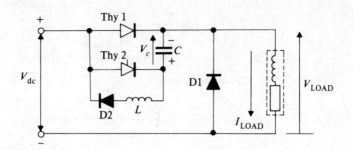

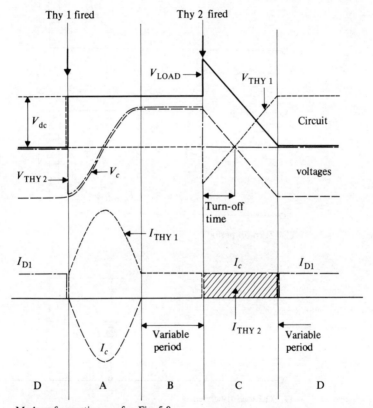

Modes of operation – refer Fig. 5.8

Fig. 5.7 The operation of a two-thyristor chopper circuit

Period A. On firing Thy1, the load current immediately transfers into Thy1 and the capacitor circulates a current through L, D2, and Thy1 to reverse its charge. When the capacitor current reaches zero, the diode D2 holds the capacitor charge.

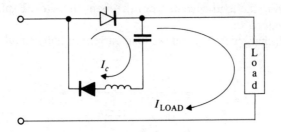

A   On-priming capacitor

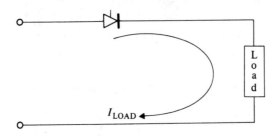

B   On-period variable

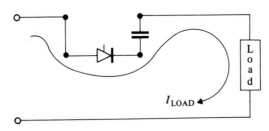

C   Turn-off period

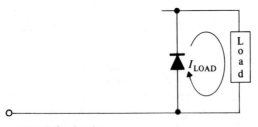

D   Off-load flywheeling

Fig. 5.8 Modes of operation of chopper of Fig. 5.7

Period B. This charge is maintained while Thy1 continues to supply the load for
   ON   whatever period of time is desired. The load current will increase during
          this period.

Period C. Firing of Thy2 initiates turn-off. The load current now flows through
          Thy2 and *C*, discharging the capacitor with a linear reduction in voltage.

When $V_C = V_{dc}$ the load voltage is zero and the load current transfers into D1.

Period D. It remains in diode D1 for as long a period as required. In practice, the
OFF   current will reduce during this period.

In this circuit the turn-off time varies with the load current as the commutating capacitor discharges through the load. The shortest turn-off time available will occur at high load current.

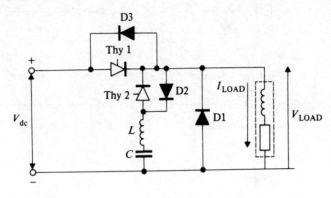

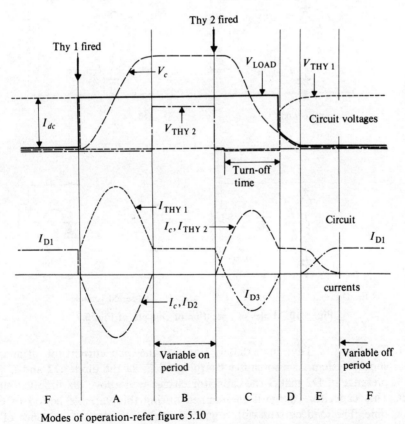

Modes of operation-refer figure 5.10

Fig. 5.9 The operation of a two-thyristor chopper circuit

95

The circuit of Fig. 5.9 operates in a different way. The capacitor charge path is now via Thy1, D2, and L and it has two discharge paths: L, Thy2, D3, and back through the supply; and secondly L, Thy2, and through the load. The supply therefore needs to be able to accept reverse current, and if it can the turn-off time of the circuit is much less dependent on load current than the previous one.

There are more modes of operation in this circuit and these are shown in Fig. 5.10. Under the initial condition D1 is carrying the load current and C is not charged.

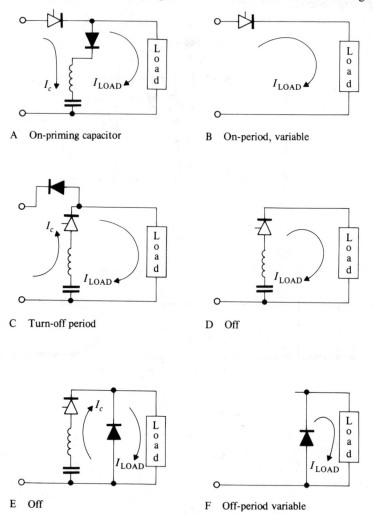

A   On-priming capacitor

B   On-period, variable

C   Turn-off period

D   Off

E   Off

F   Off-period variable

Fig. 5.10 Modes of operation of chopper of Fig. 5.9

Period A. The firing of Thy1 immediately transfers the load current into it and the supply system. It also causes charging of C via the diode D2 and L. The presence of D2 makes the capacitor charge well above the supply voltage.

Period B. This capacitor charge is maintained during this variable period of ON-
ON   time. The load current will in general increase under the influence of the supply voltage and the load inductance.

96

Period C. When Thy2 is fired, the load current is taken over by *C* and Thy1 turns off. The capacitor also discharges via the supply and D3.

Period D. When the current in D3 reaches zero, the capacitor is left only with the load current and it continues to supply this as its voltage decreases linearly to zero.

Period E. When zero load voltage is reached, the diode D1 gradually picks up the
Period F. current as allowed by *L* until during the variable period F it carries the full
    OFF   load current. Normally the load current will gradually reduce during this period as controlled by its value of inductance.

Many of the practical applications of these chopper circuits will contain additional components, usually fitted to maximize the turn-off capability of the capacitor or to protect the thyristors and diodes against excessive d*i*/d*t* and d*v*/d*t*. Their basic operating principles, however, remain unchanged.

5.5 Inverter Principles

A static inverter produces alternating current and voltage from a unidirectional d.c. source of power. A thyristor can only be used as a switch and so an inverter produces its output by the sequential switching of thyristors ON and OFF.

Figure 5.11 shows the basic principles; alternate switching of S1 and S2 results in an a.c. load voltage and therefore current. The level of voltage applied to the load is uncontrolled and fixed by the level of the d.c. supply; the frequency can be varied by changing the time of switching.

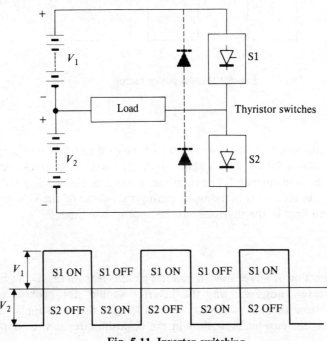

Fig. 5.11 Inverter switching

97

Type of Load

With a resistance load, the current will flow in it with the same waveform as the voltage. If the load is reactive, with either a leading or a lagging power factor, the load current will be out of phase with the voltage as shown in Fig. 5.12. During periods marked *X* and *Y* it will be necessary for the current to be flowing in the wrong direction in the load to the appropriate thyristor switch which is conducting.

This problem is solved in practice by connecting reverse diodes to the switching circuits, as shown in Fig. 5.11, such that when load current requires to reverse there is a path for such a current through one or other of the diodes. The effect is that the reactive component of the load current will feed back into the d.c. supply via the diodes during the periods marked *X* and *Y*.

The design of the supply system needs to take account of this reverse current flow. This brings out one of the primary characteristics of inverter circuits. Whatever the load power factor and kVA, the average d.c. current fed into the inverter is dependent only on the power component of the output, plus the circuit losses. A d.c. system cannot feed reactive power into the inverter.

In many cases, a d.c. capacitor across the input will allow free passage for the reverse currents and this will then effectively carry the reactive kVA, which in some circuits can be very high.

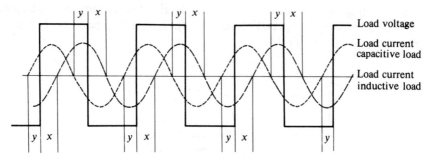

Fig. 5.12 Load power factor

Gate Firing

It is worth noting here that the power factor of the load also has another implication. Under lagging power factor load, when a thyristor switch is switched ON it will not initially carry the load current. Some time later it must be able to do so. It is therefore essential that gate current is maintained during the whole of the ON-period so that load current can flow in the thyristors at the appropriate time.

Regeneration

The normal direction of power flow in inverter circuits is from the d.c. to the a.c. sides. There is no reason, however, why the inverter should not operate as a rectifier feeding power from the a.c. to the d.c. side as long as the d.c. supply can accept it. This means that the current must flow in the opposite direction, to oppose the d.c. voltage.

When feedback diodes are fitted, the regeneration currents will flow in these diodes, frequency control still being maintained by the main thyristor switches.

Voltage Control and Waveform

The most common output waveform from inverters is a square wave or quasi-square wave, as shown in Fig. 5.13A and B (in a quasi-square wave the OFF-time is fixed at 60 degrees), this waveform being constant whatever the frequency. The magnitude of the output voltage can then only be controlled by varying the d.c. voltage supplied to the inverter.

If it is possible to switch the thyristor switches ON and OFF at will, it is possible to control the time of application of the d.c. voltage and hence the mean level of output voltage during the cycle.

Figure 5.13 also shows some of the control methods which are used so that a varying output voltage can be achieved even with a fixed input d.c. supply. They all involve turning off the thyristors more frequently and this imposes further restriction

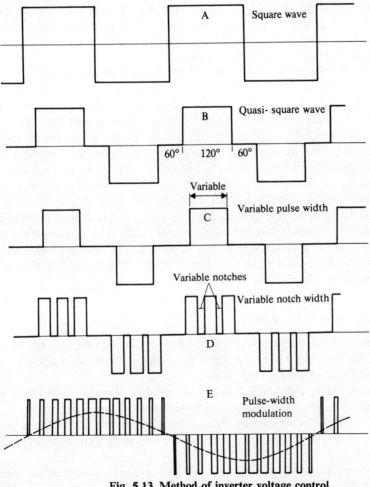

Fig. 5.13 Method of inverter voltage control

99

on the design of the commutating circuits as well as increasing the required capability of the thyristors.

Minimum Pulse Width

Up to now, the switches have been shown as perfect ones, switching from ON to OFF instantaneously. As will be seen from studying the later detailed commutation circuits, switching does take a significant time which may be well above the turn-off time of the thyristor. Once switching has been initiated, the complete commutation process has to be allowed to complete itself before further circuit switching can be considered. This results in a minimum ON pulse width and a minimum OFF pulse width similar to that existing in choppers. It limits the maximum frequency of operation, and allowance for this must be made in the firing arrangements.

Voltage-fed and Current-fed Inverters

These terms are used in connection with inverter circuits. A voltage-fed circuit is one in which the d.c. voltage applied to the inverter cannot change quickly. For example, if a large capacitor is connected across the d.c. supply, whatever short-time currents are drawn from it will not affect the input voltage.

A current-fed circuit is one in which the current drawn from the supply cannot be changed quickly. For example, a series inductance in the input circuit will prevent sudden change of current. The d.c. voltage supplied to the inverter will then depend on the extent of current changes required, and the voltage may vary considerably.

In a voltage-fed system, the thyristor circuit will decide the load voltage, leaving the current to take on any waveshape dictated by the load. The load current is controlled in a current-fed system and the voltage will vary, dependent on the load.

Most forced-commutated inverter circuits rely on a low-impedance d.c. supply to provide high commutating circuit-charging currents during short periods of time. Only a voltage-fed system is acceptable in these cases. In some instances, the load circuit is capable of providing the commutating currents required and then some benefit can be obtained in using a current-fed system. Commutating capacitors will usually be larger in a current-fed system and longer thyristor turn-off times may be allowable, but circuit response to load changes may be slow.

The Methods of Inverter Commutation

These vary considerably from one design to another, and one application to another, and it is only possible in this book to indicate the most-used methods and the overall basic principles. Three approaches are in use:
  (a) To use completely independent thyristor switches complete with their own commutating capacitors and inductors in each arm of the circuit.
  (b) To use a combined commutating arrangement for two complementary arms of the circuit so that switching of one primes the commutating circuit for the other, and vice versa.
  (c) To use one commutating unit to turn off all the arms of the thyristor circuit together (often referred to as a d.c. supply commutation).

Methods (a) and (c) can use similar commutation arrangements to those which are used for choppers, but where two arms are interrelated special circuits have been developed and are in common use. Examples of these are detailed in Sections 5.6 and 5.7.

In the *complementary commutated inverter* circuits (Section 5.6), individual thyristors are used in each switching unit (e.g., S1 in Fig. 5.11) such that turning on one switch, say S2, will cause S1 to turn off, and vice versa. The two switches are dependent on each other: they are complementary to each other.

The *auxiliary thyristor inverter* circuit (Section 5.7) uses additional thyristors in each switch to initiate turn-off of the main thyristors.

5.6 The Complementary Commutated Inverter Circuit

In its simplest form, this circuit is shown in Fig. 5.14 as one complete phase. Although it is often used with additional phases to make single- or three-phase bridge assemblies, this circuit using a centre-tapped d.c. supply is the most suitable to explain its principles of operation.

The two coils, L1 and L2, are closely coupled together and they form the commutating inductors; C1 and C2 are the commutating capacitors. If, when one of the thyristors is conducting current from the supply to the load, the other one is fired, the effect of the capacitors and inductors is to turn off the thyristor already conducting as long as its gate current has been previously removed. The diodes D1 and D2 allow the feedback of reactive load current and as will be seen later, the resistors help in the dissipation of circulating commutating current.

The process of thyristor switching will be explained step by step so that the current and voltage waveforms shown in Fig. 5.14 can be understood. For this explanation it is assumed that:

1. The load current remains constant during the switching process. This is a valid assumption as the switching time is usually short compared with the overall cycle time and the load current would normally only change by a small amount during this period in practical application.
2. The load has a lagging power factor.
3. The d.c. supply has no internal impedance.
4. The circuit does not contain any additional protective components. In practice, there will always be further components, e.g., capacitors, chokes, snubber circuits, etc., all of which will modify the circuit performance to some extent. They do not, however, significantly affect the principles of operation and they would complicate the explanations considerably.

Figure 5.15 shows the modes of operation occurring during the switching process.

Period A. Initial Conditions.
>   Let us assume initially that load current is flowing through Thy1 and L1. The circuit will then be as shown in Fig. 5.15A. C2 will be charged to $+2V_{dc}$ and C1 will be uncharged. As the load current is only changing very slowly, the voltage across L1 is very small. Thy2, D1, and D2 play no part in the action. When it is required to turn off Thy1, this is initiated by firing Thy2.

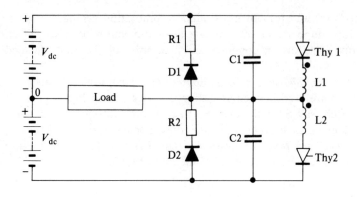

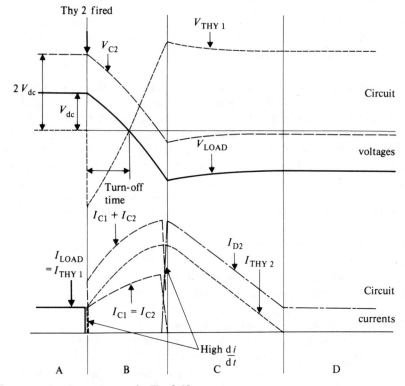

Modes of operation – refer Fig. 5.15

Fig. 5.14 The operation of the complementary commutated inverter circuit

Period B. Firing of Thy2 instantaneously changes the circuit.

Capacitor C2 discharges via L2 and Thy2. Current in L1 immediately transfers into L2 and Thy2. The C2 voltage initially occurs across L2. Due to the close coupling, this voltage also occurs across L1. L1 voltage causes Thy1 to be immediately reverse-biased, and so instantly:

The current initially in Thy1 jumps into Thy2;

The capacitor C2 discharges into L2 and Thy2 and the load circuit;

Capacitor C1 starts charging and supplying part of the load and Thy2 current.

102

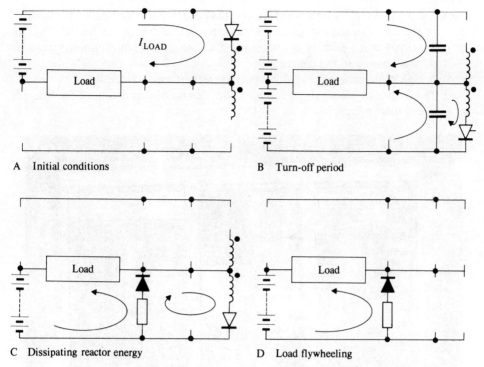

A   Initial conditions

B   Turn-off period

C   Dissipating reactor energy

D   Load flywheeling

Fig. 5.15 Modes of operation of the complementary commutated inverter

The total voltage across C1 and C2 always equals $2V_{dc}$. As the centre point of the two capacitors changes, one capacitor discharges and the other charges, both at the same rate. Therefore, the currents in C1 and C2 are always equal and opposite. At the start of this period the currents in C1 and C2 both jump to the initial load current value.

As this period progresses, the voltage across C2 reduces and hence the voltage across L2 and L1 reduce and the voltage across C1 increases. This period continues until the voltage across C2 reaches zero.

Period C. When this happens, the capacitor currents transfer into D2 over a short period of time, causing a small voltage drop across R2.

The current in Thy2 will be maintained by the inductive energy in L2 and it will circulate via D2, gradually dying away, under the influence of R2 during this period.

Period D. When Thy2 current reaches zero, D2 current will be equal to the load current and it will continue to flow this way until it reverses and transfers to Thy2.

The reverse process occurs when it is required to turn Thy2 off.

The important characteristics of this circuit are:

(a) The thyristor and capacitor voltages are positively controlled and related to the d.c. supply voltage.

(b) The time period allowed for turn-off of the thyristor does not vary very much with changes in load current.

(c) During period C, a significant energy loss occurs in the resistance. The majority of the initial stored energy in the capacitor is lost during this period. This loss has resulted in a number of circuit modifications, all of which aim to return this trapped energy to the d.c. supply.

(d) A high di/dt occurs in the thyristors when they are switched on.

(e) The frequency of switching is limited by the rate of dissipation of the 'trapped' circulating current.

Fig. 5.16 A complete 170 kVA forced-commutated thyristor drive system for variable-speed operation of induction motors. The left-hand cubicle contains a thyristor chopper, and the three-phase variable frequency inverter is in the right-hand cubicle (GEC Industrial Controls Ltd)

5.7 The Auxiliary Thyristor Inverter Circuit

The most common form of this circuit is the McMurray circuit shown in Fig. 5.17, again in a single-phase form.

A single commutating capacitor and inductor are used in the turn-off of both main thyristors Thy1 and Thy2. Thy1 is turned off by turning on Thy1A, and Thy2 is turned off by firing Thy2A.

Making the same assumptions as in Section 5.6, the process of thyristor switching will again be explained in steps with reference to the diagrams of Fig. 5.18 and the voltage and current waveforms of Fig. 5.17.

Period A. Initial Conditions.

Let us assume initially that the load current is flowing through Thy1 and at this time let us also assume that C is charged positively to an initial voltage in excess of $2V_{dc}$ due to previous operation. D1, D2, Thy2, Thy1A, and Thy2A are not effective during this period.

Period B. This commences when Thy1A is fired in order to turn off Thy1. The capacitor discharges through Thy1 via L and Thy1A and gradually takes up the load current. When Thy1 current reaches zero, period C commences.

Period C. The capacitor now discharges via diode D1 while at the same time supplying the load current. C completely discharges and recharges in the opposite direction under the influence of L.

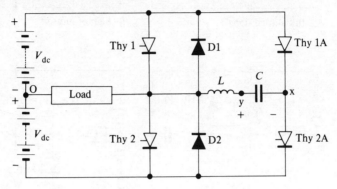

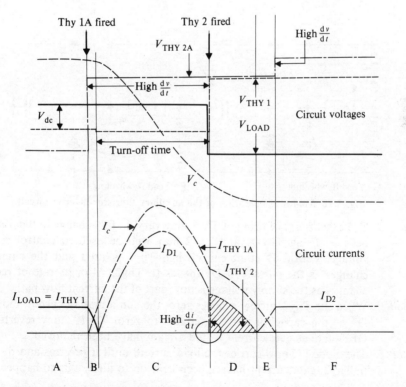

Modes of operation – refer Fig. 5.18

Fig. 5.17 The operation of the auxiliary thyristor inverter circuit

105

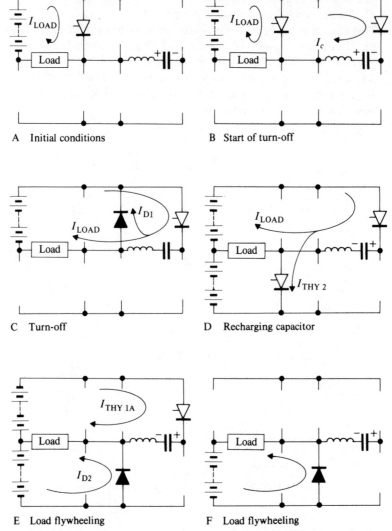

A Initial conditions

B Start of turn-off

C Turn-off

D Recharging capacitor

E Load flywheeling

F Load flywheeling

Fig. 5.18 Modes of operation of the auxiliary thyristor inverter circuit

Period D. The exact point of firing of Thy2 may vary, in fact change in the time delay between firing Thy1A and Thy2 may well be used to control capacitor voltage. Period D commences when Thy2 is fired and the circuit then changes as the current in D1 moves to Thy2. Also, its rate of reduction changes as the supply voltage is now part of the current flow path.

Period E. When the Thy2 current reaches zero, the commutating current moves into D2 as the capacitor current reduces to zero. Thy1A now reverts to the OFF-state as gate current would already have been removed.

Period F. The diode D2 now carries the load current until it reverses and then flows in Thy2 (gate current having been kept on to allow this to happen).

The reverse process occurs when it is required to turn Thy2 off; this is initiated by firing Thy2A.

The important characteristics of this circuit are:

(a) The capacitor and auxiliary thyristor voltages depend on load current and the point of firing of the incoming thyristor. Voltages well in excess of the d.c. supply are possible.
(b) The time allowed for turn-off of the thyristors is controlled by the delay time between firing of the auxiliary and the following main thyristor. It is also affected by the level of load current.
(c) The commutating energy in the capacitors remains in the circuit, reversing the capacitor voltage at each commutation. Only the normal circuit losses occur.
(d) High dv/dt occurs on main and auxiliary thyristors at the thyristor firing points and protection is required to prevent misfiring.
(e) High di/dt occurs in the main thyristor when it is initially switched on.

It must be emphasized that the explanations of the complementary and auxiliary thyristor commutating circuits are given to indicate the principles only. In practice, many differences in circuit components and detailed operating techniques are used and the circuits will then operate in slightly different ways.

5.8 The Single-phase Parallel Inverter Circuit

Figure 5.19 shows the circuit in its most regularly used form.

The two thyristors are each fired for 180 electrical degrees alternately, so applying a square alternating voltage waveform to the centre-tapped transformer primary winding. Every time a thyristor is fired, the commutating capacitor C is charged to twice the d.c. supply voltage in an appropriate direction to turn the thyristor off at the end of its conduction period. The inductance L limits the flow of capacitor charging current. The diodes D1 and D2 allow the flow of reactive load current and return the energy back into the d.c. supply. The diode D3 is included to allow trapped energy in the inductance L to discharge; sometimes a resistance is included in series with D3 to speed up the discharge of the inductive energy.

Every cycle of operation can be split up into six different periods as shown in Fig. 5.20. During most of the cycle, periods A and D apply. Periods B and E are short-time commutation periods and the times of periods C and F depend on the power factor of the load: at low power factor, periods C and F will increase in time at the expense of periods D and A respectively.

The operation of this circuit will be described using these six periods in sequence, to establish the circuit waveforms which are drawn in Fig. 5.19. In this figure, the time periods B and E have been expanded so that these periods can be fully understood.

Period A. This is the main conducting period for thyristor 1. During this the full d.c. voltage occurs across the a.c. half-primary of the transformer. As the transformer must have a constant voltage per turn, the capacitor voltage reaches twice V_{dc} with the Thy1 end positive.

Period B. As soon as Thy2 is fired, the current flowing immediately switches into Thy2, due to the action of C and L. The full capacitor voltage of $2V_{dc}$ is immediately applied to Thy1 as a reverse voltage. The capacitor voltage also instantly appears across the inductance L and forces the current in it to rise. As the period progresses, the capacitor gradually discharges and reverses, and the circuit currents rise. Thy1 must be fully turned off by the

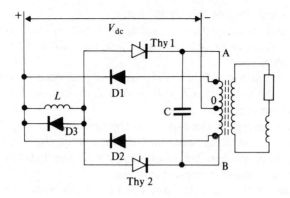

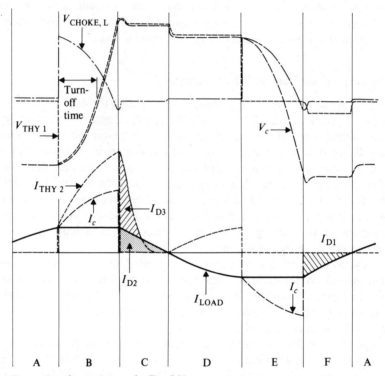

For modes of operation – refer Fig. 5.20

Fig. 5.19 The operation of the single-phase parallel inverter circuit

time its reverse voltage has disappeared. This period continues until diode
D2 becomes forward-biased.

Period C. Commences when the capacitor C has become fully charged in the opposite
direction to a sufficient level so that D2 becomes forward-biased and starts
to conduct. This diode will very quickly take over the total circuit current
while the load current continues to flow in the original direction. Current
is initially flowing in the inductance L; the diode D3 allows the energy to be
dissipated.

108

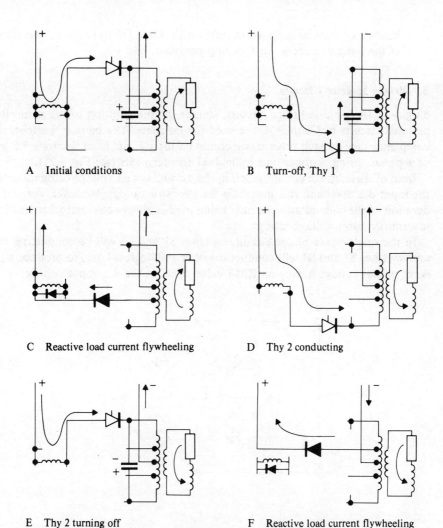

A   Initial conditions   B   Turn-off, Thy 1

C   Reactive load current flywheeling   D   Thy 2 conducting

E   Thy 2 turning off   F   Reactive load current flywheeling

Fig. 5.20 Modes of operation of the single-phase parallel inverter circuit

Period D. As soon as the secondary load current reverses, D2 ceases to conduct and current transfers into Thy2. The capacitor discharges slightly until its voltage corresponds to twice the d.c. voltage. This period continues until Thy1 is fired.

Period E. Is the reverse of period B.

Period F. Is the reverse of period C.

       And so on.

   It should be particularly noted from the waveforms that:

1. At the start and finish of periods B and E, very high rates of change of current can occur. Small inductances, usually in series with C, must be used to control the level of the di/dt in the thyristors.

2. The high level of commutating current during periods B and E is carried by the thyristors and inductance L. It will be almost independent of the value of load current.

3. Resistance may be included in series with diode D3 to speed up the dissipation of the inductive energy in L during periods C and F.

5.9 Bridge Inverter Circuits

Single- or three-phase bridge circuits, similar in configuration to the naturally commutated circuits of Chapter 4, are used for inverters. The pairs of switches may be complementary to each other using commutating circuits as in Sections 5.6 and 5.7, or separate, using chopper-type individual arrangements (see Fig. 5.21).

Both of these bridge circuits result in the normal circuit voltage being no more than the input d.c. level and this may help the thyristor ratings. However, detailed consideration of the commutating circuits being used is always essential when dealing with inverter thyristor voltage ratings.

In the single-phase bridge circuit, switches S1 and S3 will be conducting together and switches S2 and S4 will conduct together 180 degrees later, to produce a square-wave output voltage having an RMS value equal to the d.c. input voltage.

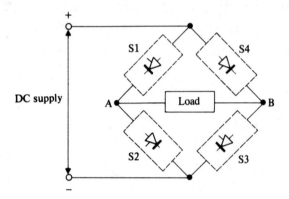

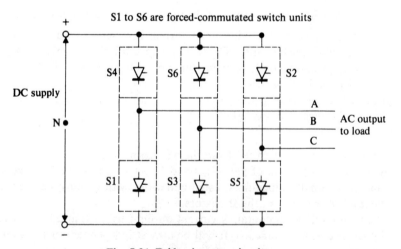

Fig. 5.21 Bridge inverter circuits

In the three-phase bridge circuit the switches conduct in the sequence shown. If they are operated as three phases each displaced by 120 degrees, i.e., if each of the phases produces square-wave outputs, then as shown in Fig. 5.22 the line-to-line ouput voltages will be quasi-square waveshapes with the full d.c. supply voltage in each direction. The RMS line voltages will then be equal to 0·816 times the input d.c. voltage.

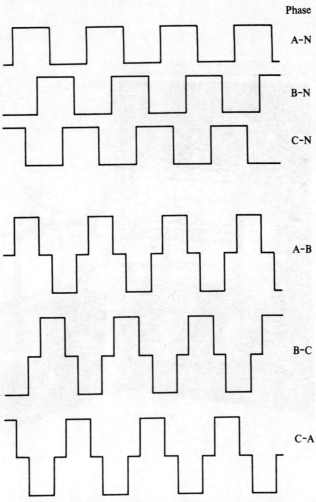

Fig. 5.22 Three-phase inverter, bridge output voltages

5.10 Thyristor Current Ratings in Forced-commutated Circuits

As will be seen from the previous sections, the currents carried by main and commutating thyristors both depend on the methods of commutation employed as well as on the normal power circuit factors. The following points need to be borne in mind in all cases:

1. Main thyristors will carry the power component of the load current and a portion of the reactive component. The feedback diodes will only carry reactive current.

111

Fig. 5.23 A 10 kVA variable-frequency a.c. induction motor drive showing the mixture of semiconductors, capacitors, reactors, and electronics needed for forced-commutated equipment (Allen Bennett Ltd)

2. The effect of power currents in the thyristors will increase at low operating frequencies and cause large junction-temperature oscillation.
3. The commutation currents will usually be much larger than the maximum load current the circuit provides.
4. The commutation capacitor charging and discharging currents may flow through main and auxiliary thyristors and diodes.
5. The losses caused by commutating currents in the thyristors, and the resulting effect on junction temperature, will increase with the frequency of commutation. These losses can become the dominating influence at higher frequencies.
6. Commutating currents will in most circuits be independent of load current; they will occur at the same level even on no load.
7. Thyristor current waveforms may include very high levels of di/dt and some means of limiting these will be necessary (see Chapter 6).

In practice, current waveforms in forced-commutation circuits are complicated and their effect on junction temperature is difficult to assess. Individual assessment as detailed in Chapter 2 is the only way to ensure maximum utilization of the thyristors. If accurate calculation is not practicable, then an appropriate safety margin should be allowed.

5.11 References

1. B. D. Bedford and R. G. Hoft, *Principles of Inverter Circuits*, John Wiley, London & New York, 1965.
2. IEC Publication 146–2, *Semiconductor Self Commutated Convertors*.
3. C. F. Wagner, 'Parallel inverter with resistance load', *Electrical Eng.*, Nov. 1935.
4. C. F. Wagner, 'Parallel inverter with inductive load', *Electrical Eng.*, Sept. 1936.
5. X. Vogel and K. Winkler, 'The solid state d.c. regulating unit and its components', *Brown Boveri Rev.*, **11**, 1971.
6. W. Farrar, 'Quasi-sine wave fully regenerative inverter', *IEE Proc.*, **120**, 9, Sept. 1973.
7. F. F. Mazda, 'Design of high frequency thyristor chopper circuits', *Electronic Eng.*, Feb. 1970.
8. B. Mokrytzki, 'PWM inverter for a.c. motor drives', *IEEE Trans.*, **IGA-3**, 6, 1967.
9. L. Hampson, 'Operation and performance of a single phase and a three phase bridge inverter', *Mullard Technical Communications*, **12**, 117, 206–222, Jan. 1973.
10. H. Zander, 'Self commutated rectifier to improve line conditions', *IEE Conference Publication 93*, 173–180, Oct. 1972.

6. Protection of Thyristors

All semiconductor devices have limited capabilities and thyristors are no exception; in Chapter 1, their limitations were explained. Reliable and satisfactory use of thyristors depends on ensuring that, at all times, the circuit conditions imposed on them are within their capabilities. To achieve this, the thyristor has to be surrounded by components chosen to protect it against the extreme conditions, so enabling an economic and easily obtainable thyristor to be used.

This chapter deals with the reasons for extreme conditions of circuit currents and voltages and the practical methods used to limit their values to within the thyristor's capabilities.

Chapters 3, 4, and 5 give some information on the normal conditions existing (i.e., the currents in thyristors and the voltages across them) for the various circuits in regular use. It is often necessary to include protection components to limit even these continuous-circuit conditions to within the thyristor capabilities.

6.1 Overvoltage Conditions

Thyristors can be damaged by excessive voltage applied even for very short periods of time. There are many such transient conditions in all electrical circuits and it is necessary to understand them to ensure satisfactory protection is provided. The conditions most important to thyristor circuits are lightning surges, transformer switching, thyristor turn-off, and load switching and these will be dealt with in turn.

Lightning strikes on overhead power lines can be passed through the supply network and appear on all thyristor circuits which are directly connected to the network. They are usually attenuated by supply system transformers and lightning arrestors, but can still be many times the normal voltage level lasting for periods up to tens of microseconds. Fortunately, their magnitude tends to reduce as the time of the transient increases. In some applications the output connections from the thyristor circuit may be exposed to lightning, e.g., d.c. transmission and traction, and ouput voltage suppression circuits will then be needed.

Transformer switching is a regular and significant source of transient overvoltages, particularly when thyristor equipment is supplied by its own transformer. When its primary current is opened or closed, transients will occur on the secondary windings. These occur even when the equipment and transformer are unloaded, due to the magnetizing conditions within the transformer.

When the supply is closed on to the transformer, the inrush magnetizing current causes voltages of up to twice normal to occur transiently. If the transformer has a large step-down ratio, capacitive coupling between the primary and secondary can temporarily boost the secondary voltage.

Thyristor turn-off. Section 1.6 explained that when any thyristor turns off at a relatively high rate of change of current, a reverse current will flow to sweep away the stored charge. Once this has been achieved the current quickly reduces to zero, inducing high voltages in the circuit inductances. These voltages can be extremely high if no protection is included to limit them; they appear as reverse voltages across the thyristor which is turning off, and they are reflected on to other thyristors in the circuit in both polarities. They occur every time any thyristor turns off and so become repetitive transients in nearly all practical applications. The stored charge and hence the level of reverse 'charge recovery' current varies between thyristors and due to temperature, so maximum values have to be used in assessing protection requirements.

The circuit of Fig. 4.5, for example, will exhibit this effect as in Fig. 6.1.

Load switching will result in overvoltages being induced in circuit inductances whether these be on the load or supply side of the thyristor circuit. Fuse blowing and the operation of protective circuit breakers are probably the most severe examples of this effect. The energy contained in circuit inductances will be given by

$$\text{Energy} = \tfrac{1}{2}LI^2$$

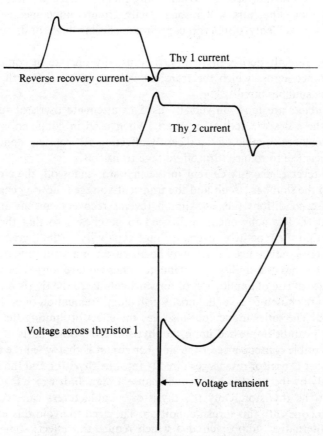

Fig. 6.1 Thyristor turn-off voltage transients

115

where I is the current flowing, and this will need to be dissipated in the protective components used, without exceeding the thyristor voltage capabilities.

Devices which open the circuit slowly, in general, dissipate this energy slowly within themselves by arcing; fast switches, i.e., fuses or high-speed switches, will usually leave most of the energy to be absorbed by other circuit components. Load-switching conditions significantly depend on the characteristics of the switch opening the circuit.

6.2 Overvoltage Protection Devices

This section deals with the components and techniques in regular use to limit the level of transient voltage surges.

Capacitor–resistor circuits are the most frequently used, the capacitor being capable of accepting energy given by

$$\text{Energy} = \tfrac{1}{2}CV^2$$

where V is the capacitor voltage, and the resistor being used to damp the circuit to prevent unnecessary resonant oscillation. Such circuits can be studied by conventional mathematical analysis and they are used widely to reduce all the transient conditions discussed in the previous section. When using them in thyristor circuits it has to be remembered that capacitors will resonate with circuit inductances; also thyristors turning on can suddenly discharge capacitors, causing high di/dt to occur in the thyristors.

When used directly across thyristors, they usually operate in conjunction with a series inductance across which the transient voltage appears. For this use they are referred to as snubber circuits.

Snubber circuits are most universally used to attenuate thyristor turn-off voltage surges and these deserve special mention. When used in conjunction with a series inductance they are capable of significantly affecting all transient conditions. Figure 6.2 shows their use to reduce turn-off voltage transients.

When the reverse recovery current in the thyristor snaps off, the circuit current is diverted into the snubber circuit and the transient voltage following can be calculated for worst-case conditions (i.e., maximum reverse recovery current and fast cut-off of this current). The components will need to be chosen so that the peak reverse voltage is within the repetitive reverse voltage capability of the thyristor.

With the series inductance (which may be air-cored or a saturating iron-cored type) the circuit also has the ability to attenuate other voltage surges occurring and to reduce the rate of rise of application of forward voltage to the thyristor. The values of R, L, and C are chosen to give the most satisfactory attenuation of each of the conditions affected. The series inductance also has the effect of limiting the rate of rise of current which can be impressed upon the thyristor from other parts of the circuit.

One undesirable consequence of the snubber circuit is that when the thyristor turns on, the snubber capacitor discharges directly into the thyristor and the inrush current is limited only by the resistor R. This will cause a high di/dt which may be above the capability of the thyristor. Only the thyristor manufacturers can accurately assess the ability to cope with this inrush condition. The need to avoid this has encouraged the use of alternative snubber circuits which reduce this effect; some examples are shown in Fig. 6.3.

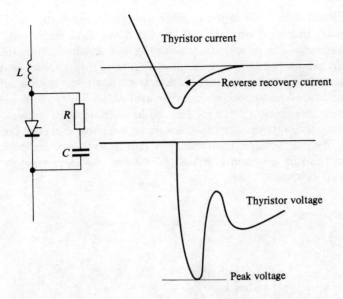

Fig. 6.2 Attenuation of reverse recovery voltage by an RC snubber circuit

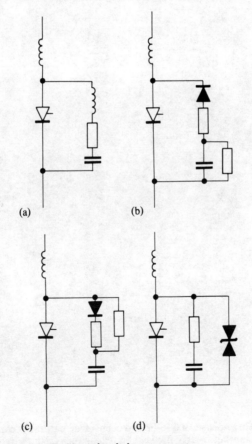

(a)   (b)

(c)   (d)

Fig. 6.3 Snubber circuit improvements

A small additional inductance in the snubber will reduce the di/dt, but the circuit is then less effective in coping with turn-off transients and those impressed from the remainder of the circuit. The polarized circuit of Fig. 6.3(c) reduces the turn-on di/dt but is not so effective on turn-off. The circuit of Fig. 6.3(b) is useful to limit reverse voltage transients when forward voltage transients or dv/dt are not present in the circuit. The addition of non-linear resistors or avalanche diodes as in Fig. 6.3(d) enables the size of the capacitor to be reduced, so limiting the di/dt inrush.

Non-linear resistors can be very useful in absorbing inductive energy at precise and controlled levels of circuit voltage. Their resistance reduces as the voltage increases and so circuit currents can be temporarily bypassed into the non-linear resistors to limit the induced circuit voltages.

Fig. 6.4 Three-phase 300 A bridge-connected, naturally commutated convertor assembly showing clearly the snubber capacitor/resistor circuits in the middle of the picture (ASEA Ltd)

The long-standing silicon carbide type, e.g., Metrosil, has found limited use as it usually produces voltages well above twice the normal circuit voltage during severe transient effects. The more recent varistor devices with a very sudden reduction of resistance will reduce transients to well within the normal economic limits. Figure 6.5 shows their comparative characteristics. When using these devices, the energy dissipated in them needs to be accurately assessed and if transients are repetitive, appropriate de-rating of the non-linear resistors may be necessary.

Avalanche diodes are semiconductor diodes which can operate in the reverse breakdown region with a high reverse current without damage. They can be used in a similar way to varistors by bypassing the current through them during the transient. They usually have the capability of absorbing significant energy in this avalanche breakdown condition.

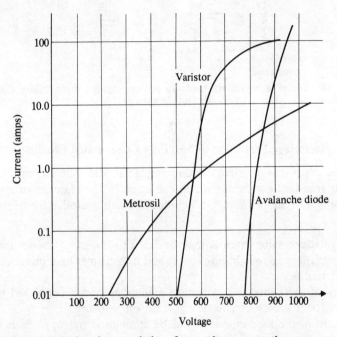

Fig. 6.5 Relative characteristics of overvoltage protective components

Selenium diodes can also be used in a similar way, but they break down at much lower voltages and many diodes have to be connected in series. Special types under various trade names are available.

Breakover diodes are semiconductor devices which, like thyristors, break over into the forward state above a specific voltage level. They are only made in small sizes and their most effective use is to provide a sudden surge of gate current when a thyristor breaks over. If used as in Fig. 6.6, the breakover diode provides an additional source of gate current if sufficient forward voltage is applied. This will then prevent thyristor di/dt failure due to the main circuit current.

A *transformer earthed screen* fitted between the primary and secondary windings is often used to prevent transient effects in the primary from being capacitively coupled through to the secondary circuit. Protection against this is usually only necessary where the transformer has a large step-down ratio. A capacitor or other voltage suppressor connected to earth from the secondary circuits can also reduce such transients.

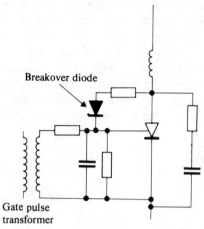

Fig. 6.6 The use of a breakover diode to protect against di/dt failure due to excessive anode voltage

6.3 Practical Overvoltage Protection in Naturally Commutated Circuits

In some simple cases it is possible for one voltage-suppression circuit to cope with all the possible transient conditions which can exist. In the majority of applications, however, a number of suppressors are included so as to optimize the overall system. For example:

> Surge voltage suppression circuits may be fitted to the input connections to limit incoming transients due to lightning strikes and transformer and inductive switching in the input circuits.
> The majority of thyristors used will have a snubber circuit connected to them to cope with thyristor switching effects, e.g., turn-off recovery.
> Surges induced in the load circuit would be attenuated by suppressors connected to the output.

Although the principal aim of each of these suppression circuits may be clear, they will in fact all affect many of the transient conditions and they will all need to be considered when assessing their individual size and the magnitude of the voltage surges remaining.

Even with all of these facilities, it is still necessary to use thyristors having non-repetitive peak voltage ratings (V_{RSM} and V_{DSM}) of at least twice the normal crest working voltage.

The exact size of components used for surge-suppression circuits varies significantly between manufacturers, the decisions being based on practical tests and experience. Nevertheless, they are all based on the same principles.

Supply-side suppression will usually be decided by supply transformer switching, the worst case normally being, opening the transformer primary circuit when no load current is flowing. Under this condition the transformer magnetizing energy has

120

nowhere to go unless suppression circuits are included, and without them high voltages result. The suppressor is chosen by assessing the transformer energy to be dissipated, and then ensuring this can be accepted by the suppressor within the peak voltages allowable. Capacitor circuits are always damped with series resistance to prevent voltage-doubling.

Typical a.c. surge-suppression circuits used are shown in Fig. 6.7.

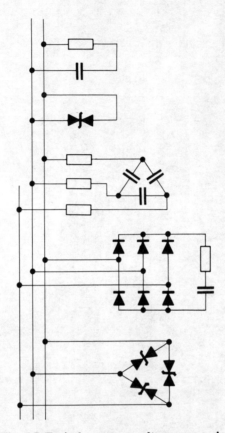

Fig. 6.7 Typical a.c. surge voltage suppression circuits

D.C. side suppression again takes the form of resistor/capacitor or voltage-dependent resistors or diodes, but it will usually be chosen by assessing the maximum d.c. circuit inductive energy which can be interrupted (probably under high-current fault conditions), the speed and energy dissipation capabilities of the switch or fuse, and the absorbing qualities of the suppressor.

6.4 Overvoltage Protection in Forced-commutated Circuits

In general, forced-commutated inverter and chopper circuits are less affected by supply system transients. Either they are fed from local battery-supported d.c. systems or they have large values of d.c. capacitance which prevents any short-time transients from getting through to the thyristors. Consequently, as long as the internally generated thyristor turn-off voltages can be limited by correctly designed snubber

Fig. 6.8 The resistor/capacitor surge suppression circuits and the snubber capacitors used in this assembly can be clearly seen (NEI Electronics Ltd)

circuits, it is possible to use the thyristors at normal peak voltages much nearer to their repetitive voltage ratings. However, as will be seen from Chapter 5, the normal applied peak voltages can be well above the d.c. supply voltage level.

Where load-switching transients can occur, capacitor/resistor circuits or non-linear devices are the most effective when mounted near to the inductances in which the voltages are generated.

6.5 Overcurrent Fault Conditions

Most thyristor circuits are fast-operating and can be controlled in such a way as to prevent the load current from rising too high to cause circuit damage or maloperation. There are, however, a number of component failures and circuit maloperation conditions where the current can rise out of control to many times the normal rated value, and steps have to be taken to limit these conditions and to protect the other circuit components against the effects of the high currents. The following paragraphs cover most of these overcurrent fault conditions.

The precise and accurate assessment of fault current in thyristor circuits is always a long and laborious job involving step-by-step circuit analysis of multiple differential equations for each circuit-switching condition. It is not intended to make an exhaustive study in this book, but only to point out the principles involved and advise a simple approach which is more useful practically. References to papers dealing with these conditions from a mathematical point of view are given at the end of this chapter.

Output short-circuits can occur on any system and in many situations gate control of the thyristors cannot prevent high currents from flowing; this will quickly result in loss of control of the thyristors due to overtemperature or commutation failure. The maximum level of the fault current during short-circuit will occur at zero delay angle α and at specific instants of the short-circuit during the cycle. It will then depend only on the system voltage and the circuit equivalent impedance/resistance. After it has been flowing for some cycles, the fault will reach a steady-state value which can be found from

$$\text{Steady-state fault current} = \frac{\text{circuit voltage}}{\text{circuit impedance}}$$

During the initial period immediately after the commencement of the fault, however, the fault current can reach higher levels depending on the circuit resistance/inductance ratios (see Fig. 6.9). Also, if the fault causes large capacitors to be short-circuited, their discharge currents can further increase the circuit fault currents; this is of particular importance in forced-commutated circuits where large filtering capacitors are used. Conversely, the presence of d.c. circuit inductance will slow up the rate of rise of fault current.

In *naturally commutated circuits* the output short-circuit current will be split up between the thyristors of the circuit, and the effective overlap angles will be much larger than under normal operating conditions. The flow path will also depend on whether the thyristors continue to be gated after the commencement of the fault or not. The most usual case is for gate pulses to continue until the circuit current causes loss of control of thyristors due to overtemperature of the junctions, as it is difficult to decide that a fault has occurred until the current has risen to high levels (see below for the effects of pulse suppression).

The maximum steady-state levels of fault current in the naturally commutated circuits of Chapter 4 with cyclic gating of thyristors at $\alpha =$ zero, assuming no d.c. inductance in the fault path, are given in Table 6.1. Under these conditions the currents in individual thyristors will be of half-sine wave shape.

These figures are obtained by ignoring thyristor circuit impedances and voltage drop, and is the worst-case condition as shown in Fig. 6.10.

Table 6.1 Steady-state fault currents in naturally commutated rectifying circuits

Circuit	D.C. short-circuit mean current	A.C. RMS short-circuit current	Thyristor peak current	Thyristor mean current	Half-cycle thyristor I^2t (amp squared-seconds)	
					50 hertz	60 hertz
Single-phase half-wave Half-controlled bridge Fully controlled bridge	I_F	$\dfrac{\pi}{2\sqrt{2}}I_F$	$\dfrac{\pi}{2}I_F$	$\dfrac{1}{2}I_F$	$\dfrac{\pi^2}{8}10^{-3}I_F^2$	$\dfrac{\pi^2}{9\cdot6}10^{-3}I_F^2$
Three-phase Half-controlled bridge Fully controlled bridge	I_F	$\dfrac{\pi}{3\sqrt{2}}I_F$	$\dfrac{\pi}{3}I_F$	$\dfrac{1}{3}I_F$	$\dfrac{\pi^2}{18}10^{-3}I_F^2$	$\dfrac{\pi^2}{21\cdot6}10^{-3}I_F^2$
Six-phase half-wave	I_F	$\dfrac{\pi}{6\sqrt{2}}I_F$	$\dfrac{\pi}{6}I_F$	$\dfrac{1}{6}I_F$	$\dfrac{\pi^2}{72}10^{-3}I_F^2$	$\dfrac{\pi^2}{86\cdot4}10^{-3}I_F^2$

Where $I_F = \dfrac{\text{rated d.c. current}}{\text{per unit reactance}} = \dfrac{I_{dN}}{X_t}$

In many practical instances, this steady level of fault current will not be reached before thyristor damage, and so the initial transient period becomes more important. Step-by-step differential equation calculations can be done to assess this initial fault period for each of the circuits concerned. Study of the results, however, shows that current waveforms as in Fig. 6.11 occur in the thyristors. Figure 6.12 gives the I^2t values from these waveforms.

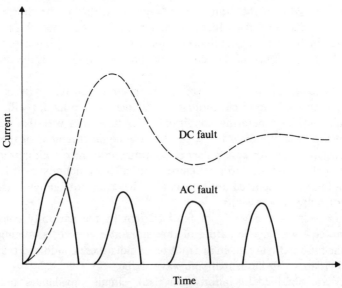

Fig. 6.9 Initial asymmetrical fault currents

Output short-circuits can occur as a result of load circuit faults, e.g., motor flashover, cable short-circuits, etc., or due to faults in antiparallel-connected thyristor circuits. They are infrequent conditions but the thyristor equipment needs to be fully protected against them. The equivalent condition can also occur if a d.c. motor load is inadvertently connected to the convertor while the motor is at rest and the convertor is controlled to give maximum output voltage. It can also be caused by control system maloperation suddenly resulting in operation at low delay angles when the motor load is running at low speed.

Forced-commutated circuits also experience output short-circuits but these will usually result in commutation failure and the results will be as explained further on in this section.

Internal faults within a thyristor circuit can also result in high currents flowing. They can be caused by the failure of a thyristor or incorrect firing of it due to interference or a faulty firing circuit. Failure of voltage-protection components, e.g., a snubber capacitor, can also cause overcurrents due to thyristor voltage or dv/dt

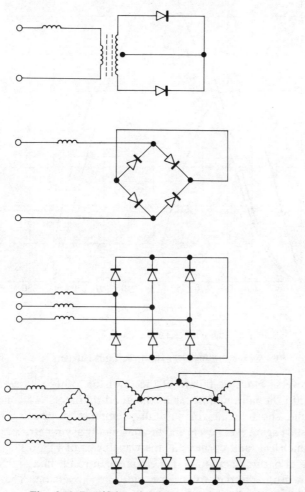

Fig. 6.10 Rectifying circuits under short-circuit conditions

breakover. Commutation failure is also an internal fault but this will be dealt with separately.

If the fault results in a thyristor failing to block forward voltage, the result will be that this thyristor will tend to carry the high fault current on its own, even during periods when other thyristors would normally carry current. The worst possible case of this condition would mean the thyristor carrying the full short-circuit current of the circuit, but in many cases the level would be less than this until such a time as other thyristors fail to block voltage due to excessive junction temperature.

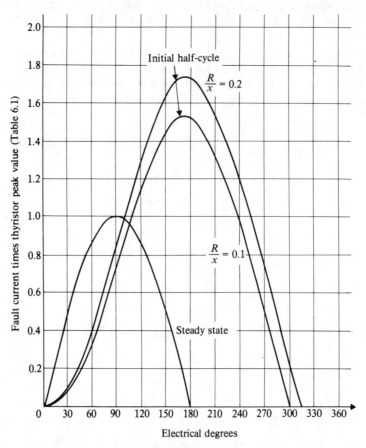

$$\frac{R}{x} = \text{Supply resistance to reactance ratio}$$

Fig. 6.11 Asymmetrical thyristor fault currents

If the fault is reverse blocking failure of the thyristor, other thyristors within the circuit may feed into the fault and as far as the good thyristors are concerned it can look like an output short-circuit. In naturally commutated circuits, however, the fault will tend to start again every cycle and be continually asymmetric, i.e., a repetitive sequence of asymmetrical fault currents as the waveforms of Fig. 6.11.

Inversion failure in naturally commutated circuits can result in a high fault current during power flow from the d.c. to the a.c. side, i.e., inversion. The condition is normally only significant with motor loads where sustained inversion can occur. This power-flow condition can only exist as long as the convertor is able to provide a voltage to balance the generated voltage of the d.c. machine. If the convertor voltage disappears or reverses a short-circuit current will flow (see Fig. 6.13).

If the convertor voltage, V_d, disappears it is equivalent to short-circuiting the motor through the circuit impedance (including the motor). This could be caused by loss of a.c. supply.

A higher fault condition may result from a firing or control circuit fault which causes the convertor suddenly to switch into the fully rectifying condition, in which case the total circuit voltage will be the sum of V_d and E_b. The total fault circuit will now,

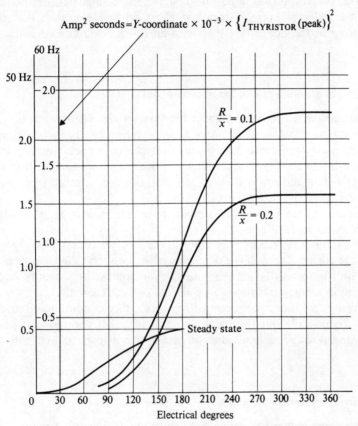

Fig. 6.12 Amp-squared seconds curves of waveforms from Fig. 6.11

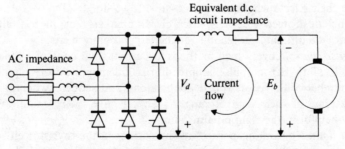

Fig. 6.13 Inversion failure

127

however, include both the a.c. circuit impedances as well as the d.c. impedance and its level and shape will depend on the relative values of the a.c. and d.c. impedances. An intermediate condition occurs if all the firing pulses suddenly disappear as those thyristors in the circuit which are carrying current at that instant will continue to do so. The total circuit voltage under this condition will be a single phase of the supply voltage, i.e., a sinusoidally changing voltage, plus the motor voltage; the fault current will flow through both the a.c. and d.c. circuits.

These inversion-failure conditions can also occur as a result of insufficient overlap angle being available. If, in Figs 4.16b, 4.22b, and 4.30b, due to reduced a.c. voltage, excessive load current, or too large a delay angle α, the angle γ is insufficient to allow for the full transfer of current from one phase to the next, then the current will remain flowing in the initial thyristors and an inversion-failure condition as above will result.

Commutation Failure in Forced-commutation Circuits

Correct operation of all forced-commutation inverter circuits depends on the ability of the commutating components to provide sufficient time for the thyristors to turn off. If, due to excessive load current, or insufficient charge on commutating capacitors, or incorrect firing of the thyristors, a thyristor does not have time to turn off, it will stay in the ON-state and this will very soon, if not instantly, result in the d.c. supply being short-circuited by the thyristors.

The fault current then flowing will depend on the circuit inductance, resistance, and capacitance, as shown in Fig. 6.14.

This figure shows that capacitance close to the inverter circuit will cause an initial high discharge current through the thyristors limited only by the local resistance and inductance near to the thyristors. An inductive input circuit, i.e., significant L and no C2, will result in a comparatively slow build-up of fault current.

If the inverter has more phases and thyristors, other conditions of commutation failure may be possible but they will all result in either the full d.c. short-circuit current flowing through an individual thyristor or it will be shared with the other phases.

6.6 Overcurrent Protection Methods

There are two approaches to overcurrent protection of thyristor circuits:
1. To use the gate pulse control to prevent overcurrent conditions occurring or to limit their effects whenever it is possible to so do.
2. To include protective devices, fuses, circuit breakers, etc., in the fault current path to provide ultimate protection for the circuit components.

Gate pulse control covers such methods as current-limit control, sudden removal of the pulses to all thyristors (pulse suppression), sudden application of pulses to all or a selected number of thyristors (pulse application), and sudden switching of the pulses to one extreme of their control range. They all have their limitations but can be extremely helpful in the right circumstances.

Current limit. Continuous control of the current in the thyristor circuit allows the current to be limited to a normal maximum level. Control can only be effected if the

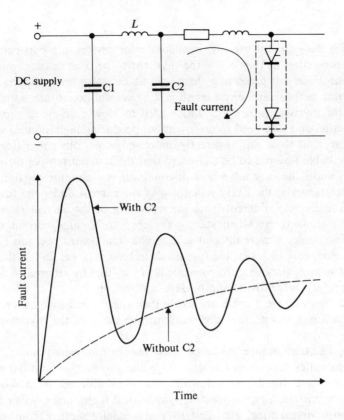

Fig. 6.14 Fault current caused by commutation failure

current rise during the interval between commutations is low. Current limit cannot prevent fast current rise.

Pulse suppression can only prevent further commutations; the thyristors already carrying current will continue to do so as dictated by the remainder of the power circuit. In certain circumstances pulse suppression can cause a fault condition, e.g., inversion failure.

Pulse application can quickly divert the fault current into a chosen path or paths assuming commutation is possible, but then some other means has to be found to interrupt the fault.

Pulse switching to the extreme of the control range can help but only if it is quick enough.

All these methods suffer from the basic limitations that:

(a) Thyristors cannot be turned off except by removal of anode current.
(b) A high thyristor current will result in a high junction temperature and loss of control.
(c) Failure of control and firing circuits causes some overcurrent fault conditions.
(d) The methods all depend on current measurements which can only indicate a fault when the current has already reached excessive levels. Also, time delay is often involved in current measurement circuits.

Fuses

Fuses, specially designed for use with semiconductor devices, are particularly useful for thyristor protection as they allow the thyristor to be used at economic levels of normal current while still protecting them against excessive levels. Special fuses are supplied for this purpose and any user should be careful not to use normal power-circuit fuses for thyristor protection. Fuses need to blow quicker, to provide satisfactory protection and they need to do it without producing high induced voltages in circuit inductance, as these can be directly impressed across other thyristors.

The most suitable fuse has to be chosen so that the total current let through by it, when it blows under the most adverse fault condition, is within the capabilities of the thyristor. Unfortunately, the likely waveform of the current under the fuse-blowing condition is usually very different from the waveform of the current referred to by the thyristor manufacturers when stating the thyristor's surge current capability. This makes fuse choice a more difficult and maybe complicated decision.

If the fault current is such that the fuse needs to blow fast, i.e., in less than 1 cycle, then the most suitable parameter to compare is $\int I^2 \, dt$ (usually referred to as I^2t) and most fuse manufacturers provide appropriate information.

If clearance times above 1 cycle are likely then the current/time curves are most appropriate to compare with the surge current/time curve of the thyristor (see Fig. 6.16).

When using fuses, allowance has to be made for the following points:
1. Fuse capabilities depend on circuit voltage and prospective fault current.
2. Fuse curves are usually plotted with parameters different from those appropriate to thyristors, e.g., prospective symmetrical fault current assuming initial asymmetry, virtual time, etc., and they are usually plotted from a.c. circuit tests, whereas thyristor currents are unidirectional.
3. Fuse arcing voltages must be within the thyristor capabilities.
4. Fuses find difficulty in breaking d.c. circuits, particularly if significant circuit inductance is present. Considerable fuse de-rating is needed compared with a.c. working.
5. Fuse RMS current ratings are based on steady levels of 50 or 60 Hz sine waves. The continuous rating may change if cyclic loads are likely and if higher frequencies are to be used.

Circuit Breakers

A.C. and d.c. electromechanical circuit breakers, including moulded-case breakers, can all be used to give protection to thyristors against overcurrents, but their relatively long opening time makes it necessary to de-rate the thyristors for their normal use. Their use may also lead to the need for an increased value of circuit impedance to limit the prospective level of fault current.

The crucial fact about circuit breakers is the time they take to clear a short-circuit type fault. Although improvements are always possible and are frequently made, in general, circuit breaker fault minimum opening times are approximately those given below, assuming they contain integral instantaneous overcurrent tripping facilities.

A.C. high- and medium-voltage circuit breakers	100–200 ms
A.C. moulded-case breakers	30–100 ms
D.C. medium-speed CB's	40–60 ms

D.C. high-speed CB's	20–40 ms
D.C. moulded-case CB's	30–60 ms

To use circuit breakers for protection, therefore, it is necessary to ensure that the thyristors can accept the full short-circuit and other fault conditions, at least for the time it takes for the circuit breakers to open.

The main difficulty in doing this is to assess accurately the effects of the transiently changing fault current against the thyristor manufacturer's stated thyristor capabilities. The thyristor rating is invariably based on a number of equal half-cycles of surge current, and few of the limiting fault conditions are directly comparable (see Fig. 6.17).

Fig. 6.15 Fuses used in series with the thyristors, and the plunger-type indicator fuses used with them (Laurence, Scott, and Electromotors Ltd)

Various methods of comparing these conditions have been developed by equipment designers; one such way based on estimating junction temperatures is contained in reference 6 for this chapter.

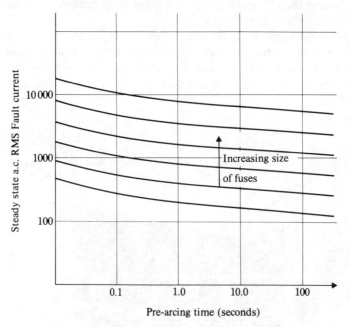

Fig. 6.16 Fuse pre-arcing current/time curves

Obviously, the circuit breaker must be included in the circuit, in a position where the fault current will pass through it. From preceding sections it will be clear that some fault currents do not flow through both a.c. and d.c. sides of convertor circuits.

Thyristor switches can be very fast and as a result are sometimes used to protect thyristor circuits.

Two forms are used, as in Fig. 6.18:
(a) Series-forced commutated switches to cut off the current very quickly.
(b) Shunt-connected 'crowbar' circuits which will bypass the current away from the main thyristors until a series circuit breaker opens the fault.

With suitable design, the series chopper-type switch can be very fast, clearing the circuit in a millisecond or so. The fault current therefore hardly has time to rise to high values and so the capacity of the series switch does not need to be very high. Obviously, back-up protection against switch failure is needed.

A 'crowbar'-type shunt switch does not need to be forced-commutated as it is only switched on when the fault occurs, but it does have to carry the full fault current until the back-up circuit breaker opens.

Refer to Chapter 16 for further application information.

6.7 Miscellaneous Protection Facilities

Most practical equipments will also include other protective devices.

Thermostats may be used to measure thyristor temperature or coolant temperature and give alarm, or switch the equipment off if the measurement is excessive.

132

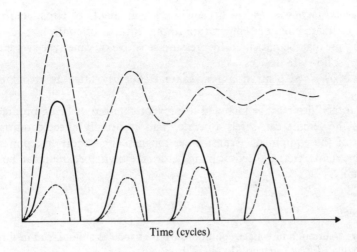

Time (cycles)

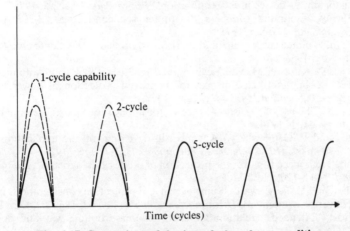

1-cycle capability

2-cycle

5-cycle

Time (cycles)

Fig. 6.17 Comparison of thyristor fault and test conditions

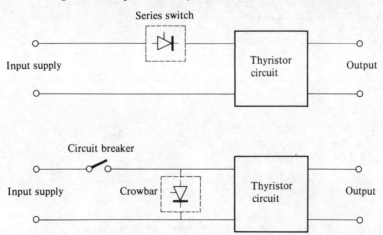

Series switch

Input supply

Thyristor circuit

Output

Circuit breaker

Input supply

Crowbar

Thyristor circuit

Output

Fig. 6.18 Static thyristor switches for protection

Special thermal analogue devices driven by measurements of circuit current have been used to estimate junction temperature to prevent loss of control.

Cooling air flow may be measured by pressure-sensitive or vane-type switches, or by flow-sensitive, solid-state devices.

Inverse time overload protection relays are frequently fitted to avoid excessive RMS loading.

Pulse-inhibit facilities may be included to prevent gate pulses being produced until such time as the circuit can safely operate. This is usually effected during initial switching on of the equipment. Transformer magnetizing conditions, power packs, commutating circuits, etc., all need priming before the thyristor circuit can be allowed to operate safely.

6.8 References

1. F. Hoelters, 'Current and voltage conditions from no load to short circuit in three-phase bridge circuits', *Direct Current*, March 1961.
2. P. de Bruyne and H. Lawatsch, 'Blocking voltage characteristics during turn off of a semiconductor power device in RC connection', *Brown Boveri Rev.*, **5**, 1975.
3. W. McMurray, 'Optimum snubbers for power semiconductors', *IEEE Conference Industry & Application Group*, 1971.
4. D. B. Corbyn, 'Voltage surge control in thyristor equipment', *IEE Conference Publication 17*, 89–101, Nov. 1965.
5. P. de Bruyne, D. Kuse, P. M. Van Iseghem, and R. Sittig, 'New voltage limiters, break-over diodes and light-activated devices for improved protection of power thyristors', *IEE Conference Publication 154*, 18–21, Sept. 1977.
6. D. M. Martin, 'The use of thyristors in convertor applications', *GEC Journal of Science and Technology*, **41**, 1, 1974.
7. J. G. Leach and P. G. Newbery, 'Advances in development and application of semiconductor fuse links', *IEE Conference Publication 123*, 1–6, Dec. 1974.
8. K. Lerstrup, 'High speed fuses for the protection of diodes and thyristors', *IEE Conference Publication 17*, 111–120, Nov. 1965.
9. P. G. Rushall and V. E. Milward, 'Some design and protection considerations in a.c./d.c. thyristor convertor equipment', *IEE Conference Publication 93*, 196–202, Oct. 1972.
10. I. K. Dortort, 'Extended regulation curves for six-phase double way and double wye rectifiers', *AIEE*, 1952.
11. E. Jacks, 'High speed fuse protection for silicon diodes and thyristors', *IEE Conference Publication 53*, 116–124, May 1969.

7. Series and Parallel Operation

Although over the years the size of individual thyristors has increased significantly and methods of cooling and protection have been developed so that they may be used to the full, high-power equipment will continue to need many thyristors effectively acting as one very large thyristor. In correct circumstances, thyristors can be connected in series and parallel to enable higher voltages and currents to be withstood. However, this cannot normally be done simply by connecting thyristor anodes, cathodes, and gates together because of the large variability between individual thyristors. Special steps have to be taken to ensure that each thyristor carries its correct share of the total circuit voltage and current during all operating conditions and that faults or thyristor failures do not impose excessive stresses on the remainder.

As an alternative or additional facility to interconnection of individual thyristors, complete circuits as described in Chapters 4 and 5 are used in series and parallel combinations to achieve higher powers and/or special performance characteristics.

In general, multiple circuits are used, where it is difficult to use series or parallel thyristors, to reduce overall system harmonics and to improve the overall system power factor. Under the right circumstances, multiple thyristors in series or parallel may be used in circuits which are themselves connected together in series or parallel combinations.

This chapter will explain the various methods of safely interconnecting thyristor and thyristor circuits to achieve optimum results. The improvements which are available by using multiple circuits will also be discussed. With these methods it is possible to make thyristor equipment large enough for all practical applications.

7.1 Parallel Connection of Thyristors

Parallel operation of thyristors is relatively easy to use in naturally commutated circuits due to the low rates of rise of current, and it is therefore regularly used. Due to the difficulties of establishing correct sharing of currents during the turn-on and turn-off periods of thyristor switching, it is rarely used in forced-commutation circuits, preference being given to parallel connection of complete circuits.

Thyristors can be connected directly in parallel with each other if they have identical forward voltage/current characteristics. This is rarely the case unless very special selection of the thyristors is made to ensure good current sharing during normal load and under overload and fault conditions.

The shape of the forward voltage curves of thyristors makes it difficult for them to achieve good sharing without assistance, as even quite a small voltage-drop difference can result in a wide divergence of load current (see Fig. 7.1).

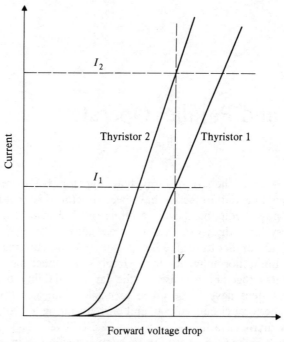

Fig. 7.1 **Divergence of currents when directly paralleling thyristors**

In addition, large thyristor equipment always involves complex runs of busbars and these can have a major influence on the sharing of current between the parallel thyristors. Both the busbar resistance and its effective inductance will be significant, and designs without forced current-balancing methods will need extremely careful consideration or large allowances for unbalance current during normal and fault operation.

There are two practical and efficient ways of improving the balance in parallel-connected thyristor circuits; these use series-connected reactors or current-balancing transformers, and they both affect the balance during the overlap angle when the currents are changing.

Parallel sharing reactors are connected one in series with each thyristor and they insert a voltage into the thyristor circuit proportional to $L \, di/dt$ such as to oppose the increase of current. A thyristor carrying more than its correct share of current during overlap and hence having a higher rate of change of current experiences a higher reverse voltage from the reactor, thus slowing the rate of rise of current, as shown in Fig. 7.2.

The reactors can be extremely effective in balancing the currents during the overlap angle but they are unable to assist during the main conduction period as the rate of change of current is low; the currents therefore tend to drift away from balance as the conduction period progresses. These reactors can be iron-cored but air-cored ones are preferable as they do not saturate at high currents and they are more able to influence the sharing of overloads and faults.

Parallel sharing transformers. This alternative method relies on using transformers to compare the currents in the many thyristors which may be in parallel. One form of this method is to compare each thyristor with the adjacent one, using an iron core

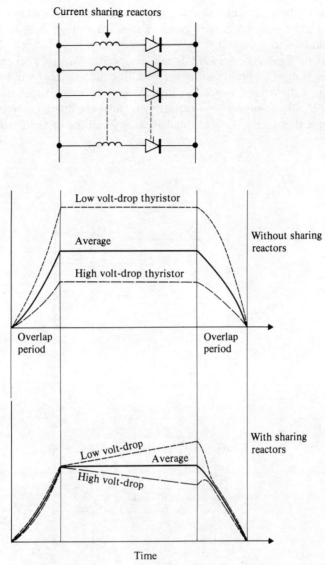

Fig. 7.2 Parallel operation of thyristors using current-sharing reactors

around a pair of opposing conductors, as in Fig. 7.3A. Any unbalance between them will then result in a voltage being induced in each conductor such as to increase the low current and reduce the high one.

This method can be very effective but it imposes severe restrictions on the physical arrangement.

Another method based on the same principles is to feed each thyristor busbar through a separate iron core, wound with a lower current secondary, and then interconnect the secondary windings, as in Fig. 7.3B. During overlap, the current which now flows in the secondaries is equivalent to the average and correct level per thyristor. The iron cores provide a voltage to each thyristor to try to match its current to the average value.

Even with these current-balancing methods it is still necessary in practice to select thyristors to be within a narrow band of forward voltage drop and to allow for the residual unbalance remaining.

If thyristor failure or forward breakover occurs in a parallel-connected group of thyristors, it must be realized that the resulting fault current will be carried solely by the faulty thyristor and hence this current may be many times its normal value. In addition, if voltage-suppression capacitor circuits are fitted, incorrect firing or break-over of one thyristor will cause the discharge of all the capacitors through the faulty thyristor.

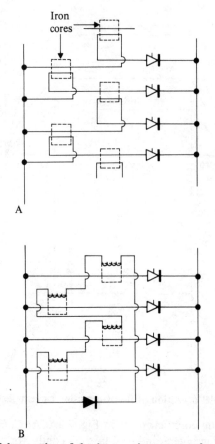

Fig. 7.3 Parallel operation of thyristors using current-sharing transformers

7.2 Series Connection of Thyristors

As with parallel operation, the problems of using thyristors in series are associated with the wide variability of thyristor parameters. Unless specially selected, thyristors will have different values of forward and reverse OFF-state leakage current, turn-on times, and turn-off recovery charge. All these factors significantly affect their use when connected in series.

Fig. 7.4 In this naturally commutated convertor the vertical rows of thyristors are connected directly in parallel using current-sharing, air-cored reactors in series with each thyristor (GEC Industrial Controls Ltd)

Leakage current. Thyristors connected directly in series will share the OFF-state voltage depending on the shape of their voltage/leakage current characteristics (see Fig. 7.5). Within the manufacturer's stated limit of leakage current there will be wide variation in the characteristics, and they will vary with temperature.

It is necessary to connect resistors, in parallel with the thyristors, which will carry a current sufficient to swamp the thyristor leakage variation. The size and dissipation of these resistors can get very large, particularly with the high-voltage thyristors normally used when series connection is considered, and either thyristors specifically made with low leakage current are used or they are selected for low, constant leakage current values.

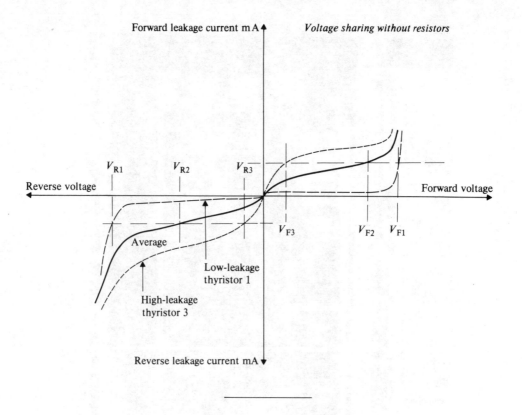

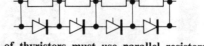

Fig. 7.5 Series operation of thyristors must use parallel resistors to equalize leakage currents

Turn-off. As explained in Chapter 1, when thyristors turn off under conditions of high rate of change of current, the current temporarily reverses and when the free carriers have been swept away the current snaps off, sometimes causing high induced voltages in circuit inductances. Unfortunately, the size of the stored charge varies between thyristors and one thyristor will turn off before another. The first thyristor to turn off will therefore attempt to accept the full circuit voltage of the series string during the short period before all thyristors have turned off (see Fig. 7.6). As selection of thyristors for storage charge is impractical, the solution to this situation is to connect capacitors across the thyristors to limit the rate of rise of the transient voltage and hence the level to which the voltage rises during the period.

Turn-on. Thyristors all have different delay times and turn-on times and the last thyristor to turn on in a series string would transiently have to accept the full circuit voltage. Again, the solution is capacitors in parallel with each thyristor.

di/dt. Unfortunately, parallel capacitors provide a hazard in that when a thyristor turns on, the capacitor can feed a high current at a high rate of change into the thyristor, a condition capable of damaging it. A small series resistor with the capacitor will limit the turn-on current and its energy to an acceptable level.

Hence, a practical thyristor string becomes that shown in Fig. 7.7.

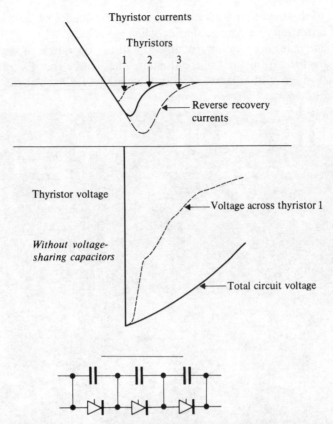

Fig. 7.6 Series operation of thyristors, parallel capacitors to equalize reverse recovery currents

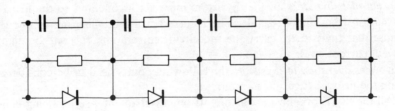

Fig. 7.7 A practical series-sharing arrangement

In very high-voltage strings used in d.c. transmission equipment, even more complicated sharing arrangements may be necessary, including series reactors with each thyristor to limit di/dt, and automatic overvoltage firing to prevent thyristor damage due to a gating circuit fault. For further reading on this see references for Chapter 16.

7.3 Firing Multiple Thyristor Assemblies

Series and parallel operation of thyristors can only take place satisfactorily if all the thyristors are fired at the same instant. Even differences of a few microseconds in the gate pulses to different thyristors can have a major influence on both current balance in parallel operation and voltage sharing when in series.

Consequently, in most equipment using multiple operation of thyristors, all the thyristors are fired from the same pulse-amplifier source (see Chapter 8). Usually, pulse transformers with separate secondary windings for each thyristor or separate pulse transformers per thyristor are used.

Fig. 7.8 Disc thyristors connected seven in series, and the series-sharing components used

With *parallel thyristors* all the thyristors must act as one and so the firing system employed must be highly reliable. The incorrect firing or misfiring of one thyristor will cause that thyristor to carry the full circuit current and this will be many times its normal current level.

With *series operation of thyristors* the following points need to be considered when selecting the firing system to be employed:

(a) All the thyristors must act as one. If one thyristor of a series string is not fired when it should be, the full circuit voltage will be impressed across it causing it to break over, and causing it to fail due to excessive di/dt.

(b) The thyristors will all be at different voltage levels with respect to earth and high-voltage insulation will be required between all the gate circuits. This complicates pulse-transformer design, as the more insulation used the slower the rate of rise of the gate pulse, and this will affect the transient sharing of the total voltage.

(c) All the thyristors must turn off at the same instant or else the last to turn off will be exposed to the full circuit voltage. Due to variation of holding currents, this can only be guaranteed if the gate pulses continue for the whole of the conduction period.

Point (b) above has led to the use of fibre-optic light guides as a means of obtaining the necessary insulation level. Unfortunately, the guides can only pass a small amount of energy to the gate and so a power source local to the thyristor is required. The simplest way is to use the voltage across the thyristor as the source of gate power but this has its limitations (see Section 16.3).

7.4 Multiple Operation of Thyristor Circuits

An alternative to the use of thyristors in series and parallel is to use complete thyristor circuits connected together to increase the total current and voltage capability. Each thyristor circuit would usually be fitted with its own firing circuit and protection components.

For parallel operation it is essential that some impedance is included in each circuit to enable current balance control via the firing circuits to be effective and to enable reasonable balance of currents during faults and short-circuits. Reactors may also be necessary to prevent the circulation of harmonic currents between the parallel-connected circuits, particularly if they are phase-displaced from each other. The output connections will be paralleled together, the input terminals of each circuit may be paralleled or may be fed from independent supplies or transformer windings, etc., as in Fig. 7.9.

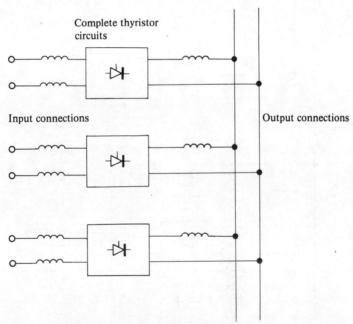

Fig. 7.9 Parallel connection of thyristor circuits

When thyristor circuits are connected in series, they will each be operating at a different voltage level and they must all be isolated from each other in some way, usually by double-wound transformers. The isolation can be done in either the input or the output sides, as in Fig. 7.10. With series connection on the d.c. side (usually used with naturally commutated circuits), the individual isolated inputs can be fed from a common supply if required. When the series connection is on the a.c. side, as is usually the case with forced-commutated inverters, the d.c. inputs may be from either separate sources or a common one.

When d.c. series connection is being used, it may be necessary to connect capacitors and/or resistors across each circuit or thyristor if ever a d.c. voltage can be impressed across the series chain when no current is flowing.

Multiple operation of circuits is not normally seen just as a direct alternative to multiple thyristors, as it provides additionally a means of improving the overall circuit performance. It can be used to cause pulse multiplication, so increasing the frequency of circuit harmonics and reducing their magnitude. Series operation of circuits can also allow sequential control of the bridges which can improve the overall power factor.

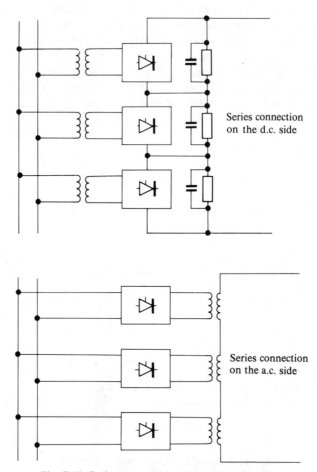

Series connection on the d.c. side

Series connection on the a.c. side

Fig. 7.10 Series connection of thyristor circuits

7.5 Pulse Multiplication

All thyristor circuits, being a sequential operation of switches, introduce unwanted harmonics into the currents and voltages. The magnitude and frequency of these harmonics are dictated by the actual circuit chosen: they are often the reason why a particular circuit is used. If the circuits discussed in Chapters 4 and 5 produce more harmonics than is acceptable, then two possibilities exist, harmonic filters or harmonic cancellation, i.e., absorbing the harmonics or arranging for equal and opposite harmonics to cancel each other. This latter method is achieved by using multiple circuits and is known as pulse multiplication or phase multiplication.

This principle involves displacing the firing of one of two circuits by such an angle that the lowest harmonics change in polarity. For example, if the firing of one of two three-pulse circuits is displaced by 60 degrees this is equivalent to 180 degrees of the third harmonic, and the third harmonic will cancel as long as the circuit currents and

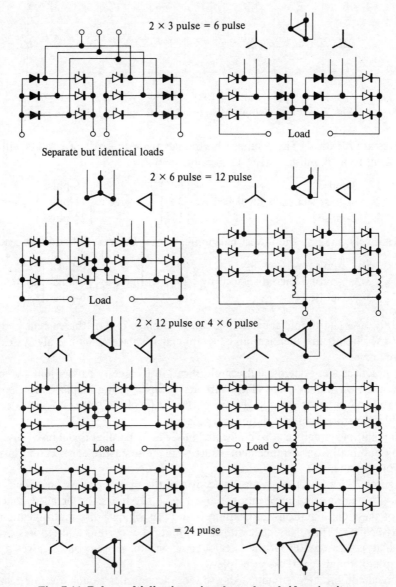

Fig. 7.11 Pulse multiplication using three-phase bridge circuits

145

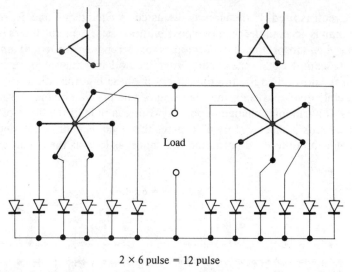

2 × 6 pulse = 12 pulse

Fig. 7.12 Pulse multiplication using the six-phase, half-wave circuit

voltages are identical. The resultant harmonics from the pair of circuits will then be equivalent to a six-pulse system. Generally:

$$\left.\begin{array}{l} \text{2-,} \quad \text{3-pulse} \\ \text{2-,} \quad \text{6-pulse} \\ \text{2-, 12-pulse} \end{array}\right\} \text{circuits displaced by} \left\{\begin{array}{l} 60° \\ 30° \\ 15° \end{array}\right\} \text{will give a} \left\{\begin{array}{l} \text{6-pulse} \\ \text{12-pulse} \\ \text{24-pulse} \end{array}\right\} \text{system}$$

Alternatively, making the lowest harmonics cancel by vectorial addition leads to:

$$\left.\begin{array}{l} \text{3-,} \quad \text{2-pulse} \\ \text{3-,} \quad \text{6-pulse} \\ \text{3-, 12-pulse} \end{array}\right\} \text{each displaced by} \left\{\begin{array}{l} 60° \\ 20° \\ 10° \end{array}\right\} \text{will give a} \left\{\begin{array}{l} \text{6-pulse} \\ \text{18-pulse} \\ \text{36-pulse} \end{array}\right\} \text{system}$$

In all cases, harmonic cancellation can take place only if the current and voltages from the circuits are identical and the angular displacements are always exactly the above angles.

In practical a.c. systems, pulse multiplication is usually carried out by combining phase shift on the a.c. side of the circuits with the firing displacement, so that the fundamental currents or voltages are corrected in phase. Most circuits also need to include transformers for isolation purposes.

The multiple circuits can be connected in series or parallel to achieve pulse multiplication but in all cases arrangements must be made to ensure equal conditions of loading for all circuits.

Figures 7.11 and 7.12 indicate a selection of the multiple thyristor circuits in use in naturally commutated applications, and Fig. 7.13 shows the detailed conditions in one of these combinations, indicating the way in which pulse multiplication is practically achieved (this example assumes a smooth d.c. current and ignores overlap for simplicity). Section 10.9 of the later chapter on d.c. motor control gives a practical example of the use of these principles.

Forced-commutated circuits also use these techniques to achieve lower harmonics in the ouput voltage, and input current, and again transformers have to be used if a

146

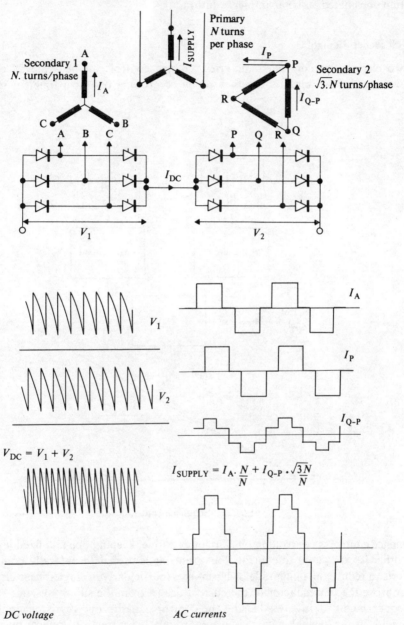

Secondary 1
N. turns/phase

I_A

A

C B

Primary
N turns
per phase

I_{SUPPLY}

I_P

P

R

I_{Q-P}

Q

Secondary 2
$\sqrt{3}.N$ turns/phase

A B C

I_{DC}

P Q R

V_1

V_2

V_1

V_2

$V_{DC} = V_1 + V_2$

I_A

I_P

I_{Q-P}

$I_{SUPPLY} = I_A . \dfrac{N}{N} + I_{Q-P} . \dfrac{\sqrt{3}N}{N}$

DC voltage

AC currents

Fig. 7.13 Pulse multiplication

single load is to be supplied. Section 10.8 gives an example of this principle applied to chopper mark-space controls where separate loads are used.

Pulse multiplication is not so frequently used with forced-commutation circuits as it is possible to build up the waveforms so as to reduce harmonics (see Fig. 5.13) and this is often considered to be a simpler solution.

7.6 Sequence Control

If two circuits are connected in series, voltage control can be achieved either by controlling the two circuits together or by controlling one at a time, in sequence.

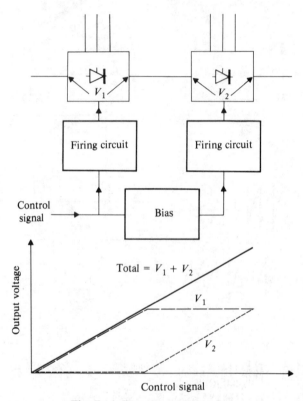

Fig. 7.14 Sequence control

Sequence control is controlling one circuit at a time, keeping one at a fixed level while the other is being used to control. This principle is used with naturally commutated circuits to reduce the magnitude of harmonics (particularly in single-phase circuits) or to improve the power factor of the current drawn from the supply system.

Sequence control involves biasing the control signal to one thyristor circuit, as in Fig. 7.14. Its use in single-phase circuits, particularly for traction applications, reduces the level of harmonic voltage produced (see Fig. 7.15).

The power factor of naturally commutated circuits varies with output voltage. Sequence control can be used to improve the power factor and reduce the input kVA to complete systems. The power-factor angle is the same as the delay angle if we

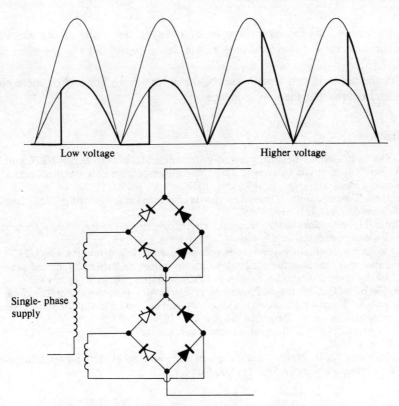

Low voltage | Higher voltage

Single- phase supply

Fig. 7.15 Sequence control on single phase

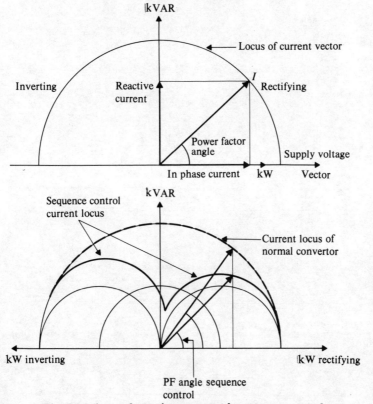

kVAR

Locus of current vector

Inverting

Reactive current

I

Rectifying

Power factor angle

Supply voltage

In phase current | kW | Vector

kVAR

Sequence control current locus

Current locus of normal convertor

kW inverting | kW rectifying

PF angle sequence control

Fig. 7.16 Power-factor improvement by sequence control

ignore overlap, as this is usually shown by drawing the locus of the a.c. current vector at a constant d.c. load current as the delay angle and voltage are changed (see Fig. 7.16).

Both of the above improvements can be taken further by connecting more circuits in series and controlling them in sequence.

7.7 References

1. I. K. Dortort, 'Current balancing reactors for semiconductor rectifiers', *AIEE*, Sept. 1958.
2. F. T. Bennell, 'Current balance in 12-pulse rectifiers comprising parallel bridges', *IEE Conference Publication 154*, 66–69, Sept. 1977.
3. J. K. Hall, 'Forced commutation of thyristors connected in series strings', *IEE Conference Publication 53*, 365–371, May 1969.
4. E. Ohno, H. Mitsuoka, and Y. Kimura, 'Thyristor strings for high voltage applications', *IEE Conference Publication 53*, 406–412, May 1969.
5. UK Electricity Council Engineering Recommendation on Harmonics, G5/3, 1976.
6. L. W. Palmer, 'Design and specification to minimise the harmonic current generation effect of thyristor drives', *IEE Conference Publication 93*, 162–169, Oct. 1972.
7. D. B. Corbyn, 'This business of harmonics', *Electronics and Power*, 219–223, June 1972.
8. K. Schmuck, 'Reaction effects on the supply system caused by hexapulse static convertors with sequential control', *Brown Boveri Rev.*, **11**, 1971.
9. I. K. Dortort, 'Phase shifting of harmonics in a.c. circuits of rectifiers', *IEEE Trans.*, **IGA-4**, Nov. 1968.
10. J. L. Hay and K. R. Naik, 'Application of thyristors to HVDC power transmission', *IEE Conference Publication 53*, 381–385, May 1969.

8. Gate Firing Systems

It is impossible to overstress the importance of the firing system to any satisfactory thyristor application or equipment. Only a correctly designed firing circuit to supply the gate currents to the thyristors will enable the full potential of both thyristors and equipment to be achieved.

The performance capabilities of a particular thyristor will depend on the magnitude and the waveshape of the gate current; it will decide whether or not the device will fire over its full operating range and whether the thyristor will be successful in accepting the circuit currents and voltages to which it is exposed.

In addition, the performance capabilities of the complete thyristor circuit will directly depend on the firing system employed; a phase-controlled system will give completely different results to an integral-cycle firing circuit.

Some systems will only operate successfully with gate current flowing during the whole of the conduction period while in others a single pulse is all that is required.

The unbalance or harmonics in an equipment will be decided by the firing system used.

The pattern of firing chosen for any forced commutated inverter equipment will dictate the output waveform.

The safe limits of operating range of the thyristor circuit are the result of the firing circuit design chosen.

In short, the firing system is the means by which the full technical performance of a thyristor equipment can be achieved. Its design is intimately involved with the thyristor circuit, and its specification and performance have to be chosen based on the particular thyristor circuit with which it is to be used and the particular performance desired from the equipment.

The first step is the definition of a firing circuit: it is the circuit which provides the gate currents for all the thyristors and which decides the particular sequence of operation of the thyristors. The firing circuit and the thyristor circuit together can be considered as a power amplifier, the output power being directly controlled by the level of a low-power input signal, as shown in Fig. 8.1.

The firing circuit itself usually has as many output channels as there are thyristors in the power circuit which it feeds. As such, it is essential for the understanding of thyristor systems and therefore must be included in this book. By contrast, although the control system in any equipment dictates the overall operating performance achieved, its specific design is not intimately involved with the thyristor circuit or firing circuit, and the understanding of these will not be simplified by further study of the control system.

151

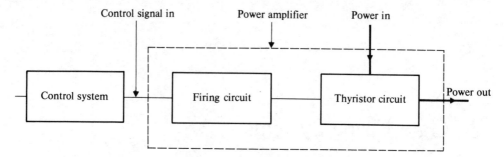

Fig. 8.1 The thyristor circuit and firing circuit combined make a power amplifier

Fortunately, many first-class books on control systems exist, and when considered as a power amplifier a thyristor equipment can be integrated into any such systems.

8.1 Design Parameters Related to Firing Thyristors

The following factors are important in all firing-circuit design irrespective of the duty of overall system, e.g., static switches, convertors, inverters, etc.; they will be followed by a study of complete circuits.

Pulse Magnitude and Shape

In Chapter 1, details were given of gate currents required to fire thyristors and particularly the wide variations that occur between thyristors due to temperature. The gate current used always has to be sufficient to fire all thyristors of the type chosen over the likely range of operating temperature; it will therefore be more than sufficient to fire most thyristors.

The gate current must be maintained until the turn-on process is complete and the device is fully conducting. In general, this means a period between 100 and 150 microseconds allowing for delay, turn-on, and spreading times.

Although with many power circuits a pulse of this length is sufficient to switch the thyristor on and maintain it conducting, some circuits require the gate current to continue throughout the conducting period while in other cases a train of short pulses during the conducting period is sufficient (see Fig. 8.2).

The most suitable system depends on the particular power circuit in use – there may not be a forward voltage at the initial point of firing or the voltage may temporarily reverse during the conduction period.

The use of a gate current just sufficient to fire may well be acceptable for many applications where the thyristor current cannot change rapidly. However, in many practical circuits the initial current flowing into a thyristor rises rapidly due to power-circuit influences, e.g., discharging circuit capacitance, etc., causing a high di/dt.

The ability of a thyristor to accept high di/dt can be improved by increasing the gate current. The current flowing in the anode/cathode circuit will initially flow only in the area of the junction near to the gate; insufficient available area will cause the power loss to be too high and the temperature of this area to exceed tolerable limits, and the device will fail. The available area increases with gate current and with its rate of application.

152

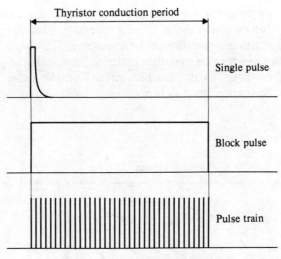

Fig. 8.2 Gate pulse waveforms

In many cases, a fourfold increase in gate current above that needed just to fire all devices, rising to this value in less than 1 microsecond, enables the optimum performance of the thyristor to be obtained.

Gate Isolation

Although in some particular applications it is possible, and may even be necessary, to obtain the necessary firing power directly from the power circuit containing the thyristors, in most cases it is obtained from a separate low-voltage source. This usually means that some method of isolation is required to separate the two power sources. This takes the form of a gate-isolation pulse transformer connected directly in the gate circuit supply to the thyristor.

The design of these transformers is a particularly specialized art because a high insulation level is required to give the necessary safe isolation and this causes high leakage reactance and hence slows down the rate of rise of gate current.

Gate Current and Reverse Leakage Current

Another characteristic of the thyristor is that the application of gate current to the device when the anode voltage is reversed, i.e., anode negative, cathode positive, results in an increase in the reverse leakage current, as shown in Fig. 8.3.

This can cause excessive reverse power loss and ultimately device failure. However, its most important effect is associated with series operation of thyristors when the increased leakage current can make the job of sharing the voltage across the series thyristors much more difficult.

Interference

As has been stated earlier, the firing circuit is the source of the technical performance of the equipment. Incorrect operation of the firing circuit can produce disastrous performance results. One of the frequent causes of firing-circuit maloperation has in the past been interference transmitted into the firing circuit either from the power circuit or from contactors and relays located near to it. Most firing circuits therefore include components to improve their noise immunity. The output stages of the firing circuit usually have protection measures included specifically to prevent interference coming from the power circuit. Earthed screens on the pulse transformer, series blocking diodes, and capacitors may be used singly or in combination for this purpose.

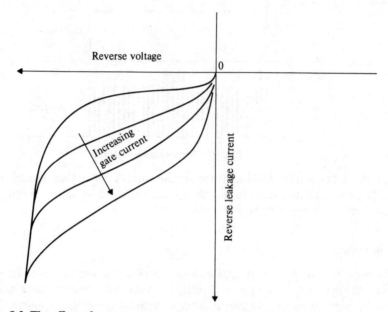

Fig. 8.3 The effect of gate current on the level of reverse leakage current

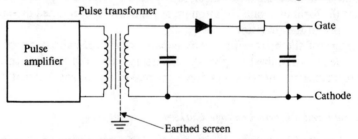

Fig. 8.4 A complete output circuit to fire a thyristor correctly

The Output Circuit of the Firing Circuit

The typical output circuit therefore consists of an arrangement as shown in Fig. 8.4.

The circuit includes the pulse transformer for circuit isolation, the resistor to limit the maximum gate current, and the diode, capacitors, and earthed screen to prevent the switching of the various thyristors from causing incorrect operation of the firing circuits.

8.2 Pulse Amplification

Three methods of driving pulse transformers are in common use and the choice between these methods is usually made after consideration of the type of gate-current waveform required, i.e., single pulse, block pulse, or pulse train.

1. *The simple pulse amplifier* is shown in Fig. 8.5. It will correctly reproduce the input signal pulse at a higher power level on the output of the pulse transformer. The maximum pulse length required must be known and the size of the transformer is directly related to this. If a large pulse transformer is required it may be difficult to obtain the necessary rise time on the leading edge of the pulse.

   The circuit consists of a direct transistor-driven pulse transformer, sometimes with preceding transistor stages to obtain the necessary amplification. The pulse transformer can have a number of separate secondary windings to feed separate thyristors, or a number of pulse transformers can be fed from one transistor pulse amplifier. The transformer core flux has to be returned to its original condition between each pulse to prevent saturation of the core. A separate winding may be included for this purpose and additional components may also be used. The power supply will usually include a capacitor to provide the initial pulse energy to ensure a short pulse rise time.

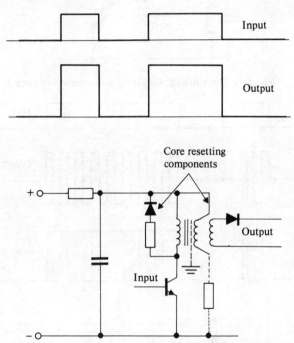

Fig. 8.5 The simple pulse amplifier output stage

2. *The blocking oscillator* pulse amplifier of Fig. 8.6 is a switchable, free-running oscillator which produces a train of high-frequency output pulses in response to a low-level input block pulse. The output pulses are usually of a low on-to-off ratio, e.g., 1 to 5.

   The circuit is made free-running by a winding on the pulse transformer being fed back into the base of the driving transistor. Again, as the pulse output is effectively of one polarity, the core of the transformer has to be reset. The circuit can be prevented from oscillating by holding the input voltage negative.

155

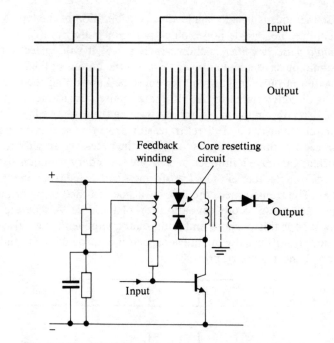

Fig. 8.6 The blocking oscillator pulse amplifier output stage

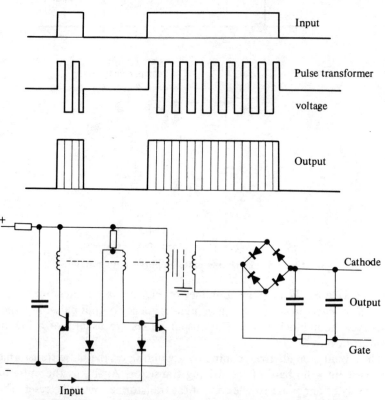

Fig. 8.7 The square-wave oscillator pulse amplifier output stage

156

When the negative bias is released, then free-running oscillation occurs at a frequency decided by the size of the transformer core and the resistor and capacitor components.

3. *The square-wave oscillator* pulse amplifier (Fig. 8.7) is again a switched free-running system, but in this case, the resulting high-frequency wave is a square wave and it can be used when rectified to make up a variable-length block pulse.

It usually consists of a transistor bistable free-running oscillator driving the pulse transformer with a balanced a.c. square wave. Relatively high frequencies can be used and, as the transformer receives alternating voltage, no additional core resetting components are required, the transformer can be relatively small and have a good rise-time performance.

Its main advantage over the other methods, however, is the possibility of rectifying the output with high-speed diodes producing a block pulse which can be of any duration. This is found to be particularly important in variable-frequency, forced-commutated applications.

Inhibiting Pulses

As will be seen later, it is useful to have an alternative input to most pulse amplifiers to allow the pulses to be turned off at the output, although the input pulse may be still being fed into the pulse amplifier. This enables other features to control the presence of gate pulses.

8.3 Pulse Generation

Within the above firing-circuit definition, the complete firing system will consist of two main parts:

1. A means of converting a control system d.c. output signal (from operational amplifiers) into the required number of output channels of low-power pulses.
2. A number of pulse transformer output stages as above to convert these low-power pulses into isolated individual gate currents for each thyristor of the power circuit.

These are illustrated in Fig. 8.8.

As described in Section 8.2, the design of the pulse amplifiers is based on the needs of the thyristors and to some extent on the pattern of firing required by the power circuit, but they only transmit the patterns generated by the pulse generator circuits and convert them into a suitable form for the thyristor. The heart of the firing circuit is the method of pulse generation and the performance of the power circuit is directly decided by the pulse generation system chosen.

The following factors are important in designs for firing-circuit pulse generators.

Synchronization

In the case of mains-commutated circuits, the pulse generator must be synchronized with the mains waveforms in some way to ensure consistent firing of the thyristor in each power-frequency cycle. In forced-commutated systems the firing is usually dictated by a separate synchronizing oscillator on which the stability of the power-circuit frequency depends. The important difference between these from the firing circuit point of view is that the mains waveforms are sinusoidal and may be distorted, whereas separate oscillators are usually more positive and predictable.

Input Signal

In some simple cases where the convertor is only used as a power switch, there will be no need for a controlled input signal, as such: it could just be a switch or relay contact or a static logic signal. In most cases, however, an analogue control signal is required and this is normally arranged to decide the level of output voltage of the total convertor. In a phase-controlled, naturally commutated convertor this signal will control the phase position of the firing pulses to the thyristors in relation to the mains wave-

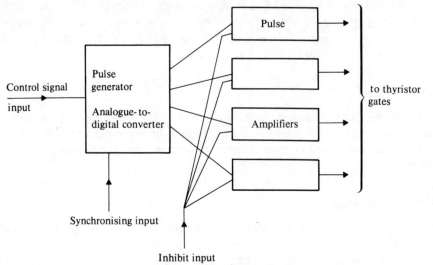

Fig. 8.8 A complete firing circuit

forms, and hence control the output voltage. In the case of an integral-cycle firing arrangement (see Chapter 3), it will control the number of cycles of output in each control period and hence the overall RMS output voltage. In the case of a forced-commutated system it is likely to control the width or pattern of the firing pulses and hence the level of the output voltage.

Phase Control

Phase-shift control is obtained by biasing a cyclic waveform with a d.c. signal voltage. The point where the two signals cross provides a detectable phase position. Although theoretically any shape of cyclic waveform can be used, only two methods are in practical use, the sinusoidal wave and the linear ramp, and these are shown in Fig. 8.9. Sine wave control is usually used in mains-commutated circuits where close synchronism with the mains waveform is essential. Ramp control has a variety of uses in both natural and forced-commutated equipment, enabling phase position or pulse length to be controlled:

As one would expect, the phase shift/bias voltage relationship depends on the shape of the cyclic waveform. The *sinusoidal* relationship is particularly useful for mains-commutated convertors as it produces an overall linear relationship between output

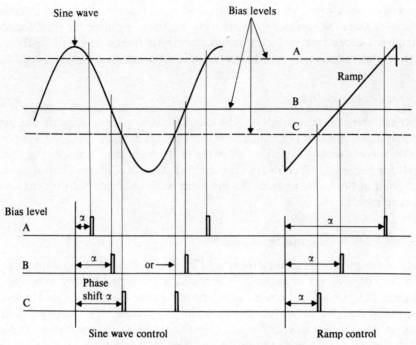

Fig. 8.9 Methods of phase-shift control

voltage and bias voltage. However, mains sine waves can be subject to variation in magnitude and to distortion. The distortion can be filtered out but the magnitude changes have to be allowed for as they will produce phase shift in the output pulses. If the sine wave is digitally generated, it will usually have some step distortion which will affect the bias voltage/phase angle curve.

Ramp or triangular waveshapes can be controlled more precisely as they are likely to be internally generated, usually by conventional resistor/capacitor/transistor

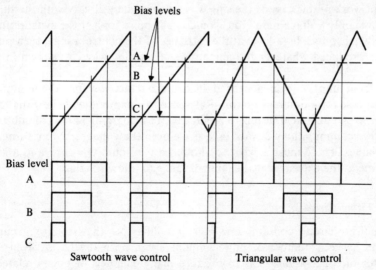

Fig. 8.10 Methods of mark-space ratio control

methods. The waveforms have to be reset and synchronized either from the mains waveform or from the internal synchronizing oscillator. In their simplest form they are frequency-dependent and this reduces their usefulness in variable-frequency circuits; digital systems may well be preferred in such cases.

Mark-space Ratio Control

Another example of ramp control is to be found in mark-space ratio control as used in chopper systems. A ramp or triangular wave is generated and a bias voltage used to decide the point of change from the ON to the OFF condition. These two methods are illustrated in Fig. 8.10, which shows that the triangular wave allows control about the central point of the wave, whereas the sawtooth wave gives control with the starting point as reference.

Phase-shift Range – Back and Front Limits

A study of the power-circuit waveforms of Chapters 3 and 4 will show that a phase-shift control system for a naturally commutated convertor ideally needs to give 180 degrees of phase shift to cover the full control range. In practice, due to overlap and inversion margin, somewhat less than this is possible, say 165 degrees. If the pulses ever move outside this control range, fault conditions will result (see Chapter 6). In the maximum rectifying condition, if one fires too early then with a short pulse the thyristor will not pick up, as the anode voltage on firing would be negative. At the other extreme, firing too late will cause inversion failure and a short-circuit fault current will flow.

Well-designed systems will therefore include limits at the extremes of the phase-shift range. Referring to Fig. 8.11, this can be done either by limiting the range of the control signal voltage or by producing a more complex synchronizing waveform. Either method is suitable with ramp control, but when mains sine wave control is used the only satisfactory way is to alter the sine waveshape. Limiting the control signal voltage cannot work in this case as the sine wave magnitude will vary with the supply voltage, and a supply voltage reduction would cause pulse loss. If the synchronizing waveform is switched to a high level at the extremes of the control range, then pulses can always be produced whatever the magnitude of the sine wave, as shown in Fig. 8.11.

Back and front limits are also needed in firing circuits for forced-commutated circuits, in this case for a different reason. Reference to Chapter 5 will show that after the turn-off process a definite time has to be allowed for recharging of the commutating circuits. Further commutations cannot take place until the voltages have returned to their steady values. There must always be allowed a minimum ON-time and a minimum OFF-time at the extremes of the control range to allow for this.

Multichannel Firing Circuits

In general, a firing circuit contains one pulse amplifier per thyristor, or group of thyristors, and hence a number of pulse amplifiers will normally be involved. The pulse generator often, therefore, has to produce many channels of pulses related in time or phase position as appropriate for the thyristors. Most pulse generators

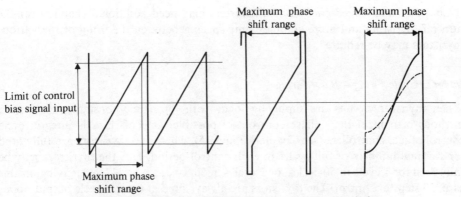

Fig. 8.11 Method of providing back and front stop limits

Fig. 8.12 A 17 kW single-phase convertor built as a complete thyristor, control, and firing circuit assembly (Brown Boveri Ltd)

contain a common phase shift or pulse pattern generator system followed by a number of low-power pulse-producing circuits, one to feed each of the output pulse amplifiers.

For example, a single-phase naturally commutated phase-shift firing circuit will contain a pulse generator producing pulses at 180 degree intervals; these will then be directed as appropriate to the pulse amplifiers so that each thyristor receives only one pulse each cycle, displaced 180 degrees from the complementary thyristors. In a three-phase, half-controlled circuit, three channels of pulses spaced 120 degrees apart are needed and the six-pulse bridge and half-wave circuits need six separate channels of pulses displaced by 60 electrical degrees.

Choppers and forced-commutated inverters may need additional channels for the turn-off thyristors and more complex time-spacing between the firing of the various thyristors may be required.

Integral Cycle Firing – Burst Firing

When thyristor circuits are supplying loads with long time constants, then other methods of control than phase control are possible. One of these is integral cycle control of a.c. controllers (see Chapters 3 and 15), where the thyristors are fully fired for varying numbers of full cycles in each control period, e.g., the thyristors may be fully fired for 1 cycle in 50 cycles, or 2 cycles in 50, or 3, . . ., or 47, etc., giving, in this case, 50 steps of control. The thyristors are always fired at the full cycle output point, i.e., free-firing. This system finds application for resistance heater or furnace supplies where time periods of 1 to 2 seconds are quite acceptable.

The firing circuit in this case consists of the appropriate number of pulse amplifiers fed with pulses to give free firing of the convertor. The switching is then done by use of an inhibit input or its equivalent. Nowadays, the switching controllers are often fully digital units synchronized from the mains and may be capable of optimization of the most satisfactory cycles to fire, e.g., if half voltage is required, every other cycle can be fired; if 25 per cent output is required, fire every fourth cycle, etc. Also, it is possible to multiphase systems to switch the phases individually to effectively increase the number of control steps.

8.4 Firing Circuits for Naturally Commutated Thyristor Circuits

From the foregoing it will be appreciated that most firing circuits for naturally commutated thyristor circuits will contain:

(a) A transformer, fed from the mains supply, to provide reference voltage waveforms for the pulse generation system. The supply to this may be filtered to prevent harmonics or distortion of the supply from affecting the firing-circuit pulses. The number of secondary windings included in this will be related to the pulse number of the circuit, and additional windings may be used to assist in the back and front limit arrangements.

(b) A pulse-generation system containing one of the methods of phase shifting in response to a single input control signal and a set of low-power pulse-forming circuits. One of the methods of back and front limiting of the phase-shift control range would also be included.

(c) An appropriate number of usually identical pulse amplifiers, 2, 3, or 6 as needed. These will include some method of switching on and inhibiting all pulse amplifiers at the same instant.

The following section illustrates the practical application of these techniques to the six-pulse firing circuit.

8.5 A Complete Phase-shift Firing Circuit for a Six-pulse Bridge Convertor

Figure 8.13 shows a typical block diagram of such a firing circuit. In this case the thyristors are fired by short firing pulses lasting 100 to 200 microseconds each. Six channels of pulses will be produced, each displaced by 60 electrical degrees from the

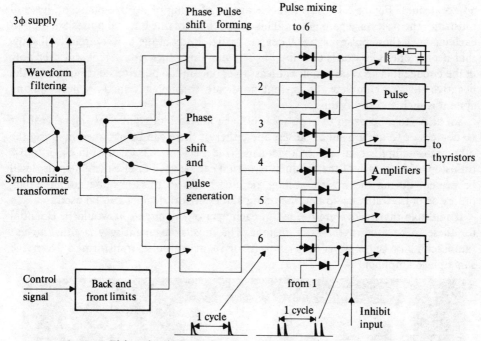

Fig. 8.13 Firing circuit for a six-pulse, naturally commutated convertor

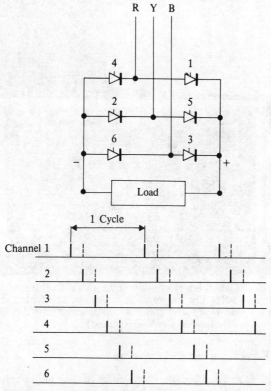

Fig. 8.14 Multichannel firing of a three-phase bridge circuit

163

adjacent ones. Figure 8.14 shows the sequence of firing of a three-phase bridge and illustrates the necessary gate pulses. This shows that not one but two pulses are used in each channel, these pulses being 60 degrees apart. Study of the power circuit will show that if only one thyristor is ever fired at any one time, then no current will ever flow in the circuit; it is necessary to fire at least two, one on the positive side and one on the negative side, to complete the current flow path through the load. A pulse-mixing system is included to do this.

An alternative to using twin pulses is either to use a block pulse lasting at least for 60 degrees or to use a train of pulses, and either of these can be obtained by using the other pulse-amplifier circuit arrangements (see Section 8.2). Only pulses or pulse trains up to the length of the conduction period can be used or else the gate pulses will be present during the reverse voltage period; hence in this six-pulse circuit, block pulses or pulse trains up to and including 120 electrical degrees can be used.

If multiple thyristors were needed in each arm of the circuit, it would be essential for these to be fired at the same instant. The most convenient way is either to use multisecondary pulse transformers or to drive many pulse transformers from the same pulse amplifier.

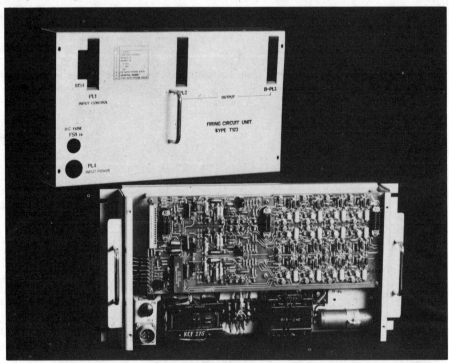

Fig. 8.15 A firing circuit which is a phase-shift unit for a fully controlled reversible antiparallel bridge assembly. The twelve pulse amplifiers are on the right-hand side of the printed circuit board and the phase-shift circuit on the left (GEC Industrial Controls Limited)

8.6 Firing Systems for Forced-commutated Inverters

A number of additional factors affect the use made of the above principles when designing firing systems for forced-commutated thyristor power circuits.

1. The commutation process itself may impose limitations on the type of pulses used to fire the thyristors and the relative timing of the pulses to the various thyristors. In some cases it will mean an increase in the number of thyristors used.
2. The frequency and sequence of firing are not dictated by outside influences, such as the mains waveform in a naturally commutated equipment, and hence these have to be internally generated and controlled.
3. Whereas in naturally commutated systems the means of control is always the point of turning the thyristor on, with forced-commutated systems the point of turning it off can also be chosen – the actual means of control is the width of the conduction periods allowed.
4. Being independent of the cyclic variations of mains supplies, etc., inverters tend to be much more variable; very wide frequency ranges are possible and complicated firing patterns may be used.
5. When a.c. inverter circuits supply inductive loads, the flow of current will be delayed after the point of firing of the thyristors. It will therefore be necessary to maintain a firing pulse on the thyristors for the whole of the conduction period to ensure that when the current wishes to flow, a gate pulse is available to ensure the device can pick up.

The specific principles employed can best be outlined by discussing the firing system likely to be used for, firstly, a d.c./d.c. chopper circuit; and secondly, a three-phase variable-frequency inverter bridge.

8.7 Firing Systems for D.C./D.C. Choppers

Most d.c. choppers will have at least two thyristors, one main power-carrying thyristor and one thyristor used to turn the main one off (see Chapter 5). The main thyristor will be operated with a mark/space arrangement at an appropriately chosen frequency

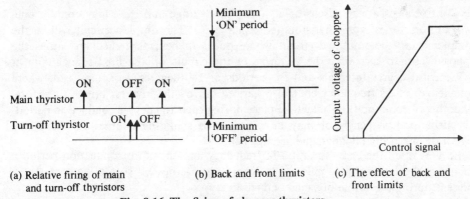

(a) Relative firing of main and turn-off thyristors

(b) Back and front limits

(c) The effect of back and front limits

Fig. 8.16 The firing of chopper thyristors

which may or many not vary. It will normally be fired for the whole of the conduction period to allow current to flow at all times. The gate pulse on the main thyristor will usually be removed at the same time as the turn-off thyristor is fired. The turn-off thyristor normally only has a gate pulse of relatively short length applied to it. Figure 8.16 illustrates the firing pattern and also shows another feature of these systems.

The needs of the commutation process require there to be a minimum length of ON-pulse and a minimum OFF-period to ensure the correct charging of the commutation capacitors. These back and front limits could be applied by restricting the range of the mark-space control signal, but this may prevent the unit from being used with zero output or with full conduction, both of which are desirable operating conditions. If the limits are applied after the mark/space control arrangements, these two extreme operating conditions can then be used and there will be a small step in the control characteristic at each end of the control range (see Fig. 8.16(c)). This characteristic shows what would be achieved by a linear or triangular wave to generate the mark-space control.

Figure 8.17 shows the block diagram of a typical firing circuit for a d.c.-to-d.c. chopper.

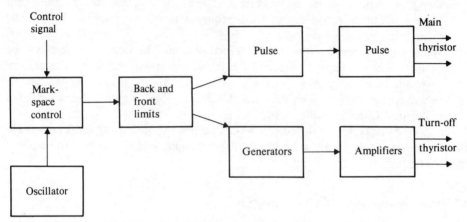

Fig. 8.17 A firing circuit for a d.c.-to-d.c. chopper

8.8 A Firing Circuit for a Three-phase Inverter Bridge

Six control arms are required for a three-phase bridge and each may contain one, two, or sometimes more thyristors (see Chapter 5). The simplest circuit will be the complementary commutated circuit where one arm being switched on causes the opposite arm to turn off. The six arms of the circuit will be fired sequentially at 60 electrical degree intervals and for periods of 180 degrees. In some cases, where voltage as well as frequency control is carried out by the inverter bridge thyristors, a number of commutations may take place during each 180 degree conduction period. The firing-pattern generator may be a simple six-step ring counter or a complex digital or mixed digital–analogue arrangement.

If, as is often the case, variation in frequency and therefore conduction period is required, then a long gate pulse or train of pulses is needed so that gate current is present during the whole of each conduction period.

All inverters suffer from the problem that incorrect operation will result in short-circuit across the d.c. power supply, for example:

(a) If, in Fig. 5.21, when arm S4 is fired, arm S1 fails to turn off – short-circuit.
(b) If gate pulses are all removed, then the current flowing will continue in those thyristors already conducting, producing a short-circuit through the load.
(c) When starting up, it must not be possible for a turn-off commutation to take place until the commutation capacitor circuits are all charged correctly, otherwise a short-circuit occurs due to commutation failure.

(d) When stopping, all thyristors have to be turned off and this requires a special sequence to ensure the commutation capacitors are properly primed to allow this to happen.

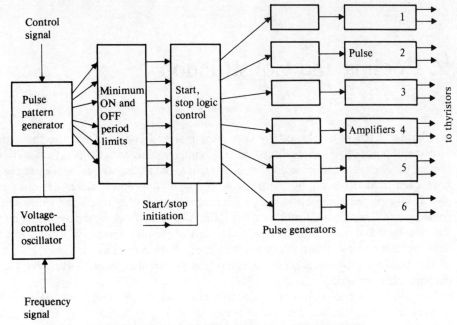

Fig. 8.18 Firing circuit for a three-phase inverter circuit

The firing circuit therefore needs to include features to limit the minimum conduction periods and minimum off-periods to allow correct capacitor charging, and means to programme the start and stop sequences, both of these features overriding all others. Figure 8.18 shows the block diagram of such a firing circuit.

The scope for technical ingenuity in the detailed design of firing circuits is clearly very wide and it would be impossible in one chapter to cover all the many ways of achieving the necessary facilities explained above. Nevertheless, if these principles are applied to detailed design, or analysis of existing systems, they will significantly help in understanding the logic and complexity of firing systems for all thyristor applications.

8.9 References

1. C. F. Battersby, 'Present techniques in gate firing', *IEE Conference Publication 53*, 146–153, May 1969.
2. G. Rayworth, 'Variable phase SCR trigger circuit', *IEE Conference Publication 17*, 121–123, Nov. 1965.
3. D. R. Armstrong, 'Zero crossing detector circuits' *Mullard Technical Communications*, No. 132, 63–68, Oct. 1976.
4. N. G. Hingorani and P. Chadwick, 'A new constant extinction angle control for a.c./d.c./a.c. static convertors', *IEEE Trans.*, **PAS-87**, 3, March 1968.
5. F. E. Spooner, 'A standard thyristor firing system integrated into the new universal Post Office Power Plant Number 233', *IEE Conference Publication 123*, 260–266, Dec. 1974.

9. Cooling and Construction

In Chapter 2 the principles of thyristor heat loss and cooling from the theoretical assessment point of view were discussed. This chapter deals with the practical methods of cooling which are available and in common use. Over the years, most cooling media have been tried, from air by natural convection or fan-blown, water or water and glycol, oil pumped along busbars and for immersion, and by freon and other super-cooled gases. There is no doubt now that after all this experience, air cooling is by far the most used and much more practical than any of the other methods. Liquid cooling does find some applications, where the heat needs to be moved away from the vicinity of the thyristors, where compact construction is essential, and where very heavy currents are involved.

The construction of thyristor equipment has always been very dependent on the cooling of the thyristors, and so this subject also is included here. Construction covers a wide area from a single thyristor/cooler unit assembly, to groups of thyristors with their cooling facilities and protection, to complete cubicle-enclosed units containing from 3 to 300 thyristors at a time with all the necessary cooling, firing, control, and protection components to make them fully operational.

9.1 Junction Temperature

A thyristor will only operate correctly, i.e., block forward and reverse voltage and be controllable by gate current, if its junction temperature is kept below a critical level. Above this temperature it will not be possible to control it by gate firing and it will not accept forward voltage without breaking over. This *critical junction temperature* usually lies between 120 and 150 °C and the practical consequences of allowing the temperature to exceed this figure can be to initiate a short-circuit fault in the equipment; it often means di/dt failure of the thyristor.

As mentioned in Chapter 2, the size of thyristor used is decided by assessing the power losses in the thyristor and the efficiency of the cooling system (heatsink) to be employed. These calculations have to be done at the highest level of load current to be carried by the thyristor for any length of time, at the highest thyristor forward-voltage drop anticipated, and they must take into account the highest ambient temperature of the cooling medium local to the thyristors. It may also be prudent to allow a modest temperature safety margin of 5 or 10 °C to make sure of satisfactory performance.

Reference should be made to Chapter 2 for more calculation details. From these it will be appreciated that allowance has to be made for power-frequency junction-temperature oscillations and the effects of cyclic loads. It is also necessary to allow for the thermal resistance of the thyristor base to cooler connection.

9.2 Air Cooling

Thyristors are mounted on cooling fins which dissipate the losses by natural convection or with fan-assisted air flow.

A very wide variety of air-cooled heatsink designs are available, and Fig. 9.1 shows a few examples. The basic principle of their design is to transfer the heat from the thyristor to the cooling area of the fins as efficiently as possible. Although other materials can be used, the majority are made of flat plate aluminium or extruded sections of the same material. In general, a design compromise is reached between the required heatsink cross-sectional shape and the limitations of the extrusion process and its dies.

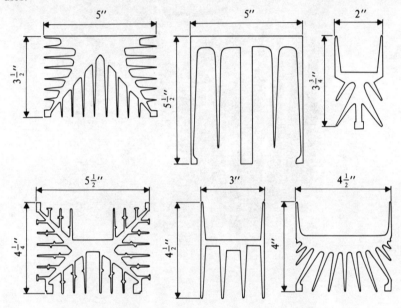

Fig. 9.1 A selection of extruded aluminium heatsinks

The performance of an air-cooled heatsink will depend on many factors:
1. The surface area exposed to the cooling air.
2. The design of the heatsink, i.e., its efficiency in transferring the heat from the thyristor to the dissipating surface.
3. The heatsink material.
4. The size of the thyristor surface in contact with the heatsink.
5. The position of the thyristor on the heatsink.
6. The ambient air temperature.
7. The volumetric flow of air over the fin surface.
8. The nature of the air flow, i.e., laminar or turbulent flow.

In addition, the efficiency of the heatsink will depend on its size in relation to the thyristor, as the heat is only put into the heatsink at one point, the heat then having to spread to the cooling fins.

Fig. 9.2 A disc thyristor clamped to a heatsink (ASEA Ltd)

Figure 9.3 demonstrates that there is a limit to the size of an efficient cooling fin, the further extremities of the cooler being less effective than those near the thyristor.

The heatsink material is also significant as different metals have different thermal conductivities, and hence they transfer the heat from thyristor to cooling surface more effectively. In this respect copper is 80 per cent more effective than aluminium but its higher cost, and difficulty of extrusion, limits its use to specialized applications.

The thyristor/heatsink contact area is also important, particularly if an aluminium heatsink is in use, as it alters both the thyristor-to-heatsink thermal resistance drop as well as altering the efficiency of the heatsink to move the heat away. The use of a special jointing compound or grease between the two surfaces can ensure that they are both in good thermal contact and all the contact area is being effective.

With regard to air flow, natural air-convection cooling is in general much less effective than fan-assisted flow as the quantity of cool air meeting the heatsink surface

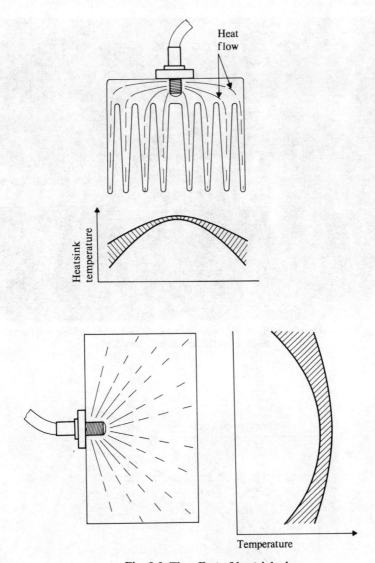

Fig. 9.3 The effect of heatsink size

is reduced, and with natural flow the air local to the fin surface tends to remain stationary or move only very slowly. Improvements of three or four times can be achieved by blowing the air (see Fig. 9.5).

The best measure of cooling-fin efficiency is its thermal resistance as measured from heat input and cooling tests equivalent to normal use. Figure 9.6 shows typical performance curves of an extruded aluminium heatsink.

Heatsinks will also have a thermal mass dependent on their size and this will result in an ability to store heat temporarily without so large a temperature rise. This is illustrated in Fig. 9.6.

Disc-type thyristors (see Fig. 1.4) can be cooled on both sides and this considerably increases their continuous current-carrying capabilities. An improvement up to twice the single-sided cooled rating can be achieved in this way. However, it does not in-

Fig. 9.4 A selection of thyristor/heatsink assemblies for natural-air and forced-air cooling (AEI Semiconductors Ltd)

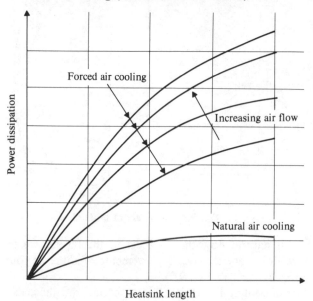

Fig. 9.5 Improved heatsink performance by forced-air cooling

crease the surge current capability and this may be the limiting factor in the allowable rating.

The drawbacks associated with air cooling are as follows and these often have a bearing on the particular cooling system chosen:

(a) Forced-air cooling involves the use of rotating fans which are noisy and are liable to break down.

(b) Blockage of the air flow paths and contamination of the heatsink surfaces can reduce overall cooling efficiency.

(c) Air flow over the thyristor itself can result in surface contamination of the insulator and resultant tracking.

Air filtering and restriction of the air flow to the cooling fins only, are methods often used to reduce these drawbacks.

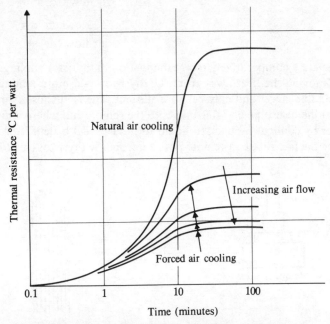

Fig. 9.6 Typical heatsink thermal resistance curves

Fig. 9.7 Double-sided-cooled disc thyristor assemblies (ASEA Ltd)

It is necessary with any air flow system design to bear in mind that the air temperature must rise to take the heat away, and this may affect the cooling of those components last in the air stream. The temperature rise can be estimated from the following formulae:

$$\text{Heatsink temperature rise (°C)} = \frac{1\cdot65 \times \text{watts loss}}{\text{air flow (ft}^3\text{/min)}}$$

$$= \frac{3500 \times \text{watts loss}}{\text{air flow (m}^3\text{/s)}}$$

Heat pipes are a comparatively recent innovation in thyristor cooling. They provide a means of moving the heat away from the thyristor to a more remote cooler which may be able to be larger and may be more efficient. The heat causes vaporization of a liquid within the heat pipe and this moves to the remote end where it gives up its heat to the cooler by condensing back to liquid form. The real benefit it provides is being able to move the heatsink to a remote position from the thyristor (see Fig. 9.8).

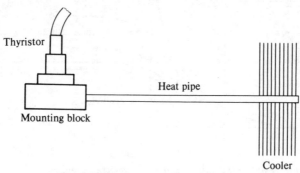

Fig. 9.8 Thyristor cooling using a heat pipe

9.3 Liquid Cooling

Cooling by liquids can be much more efficient than air cooling but it brings with it the necessity for interconnecting pipes and pumps and the potential problems of electrolytic corrosion, blockage, and possibly freezing. More compact designs can be produced using liquid cooling and the heat can be taken well away from the thyristor assembly.

Designs tend to be more special, and often they are associated with the specific application. Examples of the methods employed are:
1. Mounting the thyristor on an individual liquid-cooled block which is then interconnected with others by flexible pipes (see Fig. 9.9).
2. Mounting many thyristors on one common liquid-cooled structure.
3. Direct immersion of the thyristors (maybe with small heatsinks) into the cooling liquid.

Two liquids are in frequent use, water and oil.

Water can have a high speed of flow and can be very effective in cooling but it can, and does, cause electrolytic corrosion and it can freeze. The electrolytic action is caused by the fact that thyristors in most circuits will be at different potentials and current flow through the water can occur. Distilled, and maybe de-ionized, water

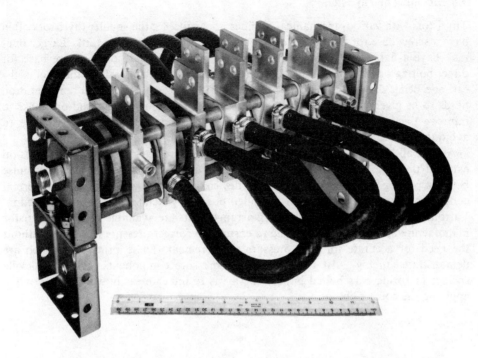

Fig. 9.9 A water-cooled stack of thyristors capable of being connected into a variety of circuit arrangements (Westinghouse Brake and Signal Co. Ltd)

may be used and water circuits will be restricted to the use of compatible metals, copper, brass, gunmetal, etc. The possibility of freezing results in the use of glycol, plus various inhibitors to prevent further corrosion. As far as is known, water-immersion of thyristor assemblies has never been attempted.

Oil is a more satisfactory medium but it is more viscous and its cooling ability is less than water. It does not allow electrolytic currents to flow and it does not freeze. It is normally, however, inflammable and this restricts its use. Non-inflammable oils are usually highly toxic. Oil immersion can be done successfully although accessibility to the components is then rather restricted.

Again, the liquid will increase in temperature to take the heat away and the following formulae will give a guide to the temperature rise which must be allowed for:

$$\text{Water (°C)} = \frac{\text{watts}}{70 \times \text{litres/min flow}}$$

$$\text{Oil (°C)} = \frac{\text{watts}}{28 \cdot 6 \times \text{litres/min flow}}$$

Liquid flow blockage or pump failure is always a possibility and flow-measuring devices will be included in any well-engineered scheme. This is particularly important if parallel liquid flow circuits are used, as a blockage in one will not be easily detectable in the total flow. Thyristors very quickly detect loss of flow by their consequent breakdown.

175

9.4 Mounting of Thyristors

Thyristors with various mechanical outlines are available; the smaller thyristors often have a screw base for bolting on or screwing into the cooler or heatsink. Larger ones may have a flat circular base with a separate clamping plate or a square base for direct bolting on to the heatsink. In all of these cases the base will be the anode, the cathode being the top or flexible braid. In all these cases, no special consideration needs to be given when mounting, except to use a mounting compound or grease to improve thermal contact and to keep within the manufacturer's stated torque to avoid damage to screw-base thyristors.

Almost all large thyristors are of the disc type, where the internal contact relies on external pressure. The mounting arrangements therefore have to be a compromise between putting sufficient pressure on the device to ensure good electrical and thermal contact, but avoiding excessive or lop-sided pressure which can damage the junction. Various patented pressurized clamping arrangements are available from the thyristor manufacturers, their main aim being to ensure the correct pressure is applied without the need for accurate force or pressure measurement. These principles, which are demonstrated in Fig. 9.10, are to use fixed pressure components such as belleville springs or spring bars bolted in such a way as to indicate easily when the spring is applying the correct pressure.

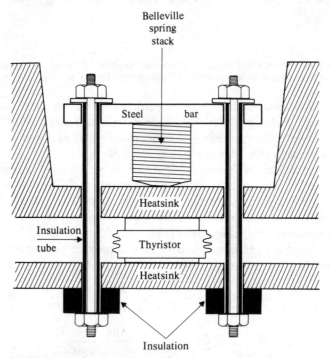

Fig. 9.10 Typical mounting arrangement for pressure-contact disc thyristor

Disc thyristors can be mounted in either polarity and this can be of significant benefit to equipment design.

In all mounting arrangements, perfect thermal connection between the thyristor and heatsink is not possible and a small thermal resistance must be included in all

176

temperature calculations to allow for this. In some cases, the manufacturer's stated thermal resistance of the thyristor may include the contact thermal drop. If not, then Fig. 9.11 can be used as a guide: this assumes correct mounting torques and the use of a jointing compound or grease.

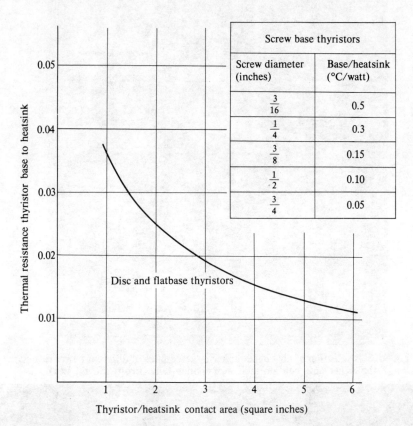

Screw base thyristors	
Screw diameter (inches)	Base/heatsink (°C/watt)
$\frac{3}{16}$	0.5
$\frac{1}{4}$	0.3
$\frac{3}{8}$	0.15
$\frac{1}{2}$	0.10
$\frac{3}{4}$	0.05

Fig. 9.11 Thermal resistance of thyristor base to heatsink connection

In the majority of situations, the thyristors are fixed solidly to the cooling structure and this is therefore operating at the appropriate anode or cathode voltage. In special circumstances this may be unacceptable, due to either the need to mount many semiconductors on one heatsink or the need to earth the cooling metalwork. Electrically insulating, thermally conducting materials are available for this purpose based on alumina, boron nitride, or beryllia. These have to be inserted between the thyristor and the heatsink and they do result in a significant thermal resistance drop which must be allowed for. This method is further complicated by the need to include current take-off from the thyristor at the same point.

9.5 Thyristor Stacks

Single-phase, three-phase, and a.c. controller assemblies of thyristor and heatsinks are available from many manufacturers and these can and do help to simplify equipment assembly.

Fig. 9.12 A selection of air-cooled thyristor assemblies of different power ratings; the larger ones contain their own cooling fans (Brown Boveri Ltd)

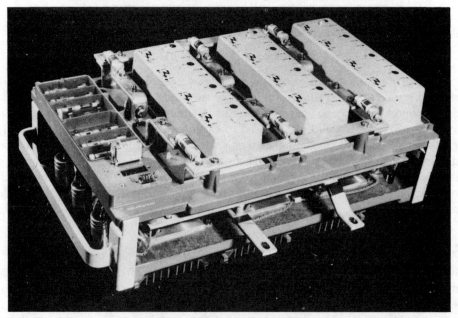

Fig. 9.13 A complete, fully controlled antiparallel thyristor bridge unit for forced-air cooling. It contains all the necessary cooling and protective components (GEC Industrial Controls Ltd)

9.6 Construction of Equipment

All manufacturers construct thyristor equipment in different ways, and here it is possible only to set down some of the main principles and show a few examples. In general, thyristor assembly construction is guided by the following points:

1. Electrical and thermal contacts are usually at the same points – electrical connection is taken from the heatsink. The heatsinks will be at different potentials.
2. The necessity to incorporate the heatsinks into an overall cooling circuit causes the thyristors to be inside the assembly, particularly with double-sided cooling, making accessibility to them difficult.
3. The thyristors need to be surrounded by reactors, surge suppression, and snubber circuits (see Fig. 4.24).
4. The thyristors, diodes, commutating capacitors, and inductors in forced-commutated circuits may need to be mounted in very close proximity to each other to avoid stray circuit inductances.
5. Construction in the form of removable sub-assemblies can considerably help in the maintenance of the equipment when in service.

Smaller power equipment involving only one thyristor in each part of the power circuit tends to be manufactured as an integrated assembly of power thyristors with protection and cooling facilities, firing circuits, and electronic control all assembled

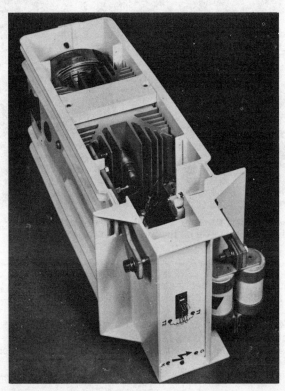

Fig. 9.14 A thyristor assembly for use in a large convertor. It contains all the items needed with each thyristor, i.e., heatsinks, series reactor, fuse, snubber circuits, pulse transformer, etc. Many of these assemblies are used to make a complete equipment (see Fig. 10.16) (GEC Industrial Controls Ltd)

179

together, as a functional assembly (see Fig. 10.20). Larger equipment, involving many thyristors, is often made in the form of many identical thyristor assemblies, each with the necessary local protection circuits. These separate assemblies are connected in parallel and maybe series to satisfy the necessary power rating.

Fig. 9.15 This oil-cooled thyristor assembly is part of a 4·8 MW convertor for driving a locomotive on the Swedish railways (ASEA Ltd)

9.7 References

1. E. J. Diebold and W. Luft, 'Thermal impedance of cooling fins', *AIEE, Paper* No. 58–926, April, 1958.
2. D. Finney, 'Convertor design for functional maintenance', *GEC Journal for Industry*, **1**, 1, 13–16, Oct. 1977.
3. P. Bachmann and H. Felkel, 'SITOR thyristor assemblies of compact design for static convertors', *Siemens Review*, No. 9, 398–399, 1976.
4. E. Hofler and G. Reich, 'A new range of modular static convertors', *Siemens Review*, No. 9, 387–391, 1975.

PART II

Thyristor Applications

In this part, all the practical applications in frequent use are explained and discussed with particular reference to the thyristor techniques necessary to be used in each of them. Where applicable the benefits, and maybe disadvantages, of using thyristors for the specific application are explained.

10. D.C. Motor Control

10.1 The D.C. Motor

Since its invention in the late 19th century, the d.c. motor has been recognized as an ideal means of obtaining controlled rotational motion and over the years its design has been refined to allow it to cope with a wide variety of variable-speed applications.

The ability to be able to control its speed by variation of the armature voltage or by change in its field current gives it great flexibility of operation. The fact that its torque is dependent on armature current and air-gap flux enables it to perform satisfactorily even under the most arduous duty cycles.

As a result, it has been extensively used in all industries and in all environments wherever variable-speed rotational drives have been required; to drive factory machines, trains, printing presses, mine hoists, pumps, cranes, steel mills, ships, fans, milk floats, theatre stages, paper-making machines, excavators, conveyors, etc.

The d.c. motors available range from fractional kW servo-motors to machines of over 7000 kW output, from 2 centimetres to 3 metres in diameter.

A full understanding of d.c. motors is not really required to appreciate the needs and design of convertors to feed and control them; a few basic points, however, will help.

The equivalent circuit of the armature from the supply point of view is shown in Fig. 10.1, in which R is the total armature circuit resistance, and L is the total armature circuit inductance.

The back-e.m.f., E_b, will be generated by the rotation of the armature in the field flux which will be the net result of separately excited fields, shunt fields, series fields, and armature reaction.

Convertor-fed d.c. motors will more often have separately excited fields rather than being shunt-, series-, or compound-wound machines. The larger motors will also be fitted with compensating windings which will cancel out the majority of the armature reaction field produced by the flow of armature current. In this latter case of the *compensated, separately excited motor*:

$$E_b \propto \text{speed} \times \text{field flux}$$

or if saturation is neglected,

$$E_b \propto \text{speed} \times \text{field current}$$
$$\text{Torque} \propto \text{armature current} \times \text{field current}$$
$$\text{Power} = \text{input power} - \text{armature losses}$$

Neglecting friction and windage,

$$\text{Shaft power} = I_A V - I_A^2 R$$

and

$$I_A = \frac{V - E_b}{R}$$

To a first approximation, therefore, speed is directly dependent on supply volts and inversely proportional to field current.

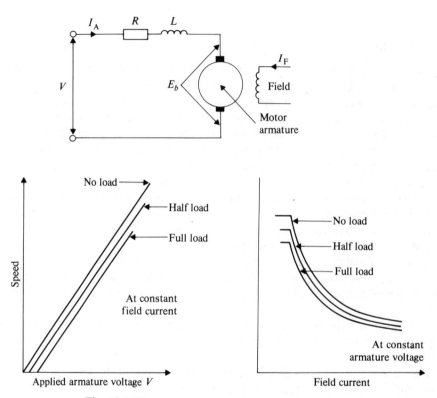

Fig. 10.1 The separately excited d.c. motor

If the motor is not compensated for armature reaction, then the flow of armature current will modify the effective field flux and hence alter the back-e.m.f. as the load current changes. Normally a reduction of back-e.m.f. occurs as load current is increased but the magnitude of the effect is dependent on the exact setting of the brush-gear. The armature reaction effect can for our purposes be allowed for by increasing the effective value of the armature circuit resistance.

The series motor uses the main armature current to provide the field; the total field resulting from both series field and armature reaction is therefore dependent on armature current, i.e.,

$$E_b \propto \text{speed} \times \text{armature current}$$
$$\text{Torque} \propto I_A^2$$

184

This gives the series motor the ability to produce very high peak torques limited only by the thermal and commutating conditions of the machine and the saturation of its iron circuit. The characteristics of the series motor are shown in Fig. 10.2.

These characteristics are ideally suited for loads where power or torque control is most appropriate, rather than constant speed. Hence they find wide application in transport drives, i.e., battery vehicles, trains, fork-lift trucks, etc.

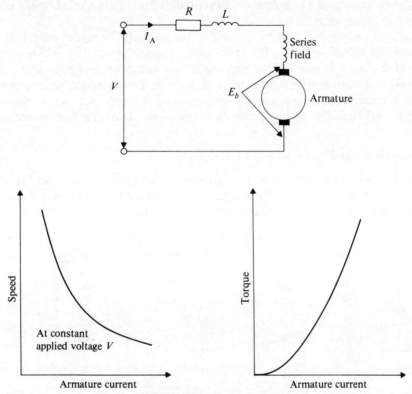

Fig. 10.2 The d.c. series motor

The choice of which motor to use for a specific application depends directly on the needs of the load, the speed/torque requirement, whether reversal of speed or torque is necessary, the range of speed or torque control, etc.

The separately excited motor can be controlled by either field current or armature voltage. Field current has its limitations, however; reduction in field current (to increase speed) reduces the torque, and in addition it cannot be changed quickly owing to the high inductance of the field windings. Hence, field control tends to be restricted to loads where constant power is satisfactory as speed increases (i.e., reduction in torque) and to loads where comparatively slow field current, and hence speed and torque change, are acceptable. Armature voltage control suffer from neither of these limitations and when used with a fixed field allows very rapid changes of speed and torque to take place. In some cases, the load requirements can be most economically satisfied by using high-speed armature voltage control for fast changes and slow field current control to set the steady-state operating point. A common term for this is *spillover field weakening* when full field is used until the limits of armature voltage are approached, the armature voltage then being used to initiate reduction of field current but still leaving sufficient armature voltage control range available for the fast changes which may be needed.

Speed control is very difficult with *the series motor* because any change in the load current will immediately be reflected in a speed change, and hence all speed-control systems will use separately excited motors. The series motor is ideally suited to systems where control of the torque or power fed to the load is needed, speed being of secondary importance.

The choice of motor will also be affected by the necessity for regenerative braking and reversal of motor direction. The series motor requires reversal of field to obtain reversal of direction. It also needs a very significant change in field connection, and maybe field supply, to achieve regeneration for braking. The separately excited motor, however, is much more flexible and reversal of direction and torque can be obtained by using the field (if slow change is acceptable) or the armature (for fast reversals).

10.2 Thyristor Control of Separately Excited Motors

Since its invention in the early 1960s, the thyristor has been used to supply and control d.c. motors, and its superior performance and economic advantages have led to its taking over the role previously fulfilled by resistor and rotating exciter field controllers,

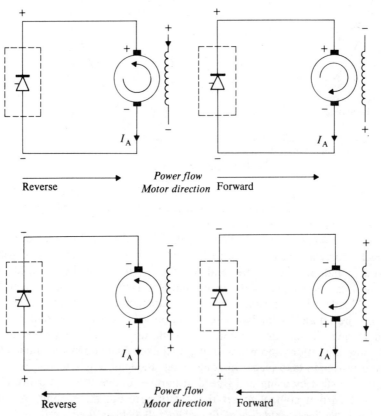

Fig. 10.3 D.C. motor control by field reversal

motor generator Ward–Leonard sets, and, more recently, grid-controlled mercury arc rectifiers.

In most cases, the thyristor performs this duty by converting a.c. mains fixed voltage and frequency into variable-voltage d.c. for either armature or field supply to the motor, or maybe both. With the more recent introduction of forced turn-off methods, it is now also used to convert efficiently constant-voltage d.c. supplies into variable-voltage d.c. to enable motor speed to be controlled; however, more of that later.

Let us start by considering the basic principles of using convertors with d.c. motors. A simple thyristor convertor will only allow current flow in one direction. It can, however, be used in a number of ways to achieve the required rotational direction and torque direction.

If field reversal is used, conditions as in Fig. 10.3 can be obtained.

The use of a single convertor allows only one direction of armature current flow and makes it necessary to use comparatively slow field direction changes to achieve operation in all four quadrants, i.e., forward, reverse, motoring, and regenerating. An alternative is to use switches in the armature circuit to avoid the need for the slow field changes, as shown in Fig. 10.4.

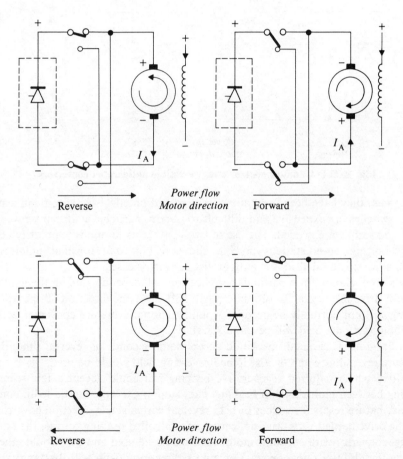

Fig. 10.4 D.C. motor control using armature reversing switches

187

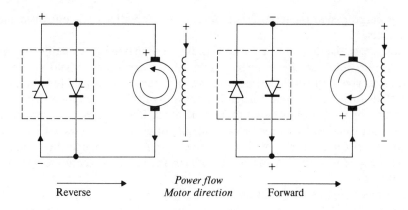

Reverse ⟶   Power flow
                 Motor direction   Forward ⟶

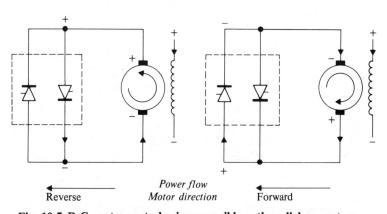

⟵ Reverse   Power flow
                 Motor direction   ⟵ Forward

Fig. 10.5 D.C. motor control using reversible antiparallel convertors

Although they have been used in many large and practical systems, main armature circuit switches are expensive and difficult to obtain, particularly if many reversals of speed and torque are needed. The use of two convertors in opposite polarity achieves the ideal of high-speed static reversal, as shown in Fig. 10.5. Constant, unidirectional field is all that is needed in this antiparallel convertor case.

The system chosen for a particular application will depend again on the load needs. A motor drive for, say, a fan or a pump will only need one direction of operation and braking will not normally be needed. A unidirectional armature convertor with constant unidirectional field will be quite suitable.

If a drive needs reversal but would accept some seconds of reversal time, then an armature reversing switch or a switched reversing field would be used.

A drive which required regenerative braking but could accept a few seconds of coasting between motoring and braking, e.g., stopping a large inertia load, could use either armature reversal switches or field reversal with a single direction covertor.

If the drive needed very fast application of controlled braking torque, then an antiparallel convertor with constant motor field would be used and this would inherently provide the ability to give reversal of motor direction, again with braking facilities.

Fig. 10.6 A three-phase, bridge-connected thyristor convertor with d.c. reversal using contactors (ASEA Ltd)

10.3 Thyristor Circuit Choice for Naturally Commutated Convertors

Any of the circuits, single-phase or multiphase, discussed in Chapter 3 can be used with d.c. motor drives.

The *single-phase bridge* is used for small drives (up to a few kilowatt) or for special applications where only a single-phase supply is available, e.g., rail traction. Only two arms need to be controlled if motoring only is required; all four arms will need to be thyristors if regenerative braking is needed. The main adverse characteristic of the circuit is the high level of ripple in the d.c. voltage at twice supply frequency, which usually means additional inductance in the motor circuit to reduce the current ripple to acceptable levels to make motor commutation satisfactory.

The *three-phase half-controlled circuit* is quite suitable for a simple variable-speed drive not requiring regeneration, but again it produces high d.c. voltage ripple at three times supply frequency and this may limit motor performance. However, it is used regularly up to 100 kW and it has been successfully used at much higher power levels.

The *three-phase, six-pulse bridge* is by far the most common circuit used for motor drives. Its d.c. ripple is much lower and quite acceptable by most d.c. motors, and it will allow regenerative braking as well as motoring. It can and is used with or without a supply transformer and for large drives, bridges may be used in series or parallel to give higher voltage or higher current operation (refer to Chapter 7).

The *six-pulse diametric or inter-phase transformer* circuit has been used in the past with mercury arc convertors and its use with thyristors is restricted to cases where mercury arc tanks have now been replaced by thyristors, but using the original transformer and circuit. Its high peak thyristor voltage for a given d.c. voltage and the expensive transformer needed make it unacceptable for newly designed drives.

Switched antiparallel six-pulse bridge circuits are the most common where high-speed reversal and regeneration is required.

10.4 Drive Control and Protection

Motor control is carried out by balancing the applied voltage to the motor against the induced back-e.m.f. of the machine. Current is established by unbalancing these two voltages, the level of current then being controlled only by the comparatively low values of motor resistance and inductance. Small changes of voltage can usually result in large changes in current and this leads to particular drive control features: namely, direct current control and current limit control, both with a high speed of operation. Direct current control allows precise control of the motor and usually takes the form of a closed inner current loop with an outer speed or voltage loop to give the drive the required overall control, as shown in Fig. 10.7.

Current limit control to give an absolute limit to the maximum level of current passed into the motor is needed to protect both the motor and convertor, and is normally included in all motor control schemes. This usually comes into play if the motor is overloaded or is stalled. A time-delayed current-measuring trip relay is often used to switch the drive off in case of lengthy operation under current limit conditions.

Protection has to be included to cover faulty operation of the firing circuit, or thyristor power circuit, or motor faults such as flashover, etc. Fuses or circuit breakers will normally be used for this purpose (refer to Chapter 6).

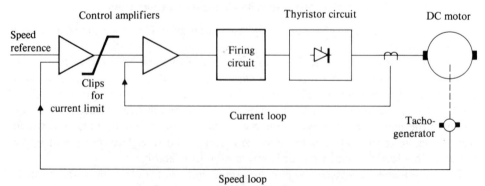

Fig. 10.7 Variable-speed d.c. drive control system

There is one additional fault condition which deserves special attention, namely, inversion failure. Control over the current can only be maintained if the convertor can match or balance the back-e.m.f. of the motor. If, due to either excessive motor voltage or low supply voltage, this cannot be done during inversion, the result will be a failure to commutate in the convertor and the motor will be short-circuited by the convertor; as it is regenerating it will then force fault current through the short-circuit.

Although protection needs to be included in the d.c. circuit to cover this, e.g., a d.c. circuit breaker, the best way to limit this occurrence is to ensure that the effect only occurs when severe reduction of supply voltage takes place, i.e., design in a suitable extra voltage into the convertor to allow for a known reduction of supply and still maintain balance. This, however, increases the convertor cost and a compromise has to be decided upon. A reasonable level is to design for a further 5 per cent supply reduction on top of the normal steady-state variation which is probably ± 6 per cent, i.e., allow for 11 per cent reduction during inversion.

10.5 Chopper Control of D.C. Motors

In Chapter 5 the principles and circuits used for chopper control were explained. This method is used to drive and control d.c. motors when only a fixed d.c. supply is available. This occurs in battery-driven vehicles and in some traction systems, and the use of a series-regulated chopper circuit allows very efficient use of the power available – a fact of particular importance when batteries, which have limited capacity, are used as the energy source.

A d.c. motor has a comparatively low value of effective resistance and hence when the full supply voltage is switched on to it the current rises rapidly. If, when the current was flowing in the motor, the supply circuit were opened, very high voltages would be

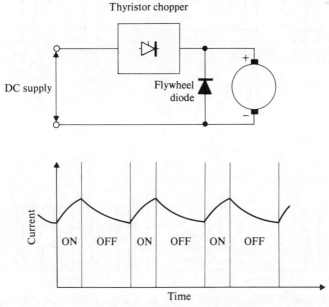

Fig. 10.8 D.C. motor chopper control

191

generated due to the motor inductance; a flywheel path therefore has to be included to allow the motor current to continue to circulate.

A chopper d.c. motor system therefore operates by alternately connecting the supply to the motor and allowing the current to rise, limited only by the circuit inductance, and then removing the supply and allowing the current to reduce naturally by flowing through the flywheel diode (see Fig. 10.8).

There will always be a ripple on the motor current and its magnitude will depend on the circuit inductance and the frequency of chopper operation.

The supply current will consist of pulses corresponding to the ON periods and hence the supply must be capable of allowing fast changes of current to occur. The system operates such that the mean chopper output voltage must match the induced back-e.m.f. of the motor, hence the mark/space ratio will change as the motor increases in speed. The rate of rise of current will depend on the voltage difference between the supply and the motor, and therefore at low speed the rate of change of current will be high and at high speed it will be low. Conversely, the rate of decay of motor current will depend on the back-e.m.f. generated by the machine; the rate of decay will be low at low speed and high at high speed. This is shown in Fig. 10.9. A constant chopper operating frequency will approximately result in a constant proportion of motor ripple current over the voltage and speed range.

An alternative method of control is to keep a constant-length ON pulse and vary the frequency to change the output voltage. This principle can be advantageous as the

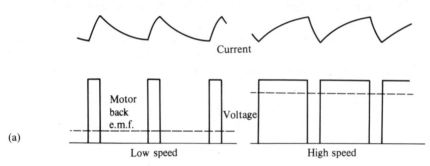

(a)

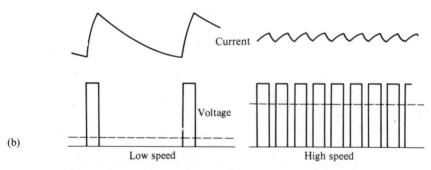

(b)

Fig. 10.9 Methods of chopper control of d.c. motors; (a) constant chopper frequency, (b) variable chopper frequency

ON/OFF period can be made automatic, the system just requiring initiation at suitable time intervals. In this case, the ripple proportion will reduce as the frequency and voltage increases.

The chopper system operates by switching pulses of current from the supply into the motor and then allowing the motor current to flywheel through the diode. The motor current is the sum of the supply current and the flywheel diode current. The supply therefore has to be capable of providing fast current pulses and must therefore be inherently of low impedance. The easiest way to ensure this in practice is to connect

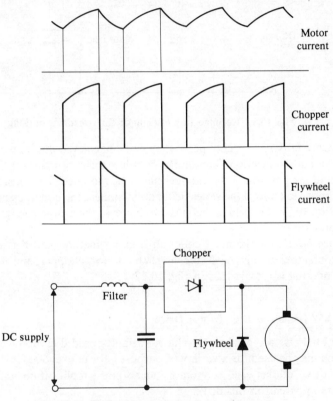

Fig. 10.10 Reduction of supply-current harmonics

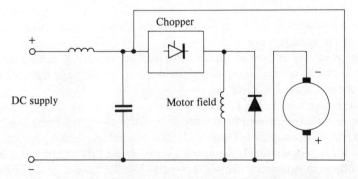

Fig. 10.11 Reconnection of chopper for regenerative braking

a capacitor across the input to the chopper and a series choke to force the current ripple into the capacitor, as in Fig. 10.10. Chopper systems can be used with either series or separately excited motors, but as vehicle control is predominant it is usually the series motor that is used.

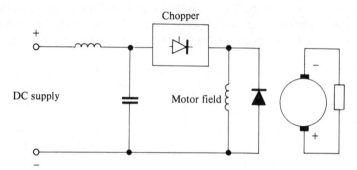

Fig. 10.12 Reconnection of chopper for resistance braking

Regenerative braking of a chopper system can be achieved but it involves significant change of circuit connection. The motor field has to be reversed with respect to the armature and the position of the chopper has to be modified. The most usual way is to use the chopper to control the series field and reconnect the circuit using contactors as shown in Fig. 10.11; the field is then used to increase the motor voltage to achieve the required braking torque.

Resistance braking is the most common braking method and it is used with field control; contactors are arranged to change the motor, chopper, and field connection whenever braking is required, as in Fig. 10.12.

10.6 A 5 kW Industrial D.C. Motor Drive

Figure 10.13 shows a typical single-phase, variable-speed d.c. motor drive of around 5 kW which may be used for a variety of purposes, for conveyors, fans, or pumps, etc.

With a drive of this size, economics necessitate simplification and a number of features are apparent on this drive.

1. The armature convertor is *controlled only in two arms* of the circuit as inversion is not required, and two particular arms have been chosen so as to allow the field diode bridge to make use of the armature convertor diodes. A flywheel diode is included to allow circulation of the motor current during the negative part of the voltage wave.
2. *Motor reversing* is carried out by interlocked reversing contactors arranged only to switch over at zero voltage by using a zero-voltage detector to operate into the contactor coil circuits.
3. Another major economic point in the design is the *direct connection between the power and electronic circuits*, the positive of the convertor being the zero of the electronic power supplies. This avoids the need for an isolating device for current and voltage measurement, the current signal being taken from a d.c. shunt, and the voltage measurement from a potential divider, placed in the circuit so that one end of each is at the electronic power supply zero.

194

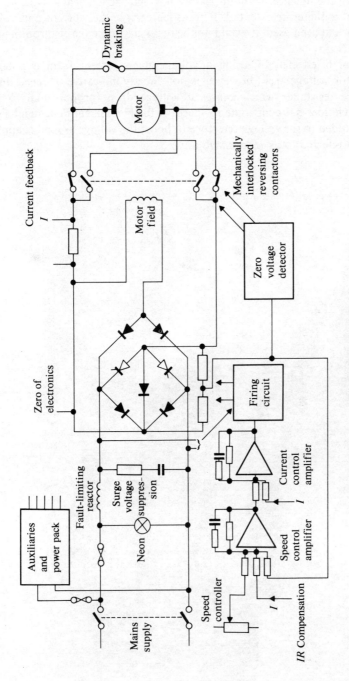

Dynamic braking

Motor

Current feedback

Mechanically interlocked reversing contactors

I

Motor field

Zero voltage detector

Zero of electronics

Firing circuit

Auxiliaries and power pack

Fault-limiting reactor

Surge voltage suppression

Neon

Current control amplifier

I

Speed control amplifier

Mains supply

Speed controller

IR Compensation

I

Fig. 10.13 A typical 5 kW industrial d.c. motor drive

195

It is worth while noting here that in circuits with flywheel diodes, the a.c. current to the convertor is not proportional to the d.c. current as some of it flows through the flywheel without passing through the a.c. leads. D.C. current measurement is therefore essential. If transductor-type d.c. current and voltage transformers had been used, it would not be necessary to tie the electronics to the power circuit.

4. *Speed control* is effected by using a voltage measurement from a potential divider. Motor voltage itself, however, is not directly indicative of speed due to the armature resistance which causes a voltage drop (proportional to load current) which does not contribute to speed. A further current-dependent signal is therefore added to the voltage reference to boost the voltage as load is applied. This is often referred to as *IR compensation*.

Fig. 10.14 Integrated thyristor/firing/control assembly specially designed for single- and three-phase convertors for d.c. motor drives (Siemens Ltd)

196

5. *The control system* shown is appropriate for a firing circuit which increases the d.c. voltage when a more positive signal is applied to its control input. The polarities of current and voltage measurement are as shown and allow the complete inner current loop/outer speed loop system to be performed with only two reversing operational amplifiers.

10.7 A 200 kW Industrial D.C. Drive

Figure 10.15 shows a schematic diagram of a typical antiparallel reversing drive of about 200 kW.

The drive operates *directly from the mains supply*, the rated motor voltage being chosen to correspond to it (with appropriate safety margins). Fault-limiting reactors are included to limit the potential level of fault currents and the d.c. circuit breaker (DCCB) is included to protect against inversion failure due to loss of supply or excessive drop or distortion in the supply voltage.

The convertor consists of *two antiparallel-connected six-pulse bridges* with one thyristor per arm of the circuit; fuses and RC circuits are included for protection. Separate gate circuit pulse amplifiers with independent switching facilities feed each thyristor bridge to ensure that only one of the two bridges is fired at one time. Control over the pulse amplifiers is effected by a logic circuit initiated by error-signal polarity measurement and changeover is conditional upon a zero current measurement.

A *relay circuit* (not shown on the diagram) would be included to ensure that the DCCB could only be closed if all the auxiliary items are functioning correctly, i.e., power pack, field supply, cooling fans, fuses intact, and in addition the low-voltage relay (LVR) ensures that the breaker can only be closed if a low voltage exists on the d.c. output of the convertor.

The *drive speed is controlled* from a tacho-generator by the closed-loop system which includes an inner current loop with current limit. The output of the speed control amplifier is the current reference and this is compared with the actual current measured from three a.c. current transformers in the current loop. Current limit is carried out by limiting the output of the speed amplifier by means of adjustable clip circuits. This drive shows two speed references with individual setting and switching: the jog reference to cause low-speed inching movements of the drive, and the run controller capable of control over the full range. The reference ramp is included to ensure control over the drive rate of acceleration. Stabilizing RC feedbacks, both adjustable across the speed and current amplifiers, are used to trim out any tendency to motor hunting. The reversing amplifier is necessary because the current measurement signal does not reverse if the d.c. current reverses.

The *principles of antiparallel switchover* deserve more detailed mention. If the output of the speed amplifier, i.e., the current reference, calls for a reversal of current then immediately the bridge carrying the current will be phased back by the control signal and the current will reduce. The reversal of the current reference will be detected by the polarity detector and this primes the logic changeover. When zero current is detected, the logic changeover is allowed to switch off the operating pulse amplifiers and after a short time delay to switch on the other set to fire the required bridge. The logic also has to cause a polarity change in the control system as reversal of torque or speed both cause the output of the speed amplifier to reverse; the current feedback,

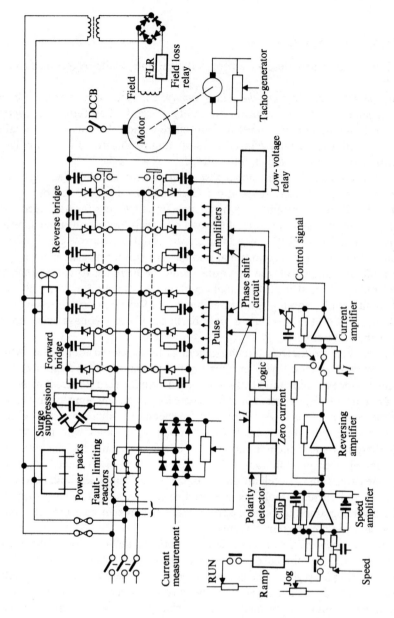

Fig. 10.15 A 200 kW antiparallel d.c. motor drive

198

Fig. 10.16 A 1500 kW thyristor convertor which is a fully reversing, antiparallel bridge unit for driving a steel rod rolling mill stand. The cubicle suite contains all the necessary apparatus for the drive; the switchgear is on the left; the thyristor modules in the large central cubicle; the regulating cubicle contains the firing circuits, the closed-loop control, the measuring attenuators, and the field supply thyristor unit (GEC Industrial Controls Ltd)

however, does not reverse and therefore the current reference has to be changed in polarity.

10.8 A Multiple-unit Train with Chopper Control

Many trains and trolley buses are supplied by d.c. from track-side mounted sub-stations containing rectifiers. In such circumstances, chopper-controlled d.c. motor drives are the most efficient method of driving and controlling the vehicle. Such power supplies are always characterized by:

(a) a relatively high voltage level;

(b) a wide variation in voltage due to distance and loading;

(c) a high likelihood of voltage transients due to other trains and atmospheric effects (lightning, etc.).

There is almost always an additional requirement of minimizing transient and harmonic currents in the supply system owing to the close proximity of telephone and signalling systems.

These factors directly decide the design of the chopper controllers, and Fig. 10.17 shows one such design chosen to point out these principles.

Most systems will have a number of motors; for convenience two have been shown in this case, each being fed by its own controller; both controllers, however, being controlled together from a common closed-loop control system.

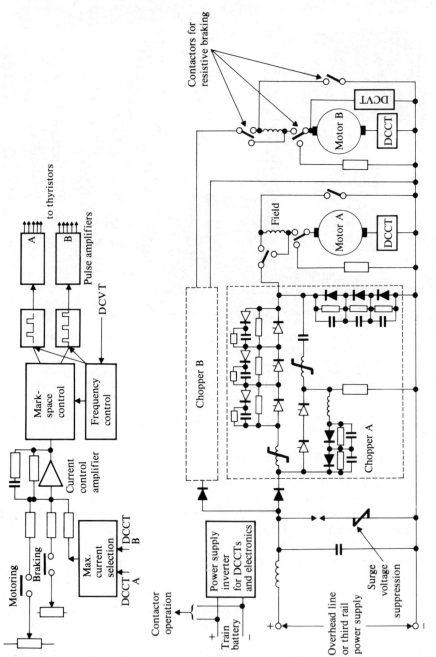

Fig. 10.17 A train chopper controller

Due to the relatively high supply voltage, the chopper controllers contain *series-connected diodes and thyristors* and therefore appropriately chosen voltage-sharing networks are connected in parallel with the semiconductors. As indicated in Chapter 7, these circuits will help to share the voltage due to differing turn-on characteristics and hole-storage capacitance.

Parallel connection of the chopper thyristors has been avoided on this design by feeding each motor individually. When it is required, complete choppers are usually used in parallel with reactance included in each chopper circuit to ensure the correct sharing of the total motor current.

The power supply is fed to the choppers via a single choke/capacitor filter followed by a surge diverter to reduce voltage surges. In order to minimize the harmonic currents flowing in the capacitor, two features are included in this system:

(a) The two choppers are phase-displaced from each other so as to double the frequency of input current harmonics. The same mark/space ratio is employed on both choppers but the firing points are displaced by, in this case, 180 electrical degrees within the operating cycle. With more choppers, separate phase displacement can improve still further the input harmonic currents so as to reduce the duty on the input filter capacitor.

(b) In addition, the frequency of chopper operation is programmed to vary over the operating voltage range in such a way as to equalize the RMS harmonics over the working range. A frequency rising to a maximum at half voltage is ideal from this point of view when a constant current load is considered. Unfortunately, interference with trackside signal circuits has, up to now, limited the application of frequency varying arrangements.

The control system uses operational amplifier techniques to give an overall current control as is conventional on electric vehicles. The maximum of the motor currents is used as the control function. The motoring reference would be ramped to avoid jerking of the drive. The electronics and measurement systems obtain their power supplies from an inverter/regulated rectifier unit from a low-voltage train battery (24 V).

Train braking is by resistance rather than regeneration into the supply. Contactors change over the circuit so that the field is reversed, the armatures are disconnected from the choppers and connected to braking resistors; the choppers are used to regulate the field currents only and hence the braking effort. As in motoring, the choppers are controlled by armature current measurements to a separate brake-current reference. Electrical braking may well be used in conjunction with mechanical or pneumatic brakes.

10.9 A Large 4000 kW D.C. Motor Drive for a Mine Hoist

A mine hoist or winder, used for transporting men, materials, and rock to and from the bottom of a mine, is a very important drive as the whole operation and output of the mine will depend upon it. It is also important from the reliability and safety point of view as men's lives will depend on it. Equipment is therefore designed with safe operation and protection as the priority factors.

From the performance point of view the drive has to be capable of operating over a wide speed range, low speeds for levelling at stopping places and general inspection, and high speeds for maximizing the rock/ore output. As the mechanical systems are

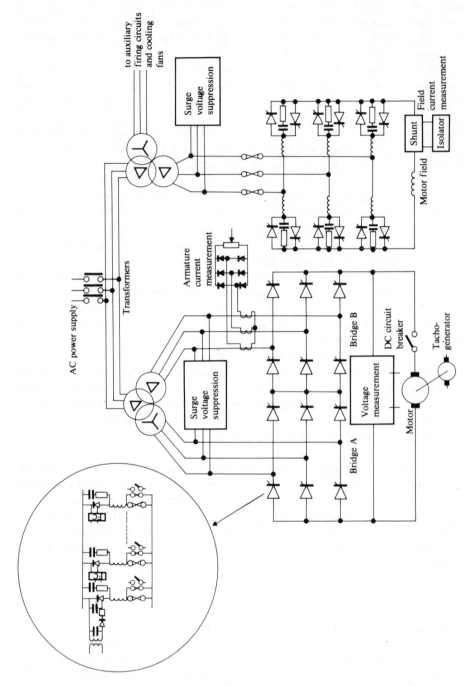

Fig. 10.18 Power circuit of a mine-hoist convertor d.c. drive

to auxiliary
firing circuits
and cooling
fans

Surge
voltage
suppression

Field
current
measurement

Shunt

Isolator

Motor field

Transformers

AC power supply

Armature
current
measurement

Bridge B

DC circuit
breaker

Tacho-
generator

Surge
voltage
suppression

Voltage
measurement

Motor

Bridge A

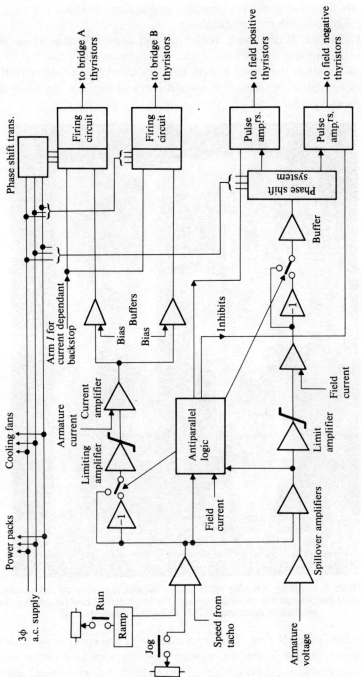

Fig. 10.19 Control system of a mine-hoist drive

To bridge A thyristors
To bridge B thyristors
To field positive thyristors
To field negative thyristors

Phase shift trans.

Firing circuit
Firing circuit
Pulse amp.rs.
Pulse amp.rs.
Phase shift system

Buffer

Arm I for current dependant backstop

Bias
Buffers
Bias

Inhibits

Cooling fans

Armature current
Current amplifier

Antiparallel logic

−1

Field current

Limiting amplifier

−1

Power packs

Field current

Limit amplifier

3φ a.c. supply

Spillover amplifiers

Run

Ramp

Speed from tacho

Jog

Armature voltage

usually balanced, the drive has to be capable of operating under motoring or regenerating conditions at any speed. The changing weight of the rope as the system operates alters the drive power requirements and makes transition from rectification to inversion fairly smooth and predictable.

Figures 10.18 and 10.19 show a convertor and control system which would be suitable for this application. Reversal and regeneration are provided by using a unidirectional armature convertor and an antiparallel reversing field convertor.

The following points are relevant to large drives and they are explained using this hoist drive as an example.

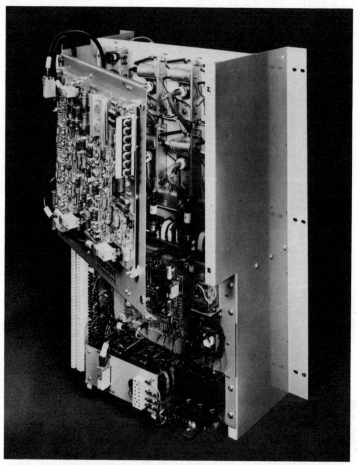

Fig. 10.20 A complete assembly specifically designed to control the speed of d.c. motors. It contains all the necessary power thyristors, firing, control, cooling, and protective apparatus (GEC Industrial Controls Ltd)

The armature convertor needs to use *parallel connection of thyristors* to achieve the necessary current output. In this, as in many cases, the economic motor voltage is in excess of the economic single-bridge convertor capability and *series operation of bridges* is used. When series bridges are used, it is sensible to phase-displace the transformer secondary windings, feeding them to improve the d.c. and a.c. harmonics present. These principles are explained more deeply in Chapter 7.

The field convertor would be designed with a much higher voltage capability than that required to circulate full field current so that the speed of changing the current can be increased. This is known as *field forcing* and often ten times normal voltage is included to reduce the effective field time constant to one-tenth of its normal value.

Although mine hoists are not normally operated in this way, such a drive could be operated at full field current at all speeds up to, say, 70 per cent maximum speed, field weakening being used to increase the speed on a constant power-loading basis. A *spillover field-weakening system* could be used so that one overall speed control could be applied. When, say, 95 per cent of maximum armature voltage has been reached, then field current reduction would be commenced automatically until the minimum field current allowable is reached, at which point the armature voltage will be 100 per cent.

This sort of drive can operate in the regenerating mode for long periods of time and in these conditions loss of supply will result in inversion failure and therefore tripping of the protective circuit breakers. This can also happen if a reduction of supply voltage occurs. This fault can be minimized if the inversion backstop on the armature firing circuits is changed as load current is applied, allowing a larger safety angle to cater for supply voltage reduction whenever the load current is low. The *current-dependent backstop* can mean that the drive is only operating close to its inversion limits for a short period of time and the likelihood of failure is reduced.

This leads to the subject of *protection*. On a large drive it is essential for all system and circuit fault conditions to be dealt with by the a.c. and d.c. circuit breakers so that a minimum outage time occurs on fault. The fuses in series with each thyristor in the armature convertor would be used only to disconnect a faulty thyristor when a fault occurs either with the thyristor itself or with its local surge protection or gate circuitry.

10.10 References

1. American National Standard ANSl, C34.3–1973, Part 1, *Convertors for DC Motor Armature Supplies.*
2. R. H. Burch and G. A. Thompson, 'Electrical variable speed drives', *IEE Conference Publication 93*, Oct. 1972.
3. R. R. Jones and N. A. Dugard, 'Bi-directional thyristor drives', *GEC Journal of Science and Technology*, 34, 3, 98–108.
4. W. D. Sinclair, 'Thyristor power convertors for d.c. machine drives', *AEI Engineering*, 7, 3, 118–127.
5. 'Traction equipment', *Brown Boveri Review*, 62, 12, 1975.
6. C. E. Band and J. H. Stephens, 'Development of, and operation experience with, a high power d.c. chopper for 1500 V d.c. railway equipment', *IEE Conference Publication 53*, 277–288, May 1969.
7. J. M. W. Whiting, 'Thyristor control of "Sprinter" 1500 V d.c. train sets', *IEE Conference Publication 154*, 126–131, Sept. 1977.

11. A.C. Motor Control

Variable-speed operation of a.c. motors has been the aim of the researchers throughout this century and many unusual rotating machines have been developed capable of achieving this. The more recent increasing capability of thyristors has made speed variation, of even standard a.c. motors, not only possible but in many cases economic compared with alternative drive systems.

There are many static systems which can be used, and in this chapter each is covered with particular reference to its capabilities. Firstly, however, we will consider the characteristics of a.c. motors which are relevant to static controlled variable-speed operation.

11.1 A.C. Motors

A.C. motors generate torque by the interaction between a rotating electrical field on the stator and another on the rotor. These two fields must be in synchronism in the air gap and the torque produced will depend on the phase relationship between them. A three-phase stator winding is able to produce a smoothly rotating field and hence the majority of efficient a.c. motors in industrial use are three-phase. The speed of the rotating field is decided by the frequency of the voltages applied to the stator, and as a result the motor speed is directly related to the supply frequency.

In the case of the synchronous motor, the rotor must be completely synchronized with the stator rotating field if torque is going to be developed. In the induction motor, currents are induced in the rotor by the relative speed between the stator rotating field and the rotor, i.e., the rotor always travels at a different speed to the stator field if torque is being produced. However, since the rotor currents are at a frequency decided by the relative speed between the rotor and stator field, their effects in the air gap occur in synchronism with the stator rotating field at all times. The direction of the stator rotating field decides the direction of motor rotation.

The *synchronous motor* has a three-phase stator winding and a d.c. field system on the rotor. Steady torque can only be produced if the rotor turns at exactly the same speed as the stator rotating field. The application of torque to the shaft causes the rotor to lag behind the stator field by the load angle (σ). Up to a load angle of 90 degrees, the torque increases as shown in Fig. 11.1.

The level of torque developed depends on the magnitude of the stator currents and the strength of the air-gap field as well as the load and power factor angle:

$$\text{Torque} \propto \text{stator current}$$
$$\text{Torque} \propto \text{air-gap field}$$
$$\text{Torque} \propto \sin \sigma$$

The rotating field of the motor induces a back-e.m.f. in the stator winding and this opposes the supply voltage, the difference between the two dictating the stator current flowing. The induced voltage will vary with the speed of the motor and the strength of the field:

$$\text{Induced voltage} \propto \text{speed} \times \text{air-gap flux}$$

When supplied by a variable-frequency system, the speed will follow the frequency and so will the magnitude of the induced voltage. If we ignore stator resistance and reactance, the applied voltage will need to increase with frequency (to keep a balance between applied voltage and back-e.m.f.) on a constant V/f ratio basis.

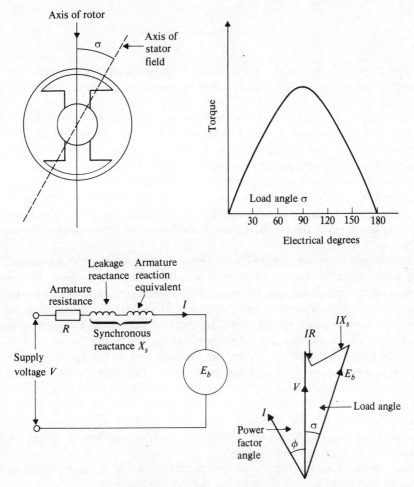

Fig. 11.1 The a.c. synchronous motor

The operation of the machine is complicated by the presence of an armature reaction field produced by the stator currents. This modifies the effective air-gap flux by an amount depending on the level and power factor of the stator current. The effect of this armature reaction field can for our present requirements be considered to be the same as a series inductance in the stator circuit. (This can be combined with the stator leakage reactance and is known as the synchronous reactance, as shown in Fig. 11.1.)

Using this equivalent circuit, the vector diagram can be drawn in order to assess the interdependence between applied voltage, stator current, applied field, and torque.

The vector diagram of Fig. 11.1 indicates the general case; V is the applied voltage, E_b the induced voltage due to the applied field only; the voltage drop IX_s allows for the effects of armature reaction.

From this, the power passed to the rotor,

$$P_r = I \times E_b \cos(\phi + \sigma)$$

and

$$\text{Torque} \propto \frac{I \times E_b}{f} \cos(\phi + \sigma)$$

When a synchronous motor is fed from a variable-frequency convertor source, its operation will depend on the way in which the motor variables are controlled by the convertor.

For example, when the motor is fed from a low-impedance voltage source, the power factor of the input current will be allowed to vary dependent on the applied excitation and the load torque required. This would be the case if it were fed from a forced-commutated, voltage-fed inverter, as explained in Section 11.7.

If, however, a current source convertor was used and the control arranged to feed the current into the motor at a constant power factor angle to the back-e.m.f., i.e., σ constant, then the current level would have to be varied to control the motor torque. This is approximately the condition which applies in the synchroconvertor explained in Section 11.6.

The synchronous reactance we have referred to up to now is the steady-state value – the value which is effective for conditions which last a long time. The armature reaction effects, which account for most of X_s, however, cannot appear instantly and for short time effects a lower value of reactance, the subtransient reactance, will exist. If the machine reactance appears in the thyristor commutation arrangements, then it is likely that the lower subtransient reactance is the one to use.

The field of a synchronous motor can be produced in various ways: permanent magnets can be used or a d.c. current can be fed to the rotor by slip rings. In recent years, many synchronous motors have been brushless, using a rotating exciter having its generator winding on the rotor along with diodes, and maybe thyristors, to produce the necessary d.c. for excitation of the main machine. If this method is used for variable-frequency, convertor-fed drives, a method capable of giving sufficient excitation at low speed will be needed.

Some synchronous machines also incorporate induction windings which allow the motor to operate as an induction motor for starting purposes.

The synchronous motor can operate as a generator and it will do so if the applied voltage or back-e.m.f. is altered to allow power to be fed from the motor to the supply.

The *induction motor* is even more complex to understand as the torque in it is produced by the interaction of the stator rotating field and the rotor current which is induced by it. The current in the rotor is induced as a result of speed difference between the rotating field and the rotor, and its frequency is dependent on this speed difference, the *slip*. The torque is produced by interaction between the rotor currents and the stator field flux.

The field flux is produced by a stator magnetizing current, the total input current consisting of this plus the power and reactive components of the load. The conventional equivalent circuit shown in Fig. 11.2 can be drawn to combine stator and rotor circuits as the net effect of rotor frequency and slip speed appears at the stator frequency when looked at from the input side.

From this,

$$I_2 = \frac{E_1}{\sqrt{[(R'_2/s)^2 + (2\pi f_1 L_2)^2]}}$$

$$E_1 = 4 \cdot 44 \phi f_1 T_p$$

where

$$\phi = \text{air-gap flux}$$
$$T_p = \text{number of turns on primary}$$

The motor torque can be deduced as follows:

$$\text{the power passed to the rotor} = I_2^2 \times \frac{R'_2}{s}$$

Therefore

$$\text{the air-gap torque} \propto \frac{I_2^2 \times (R'_2/s)}{f_1}$$

$$\propto \frac{\phi^2 \times f_1 \times (R'_2/s)}{(R'_2/s)^2 + (2\pi f_1 L_2)^2}$$

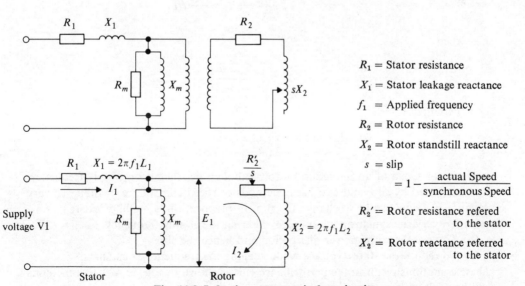

$R_1 = $ Stator resistance

$X_1 = $ Stator leakage reactance

$f_1 = $ Applied frequency

$R_2 = $ Rotor resistance

$X_2 = $ Rotor standstill reactance

$s = $ slip

$$= 1 - \frac{\text{actual Speed}}{\text{synchronous Speed}}$$

$R_2' = $ Rotor resistance refered to the stator

$X_2' = $ Rotor reactance referred to the stator

Fig. 11.2 Induction motor equivalent circuits

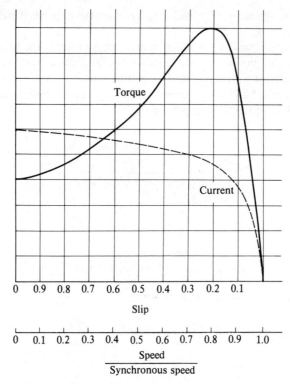

0   0.9   0.8   0.7   0.6   0.5   0.4   0.3   0.2   0.1

Slip

0   0.1   0.2   0.3   0.4   0.5   0.6   0.7   0.8   0.9   1.0

Speed

$$\overline{\text{Synchronous speed}}$$

Fig. 11.3 Induction motor curves at constant applied frequency

At any specific applied frequency these relationships can be shown as the graphs of Fig. 11.3. The maximum value of the torque curve occurs approximately when

$$\frac{R'_2}{s} = X_2' = 2\pi f_1 L_2$$

i.e., when

$$s = \frac{R'_2}{2\pi f_1 L_2}$$

and therefore

$$\text{Maximum torque} \propto \phi^2$$

The rotor speed of an induction motor, although dependent on supply frequency, is also affected by slip, and two basic methods of speed control are possible: to vary the applied frequency or to change the slip. In practice, three methods exist:

(a) To vary the synchronous speed by altering the supply frequency.
(b) To vary the rotor power dissipation and hence the slip.
(c) To reduce the stator voltage while keeping the frequency constant.

These conditions result in the performance curves shown in Fig. 11.4. These methods will be dealt with in the following sections.

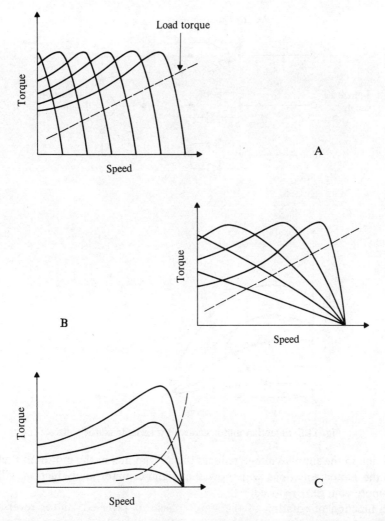

Fig. 11.4 Methods of induction motor speed variation. A: variation of applied frequency (constant air gap flux). B: variation of rotor resistance. C: reduction of stator voltage

11.2 Induction Motor Control by Variable Stator Voltage

A phase-controlled thyristor a.c. controller in the supply to an induction motor can be used to apply constant frequency, variable voltage to the motor, as in Fig. 11.5. The applied voltage can then be reduced, so reducing the air-gap flux; this increases the slip and so alters the motor speed. A relatively high rotor resistance will enable stable speed control to be achieved, giving the speed–torque curves as shown.

To obtain reasonable control, a full thyristor controller as described in Chapter 3 is needed with back-to-back thyristors in each line. Simpler arrangements of thyristors in one phase only or a thyristor and a diode in each phase have been used but they will always produce poor, noisy motor performance due to the unbalanced operation and d.c. saturation of the iron core which these methods produce.

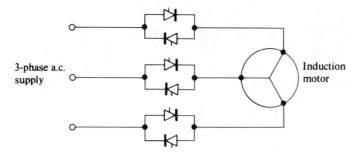

AC thyristor controller

3-phase a.c.
supply

Induction
motor

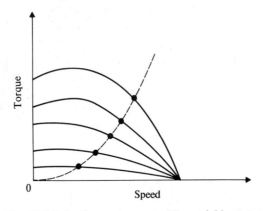

Torque

0

Speed

Fig. 11.5 Induction motor control by variable stator voltage

Reduction in the supply voltage reduces the air-gap flux in the motor and reference back to the motor equations will show that significant torque reduction will occur as the supply voltage is reduced.

If the direction of rotation of the stator phases is reversed, motor reversals and regenerative braking are possible and this can be achieved using additional thyristor a.c. switches A′ and B′, as in Fig. 11.6. The additional switches would be used only when B and C are fully switched off, similar to antiparallel switching in d.c. drive convertors. Full four-quadrant operation is then possible as shown.

This method of speed control has a few limitations, however:

(a) Reference back to Chapter 3 will show that the ouput voltage from an a.c. controller is dependent not only on the delay angle of the gate firing pulses but also on the periods of current flow which are dictated by the load power factor. An induction motor will draw a varying power factor and this will influence the voltage being applied to it (see Fig. 3.7). Whenever the load current is continuous, the a.c. controller will have no influence on the circuit conditions at all.

(b) Control is achieved by distortion of the voltage waveforms and by the reduction of current flow periods. Significant amounts of stator and rotor harmonic currents will flow and eddy currents will be induced in the iron core. These will cause additional motor heating and alter the motor's performance compared with sinusoidal operation.

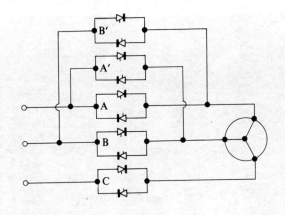

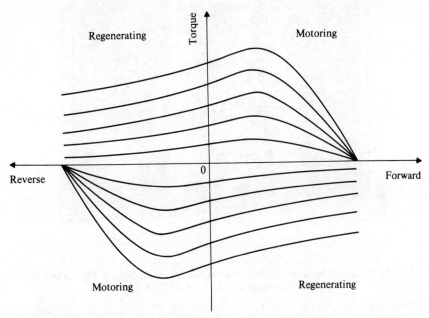

Fig. 11.6 Reversing/regenerating voltage controlled induction motor drive

The practical results of these limitations are that:

1. The motor's performance can only be predicted after a full understanding of the motor, thyristor convertor, and the load.
2. A closed-loop speed control based on a tacho-generator speed measurement is essential to ensure stable performance.
3. The system gains most practical application where the load is predictable and where the load torque required at reduced speed is relatively low.

As far as the thyristor voltage ratings are concerned, the normal crest working voltage is the peak of the supply line voltage, but high transients can occur if the circuit is opened while in operation by switches or fuses. The stored energy in the motor has to be allowed for in the assessment of thyristor voltage safety margins and surge-suppression requirements.

Fig. 11.7 An a.c. thyristor controller designed for crane control which has a continuous output of 120 kVA (ASEA Ltd)

The most significant factor in current ratings is the possibility of thyristors having to carry the normal motor starting currents during a period when the thyristors are unable to influence the circuit due to adverse load or power factor conditions.

11.3 Induction Motor Control by Rotor Resistance

A slip-ring induction motor can be slowed down by introducing additional resistance into the rotor circuit, and this has been done for many years using contactors to switch the resistance in steps or using liquid resistors. Increased resistance causes increased slip and therefore speed reduction, as in Fig. 11.4(B).

Recently, thyristors have been used to allow smooth change in effective resistance, to minimize the number of resistors and contactors required, and to reduce maintenance.

Although many schemes have been tried using thyristor naturally commutated bridge circuits to rectify and control the rotor currents, these all suffer from the variable frequency in the rotor circuit and the change in rotor power factor which they introduce. The most suitable system is shown in Fig. 11.8, where the rotor currents are rectified and a chopper controls the effective rotor resistance. The chopper is controlled at relatively high frequency, giving control in the area shown on the graph by switching from a rotor resistance of R to a low value. More complex arrangements using more resistors, and choppers to bypass them, can widen the range of control possible. If the chopper frequency is high, the harmonic components in the current so produced will have very little effect on motor performance.

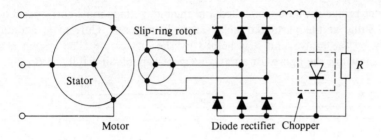

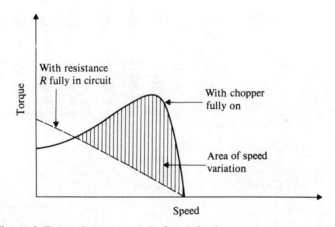

Fig. 11.8 Rotor chopper control of an induction motor

Any of the mark/space patterns of control can be applied to the choppers and many detailed chopper circuit designs can be used (see Chapter 5).

The rotor voltages and currents in an induction motor depend on slip, the induced voltage being highest at standstill and the current being maximum at synchronous speed. The thyristors and diodes used must allow for these extremes if they are permanently connected to the rotor circuit. In some schemes, the semiconductors may only be switched in after starting up, in which case they will not be exposed to the high standstill induced rotor voltage.

In general, rotor resistance control is relatively inefficient at low speeds, the unused power being dissipated in the rotor resistance. The efficiency can be improved by feeding rotor power back into the supply system using the scheme described in the next section.

11.4 Slip Power Recovery from an Induction Motor (the Kramer Scheme)

The slip of an induction motor, and therefore its speed, can be altered by extracting power from the electrical circuit of the rotor. With a Kramer scheme, the power is then fed back into the supply system. When the scheme was first introduced, a motor generator was used to recover the energy, but now static systems using thyristors are preferred.

The principle is to rectify the rotor current with a diode bridge and then to use a naturally commutated thyristor bridge to invert this power into the supply system, as shown in Fig. 11.9.

The inverter bridge is phase-controlled and the d.c. voltage must correspond to the appropriate value at the particular delay angle being used. Current is maintained continuously by the motor and it is helped by the d.c. choke. The system characteristics are shown in the figure for an arrangement capable of a full speed range and

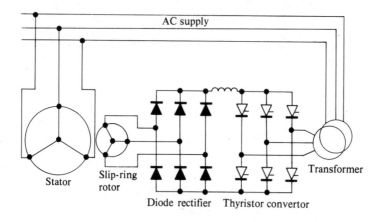

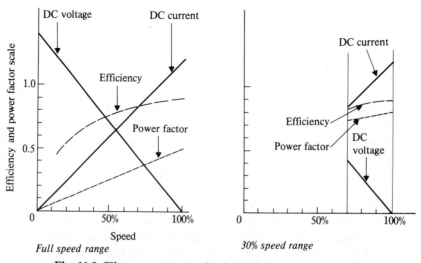

Full speed range

30% speed range

Fig. 11.9 Slip-power recovery for induction motor speed variation

for a relatively small speed reduction from full speed. In the latter case, the static equipment would be disconnected during starting, which would be done by other means.

The ratings of the thyristor and diode equipment have to take into account the fact that rotor voltage is high at low speed and rotor current is high at high speed. The effective kW rating of the convertors is therefore significantly more than the actual power fed back into the supply. For example, for a full-range controller, the convertor equipment will need to be rated at four times the maximum power actually fed back into the supply system. As the range of the allowed speed control using slip power recovery is reduced, the excess capacity in the convertor reduces; with a 30 per cent speed range the convertor rating will be 1·5 times the maximum power feedback. In practice, the scheme is therefore used where only a modest reduction of speed from the synchronous speed is needed.

The poor power factor of the feedback power at high speeds can be improved by altering the ratio of the inverter transformer, either by tappings or by using a smoothly variable regulating transformer. The use of multiple circuits in the inverter, arranged to be switched in series or parallel, can also help in power factor improvement.

This system has one other disadvantage which will be of significance. The feedback of power into the mains supply depends on the mains voltage being sufficiently high to give a voltage balance in the rotor circuit. If the supply voltages are lost, or reduce too far, inversion failure (see Chapter 6) can occur, causing a short-circuit through the thyristor bridge. The circuit protection has to allow for this and with some less-reliable supply systems, regular operation of this protection is likely as the equipment is inverting continuously.

11.5 The Cycloconvertor

Naturally commutated thyristor circuits can be used to produce variable frequency to control the speed of both synchronous and induction motors using the cycloconvertor principle. This can best be understood by considering two fully controlled thyristor convertors connected antiparallel to each other, as shown in Fig. 11.10 (refer also to Chapter 10).

Such an arrangement is capable of feeding either polarity of voltage to the load and either polarity of current. As both bridge circuits can each produce full voltage in either direction, as long as current is flowing the right way, any combination of output current and voltage can be supplied.

If the firing circuits are supplied with a cyclically changing input signal, then the current and voltage to the load can also be cyclically changed. The principle of the cycloconvertor is to supply low-frequency a.c. to the firing circuits to produce low-frequency a.c. in the load.

The above system will give a single phase of low frequency. Three such systems in delta connection, as in Fig. 11.11, can give a three-phase output, suitable to drive an a.c. motor, and able to provide the wide range of frequency and voltage control to enable high torque to be produced in the motor over the whole speed range, as shown in Fig. 11.4(A).

As the power factor of the current drawn by an a.c. motor will vary over the speed and load range, the convertor needs to be capable of supplying both directions of current and voltage in any combination (see Fig. 11.12).

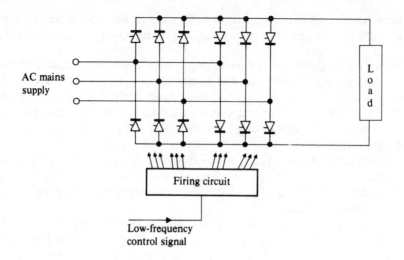

AC mains supply

Load

Firing circuit

Low-frequency control signal

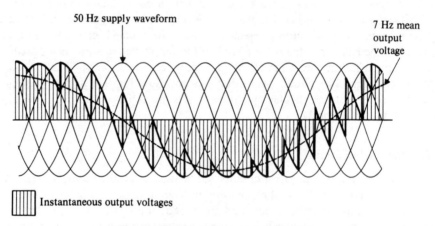

50 Hz supply waveform

7 Hz mean output voltage

||||| Instantaneous output voltages

Fig. 11.10 The cycloconvertor principle

Cycloconvertors have the following performance characteristics:

(a) Reasonably sinusoidal output waveforms can only be achieved up to about one-third of the supply frequency. Although systems can be made to operate above this, the motor performance will deteriorate. The cycloconvertor drive is essentially a high- to low-frequency convertor.

(b) The motor can be driven in either direction at will, purely by electronic control changes to alter the phase sequence of the convertors.

(c) The motor can be driven by power from the a.c. supply system or it can be braked by extracting power from it and feeding it back into the supply system. Again, this can be achieved solely by electronic changes within the convertors.

(d) The output voltage can be sinusoidally controlled until the maximum convertor voltage is reached. Up to this point, the output voltage can be increased in step with frequency to keep the motor air-gap flux constant and therefore the torque capability high.

(e) Operation is possible above this point if the output waveform is allowed to become trapezoidal. This can improve the overall input power factor at high

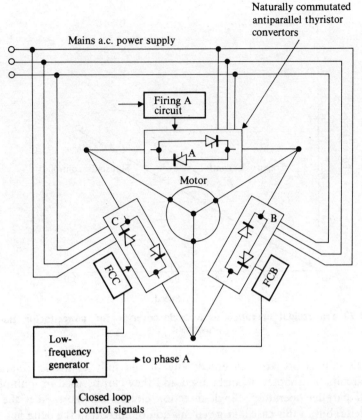

Naturally commutated antiparallel thyristor convertors

Mains a.c. power supply

Firing A circuit

A

Motor

C

B

FCC

FCB

Low-frequency generator

to phase A

Closed loop control signals

Fig. 11.11 The cycloconvertor

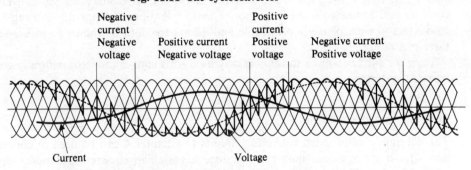

Negative current Negative voltage

Positive current Negative voltage

Positive current Positive voltage

Negative current Positive voltage

Current

Voltage

Fig. 11.12 Both directions of current and voltage are required

speeds but voltage control using the convertors is not available in this condition of control and additional harmonics are produced in the motor.

(f) The input power factor to a cycloconvertor is low and with most circuits, power factor change is continually occurring at the output frequency. As the motor requires an output voltage proportional to speed and frequency, the input power factor at low speeds is very low. Trapezoidal waveform control at high speeds can improve the power factor (see Fig. 11.13).

(g) The number of thyristors is relatively large and most practical circuits involve a minimum of eighteen.

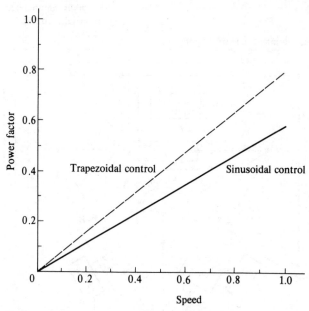

Fig. 11.13 Trapezoidal operation of a cycloconvertor for power-factor improvement

As far as the convertors are concerned, any of the fully controlled, naturally commutated circuits of Chapter 4 can be used and they can be used in multiples in either series or parallel operation. Single-direction circuits can be used if they are connected in delta, but in this case a large circulation of current in the delta has to be allowed to enable the motor line currents to reverse. This increases the convertor currents and reduces the effective power factor. Antiparallel operation using two convertors in each phase is preferable and allows freedom of choice as to how the three phases are arranged.

Thyristor ratings will be those normally used for mains-connected, naturally commutated systems.

11.6 The Synchroconvertor

The naturally commutated convertor circuits of Chapter 4 can be used in conjunction with a synchronous motor to produce a variable-frequency a.c. motor drive system. Two thyristor convertors are involved, as shown in Fig. 11.14; the supply convertor produces d.c. from the mains supply and the motor convertor normally operates in the inversion mode to convert the d.c. power into a.c. for the motor. The generated voltages in the motor are used to allow natural commutation of the motor convertor. As a result, it is essential for the motor to be a synchronous motor.

The supply convertor is a conventional phase-controlled circuit with its firing circuits synchronized to the mains supply. The thyristors of the motor convertor have to be fired in synchronism with the generated voltages of the motor as the frequency will change with motor speed. This is achieved using either a rotor position encoder or a signal from the motor terminal voltages.

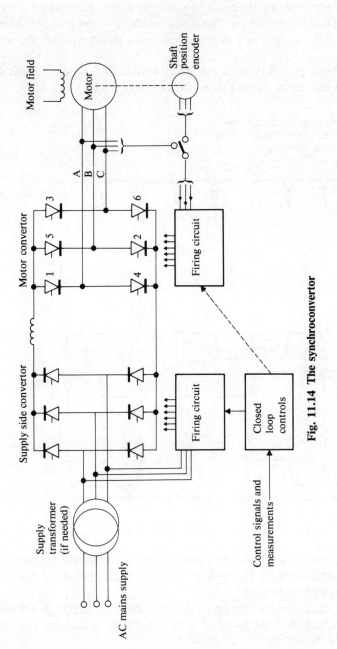

Fig. 11.14 The synchroconvertor

Motor field

Motor

Shaft position encoder

A
B
C

Motor convertor

3
5
1
6
2
4

Firing circuit

Supply side convertor

Firing circuit

Closed loop controls

Supply transformer (if needed)

AC mains supply

Control signals and measurements

The motor convertor then acts like a static commutator and the motor and motor convertor together behave like a d.c. motor, in that change in the d.c. voltage will change the motor's speed, as will change in its field current.

This mode of operation can only continue while the motor-generated voltages are sufficient to commutate the convertor. These will normally be proportional to motor speed (with constant excitation) and hence at low speed another mode of operation must be used.

At low speeds, the supply convertor is used to turn the current off during switchover or commutation of the motor convertor, as shown in Fig. 11.15.

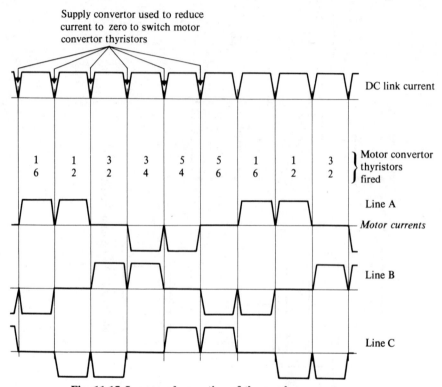

Fig. 11.15 Low-speed operation of the synchroconvertor

With these two modes of operation the synchroconvertors performance is as follows:

(a) A full range of motor speed and frequency can be obtained, limited only by the mechanical capabilities of the motor. Motor frequencies above the supply frequency can be readily used.

(b) Field control of the motor can be used, when maximum applied voltage has been reached, to extend the range of speed control at constant power; this is similar to field weakening of a d.c. motor.

(c) Either direction of motor rotation is possible and can be selected by electronic changes in the sequence of firing of the motor convertor thyristors.

(d) The system is fully reversible in that power can be fed to the motor or it can be absorbed from the motor and fed back into the supply system. In this latter case, the motor convertor will rectify the motor voltages and the supply convertor will invert the power into the supply; the d.c. voltage will reverse, the current continuing to flow in the same direction.

(e) Although the motor operates at a leading power factor (in order that the motor convertor can operate in its inversion mode), the power drawn from the supply system will be at a lagging power factor, increasing with d.c. voltage and motor speed.

(f) The system is a current-fed one, having a d.c. choke to smooth the d.c. current. The motor current will be square wave similar to the input current of a normal naturally commutated convertor (see Chapter 4). This will increase the motor heating but it does have the effect of assisting the motor-generated voltages to be sinusoidal.

Fig. 11.16 This 5 kVA variable-frequency inverter a.c. induction motor drive uses the circuit shown in Fig. 11.17/C. All the power components including thyristors are immersed in an oil-filled tank (Danfoss Ltd)

11.7 Forced-commutated, Variable-frequency A.C. Motor Drives

The many inverter circuits referred to in Chapter 5 can be used to provide variable-frequency, variable-voltage supplies to alter the speed of induction motors or synchronous motors. Reference should be first made to this previous chapter dealing with forced-commutation circuits.

These circuits, as previously explained, are only switching circuits and pure sinusoidal waveforms cannot be produced to give ideal motor performance. Two waveforms are in regular use for practical a.c. motor drives: the quasi-square wave and the synthesized sine wave, pulse-width modulated (PWM) waveform as shown in Fig. 5.13B and E.

Motors will operate quite successfully at high speeds with quasi-square applied waveforms but at low speeds the rotating fields within the machine will be stepped around rather than moving smoothly. The PWM waveform allows sinusoidal currents to flow in the motor even at low frequencies, giving smooth rotation of the motor field flux and smooth performance of the motor.

In general, the applied voltage to the motor must increase with increase in frequency. When the motor is supplied with the same waveform at any frequency, e.g., the quasi-square waveform, then the level of the d.c. voltage will need to change to control the motor voltage.

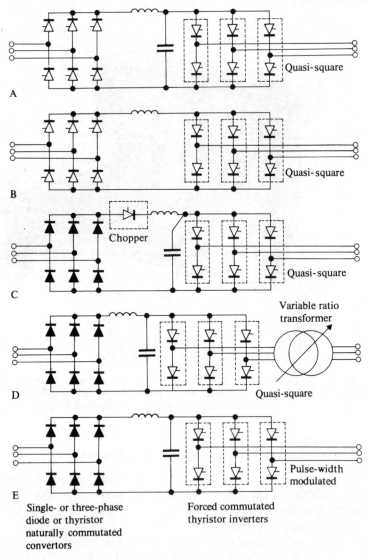

Fig.11.17 Forced-commutated inverter motor drive methods

224

Fig. 11.18 A forced-commutated, variable-frequency inverter rated at up to 250 kVA for induction-motor control (Emerson Electric Industrial Controls Ltd)

There are many overall schemes for forced-commutated, a.c. motor drives, and Fig. 11.17 shows a few. In most cases, power is drawn from a standard-frequency power system involving a naturally commutated circuit to produce a d.c. link. Where a d.c. battery supply is to be used, all those circuits shown which use a diode input bridge can be used (without the input bridge), i.e., circuits C, D, and E.

The following factors, related to Fig. 11.17, have to be considered when the correct choice of circuit is to be made and they may explain the reasons for a particular choice.

1. A thyristor-controlled input bridge as in circuits A and B will give smooth control of the d.c. link voltage but fault currents cannot be turned off in less than

one half-cycle of the supply frequency. The input power factor will change with motor speed.

2. A diode input bridge will give a constant input power factor but other means of voltage control will be needed.

3. The series d.c. link chopper of circuit C allows full control of d.c. voltage and if operated at high frequency it can be turned off quickly when a fault occurs.

4. Output voltage control with a motorized regulating transformer as in circuit D is satisfactory as long as output frequency and motor speed changes are relatively slow. With this arrangement, very high currents can be fed to the motors at low speed to achieve very high torques, as the full inverter kVA is available at all speeds.

5. The voltage-fed circuits (A, C, D, and E) will provide approximately sinusoidal currents into the load motors. In the current-fed circuit B, the d.c. link choke will smooth the d.c. current and lead to square-wave currents in the load. In this case, the output voltage will follow a sinusoidal shape but with large transient voltage spikes.

Fig. 11.19 A 5 kVA variable frequency inverter drive which is naturally air-cooled and provides control over the range 5–60 Hz from a 50 Hz input supply (GEC Industrial Controls Ltd)

6. The voltage-fed circuits will usually have a relatively large d.c. link capacitor to filter the d.c. ripple and provide commutating currents. Under fault conditions in the inverter or load, this capacitor will discharge through the inverter thyristors.

7. Where the d.c. link voltage varies and when this is used to charge commutating capacitors, the ability to commutate load current may reduce as the d.c. link voltage reduces. It is usual to provide another constant voltage feed for charging commutating capacitors to avoid this effect.

8. In the pulse-width modulated circuit E, both voltage and frequency control are carried out with the inverter thyristors. This complicates the operation and waveforms of the inverter.

9. The current drawn from the input convertor by the inverter circuit will be related to the power component of the load. The reactive current required by the load will circulate within the inverter.

10. All the inverter circuits can operate as rectifiers and regenerate load power back to the d.c. link. In the voltage-fed circuits (A, C, D, and E), the power is fed back via the feedback diodes in the inverter and a means of dissipating the feed-back power or feeding it back into the input mains supply will be needed. Figure 11.20 shows the alternative possibilities.

In the current-fed circuits, regeneration can be performed without reversing the current; voltage reversal is all that is needed and hence no further equipment is needed to feed back the load power into the input supply system.

11. Diode input rectifiers can be used to supply a number of inverter circuits, each with separate motor loads.

Forced-commutated a.c. motor drives have a number of practical benefits:

(a) They can be used to control cage induction motors which are robust, cheap, reliable, and brushless.

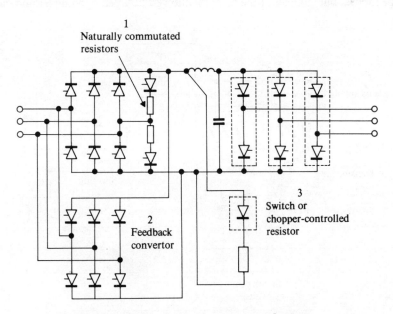

Fig. 11.20 Methods of removing regenerated power

227

(b) A wide range of frequencies from zero to many kilohertz can be provided by using these techniques. The present upper frequency limit of forced-commutated inverters is well above the needs of a.c. motors and their applications.

(c) Many motors can be connected to the same inverter. If these are either synchonous or synchronous reluctance motors, then they will all run at exactly the same speed, i.e., in synchronism.

(d) The speed of inverter motor drives can be very accurately controlled and they can be synchronized with a process or with other inverters by digital means.

(e) They usually provide control over motor frequency, voltage, current, and flux. Using this high degree of flexibility, the motor's performance can be fully optimized.

(f) Full torque can be obtained over the whole of the speed range without high input currents (see Fig. 11.4(A)).

11.8 Injection Braking of Induction Motors

Induction motors can be slowed down by applying a fixed d.c. field to the stator windings. The rotor then induces voltages and currents, and a reverse torque is produced. The necessary power can then be dissipated in the rotor resistance. Thyristors are now being used to provide the d.c. for this purpose, usually accompanied by some form of variable rotor resistance to control the braking torque, as in Fig. 11.21. Slip power recovery can also be used to provide the necessary braking control.

The naturally commutated convertor would be switched into operation after the main switch S1 had been opened by closing S2. It would normally be constant-current controlled from a measurement of d.c. current.

The convertor used need only be of low voltage capability decided by the effective stator resistance and the current required. The system can be used even for high-voltage motors but sufficient time must be allowed between opening S1 and closing S2

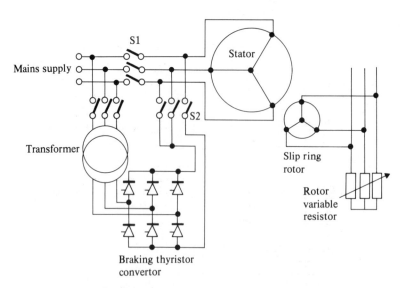

Fig. 11.21 Dynamic braking of induction motors

228

to ensure that stator-induced voltages have reduced to within the withstand capabilities of the convertor.

11.9 References

1. R. H. Burch and G. A. Thompson, 'Electrical variable speed drives' *IEE Conference Publication 93*, Oct. 1972.
2. H. C. J. DeJong, *AC Motor Design with Conventional and Convertor Supplies*, Clarendon Press, Oxford, 1976.
3. P. J. Tsivitse and E. A. Klingshirn, 'Optimum voltage and frequency for polyphase induction motors operating with variable frequency power supplies', *IEEE*, **IGA-7**, 4, 480–487, 1971.
4. 'AC motor supply with thyristor convertors', *IEEE*, **IGA-2**, 334–340, 1966.
5. V. Willisits, 'Lifting gear applications of thyristor convertors for a.c. regulation systems', *Brown Boveri Review*, **5**, 308–312, 1976.
6. J. D. Van Wyk, G. W. Loots, and W. J. Louw, 'Dissipative rotor chopper cascades for control of wound rotor induction motors', *IEE Conference Publication 154*, 92–96, Sept. 1977.
7. W. Shepherd and J. Stanway, 'Slip power recovery of an induction motor by the use of a thyristor inverter', *IEEE*, **IGA-5**, 74, 1969.
8. A. B. Goldhammer, 'Modern Kramer drives', *Electrical Review*, **4**, Aug. 1967.
9. U. Putz, 'The convertor-fed brushless synchronous motor', *IEE Conference Publication 123*, 71–76, Dec. 1974.
10. T. Peterson and K. Frank, 'Starting of large synchronous motor using static frequency convertor', *IEEE*, **PAS-91**, 1, 172–179, Jan. 1972.
11. 'The application of a cycloconvertor to the control of induction motors', *IEE Conference Publication 17*, 137–145, Nov. 1965.
12. T. Salzmann, 'Cycloconvertors and automatic control of ring motors driving tube mills', *Siemens Review*, **45**, 1, 3–8, 1978.
13. K. H. Williamson, 'Simple 3 phase a.c. motor control system for motors below 5 HP', *IEE Conference Publication 53*, 320–327, May 1969.
14. A. Jenson, 'Decisions and considerations concerning the determination of basic principles for a frequency convertor for standard motors', *IEE Conference Publication 93*, 29–36, Oct. 1972.
15. B. Mokrytzki, 'Pulse-width modulated inverters for a.c. motor drives', *IEEE*, **IGA-3**, 6, 493–503, 1967.
16. W. McMurray, *Theory and Design of Cycloconvertors*, MIT Press, Cambridge, Mass., 1972.

12. D.C. Supplies to High-inductance Loads

When thyristors are used to provide controlled d.c. power for high-inductance loads, special problems are encountered. In this chapter these peculiar conditions are covered and some of the most frequent uses of thyristors to supply such loads are explained. In the terms of this chapter, a load is a high-inductance one if it is equivalent to a resistance and an inductance only (i.e., no back-e.m.f. or capacitive components) with a time constant which is relatively long compared to the thyristor period between commutations.

The majority of such loads are the excitation coils for magnetic circuits:

(a) Field excitation coils on a.c. and d.c. machines.
(b) Electromagnet excitation coils.
(c) Excitation of bending magnets used particularly in research into fundamental particles (atomic physics).
(d) Excitation of eddy-current couplings, contactor coils, degaussing coils, and the like.

In all these applications, it is the value of current which is important and even without other improved performance requirements, some means of controlling the voltage to compensate for resistance changes with temperature is needed. Thyristors provide an ideal method of obtaining fast and accurate control of the current.

Feeding a high-inductance load from thyristors brings with it specific problems not encountered in other applications:

(a) If the load has a long time constant, the current will take a long time to build up. When this current is switched on via a thyristor, the current may not reach the thyristor latching current by the time the gate pulse has ended.
(b) Once the current is established, it results in a high stored energy in the load inductance. If one tries suddenly to stop the current from flowing, very high voltages can be induced in the load. If the current and energy are allowed to die away by short-circuiting the load, it may take a long time before the current has ceased.
(c) The load current will only cease if the load voltage is zero or negative. Even a very low pulsed positive voltage will maintain the load current above the holding current of the thyristors.
(d) In addition, if the load coil is part of a complex magnetic circuit such as a rotating machine, unusual currents and voltages can be induced in it due to the other m.m.f.s affecting the flux in the iron core.

The immediate technical implications of high-inductance loads on the design of thyristor circuits used to feed them will be discussed in the next few sections, prior to more detailed assessments of the most frequent practical applications.

12.1 Load Time Constant

With an inductance load, the current can only change at a rate decided by the applied voltage and the load inductance. A voltage V suddenly applied to a load having resistance R and inductance L will, as in Fig. 12.1, cause an initial rate of rise of current equal to V/L, the current subsequently rising according to

$$i = \frac{V}{R}\left[1 - \exp\left(-\frac{R}{L}t\right)\right]$$

The current will rise to 63·2 per cent of its steady value (V/R) in a time equal to L/R seconds (curve (a)). With magnetic-coil loads, this time constant can be too long to achieve satisfactory control. However, increase in the value of the applied voltage V will effectively reduce the time constant and increase the rate of rise of current. For example, the application of twice the normal voltage will cause the current to reach the previous steady value (V/R) in 70 per cent of the load time constant (curve (b)). This process has acquired the name of *field forcing* and is a regularly used principle with high-inductance loads. Figure 12.1 also shows one of its limitations, namely, that if the high voltage is applied continuously the current will rise to a much higher level than normally required. Field forcing is therefore only applicable when the supply voltage can be controlled to limit the level of load current and even then protection against its maloperation will be needed to avoid damage due to overloading.

If it is required to reduce the load current after it is flowing steadily, the removal of the applied voltage will cause the current to decay exponentially according to

$$i = I_1 \exp\left(-\frac{R}{L}t\right)$$

where I_1 is the initial value, assuming that a flow path is available through the supply.

Again, this can be a long time and it may be too long to ensure satisfactory operation. In addition, the initial rate of drop of the current will be dependent on its initial value. A more predictable and faster response can be achieved by inserting a negative voltage in the current path to speed its reduction. This is known as *negative field forcing* and is shown in Fig. 12.1. An applied negative voltage V will cause the current to reduce according to

$$i = \frac{V}{R}\left[\exp\left(-\frac{R}{L}t - 1\right)\right] + I_1 \exp\left(-\frac{R}{L}t\right)$$

giving an initial rate of reduction of

$$\frac{di}{dt} = \frac{V + RI_1}{L}$$

giving the curve (d), as against curve (c) when no negative forcing is available.

This condition transfers the load energy $(\frac{1}{2}Li^2)$ back into the supply and it must be capable of accepting this energy. When supplied from a thyristor convertor, this energy can be returned to the mains by using the techniques of inversion by reversing the d.c. voltage while the current is still flowing in the original direction. If a supply system is unable to accept the load energy, then negative forcing is not possible although suitable additional voltage for positive forcing can be provided. In this case, the rate of rise of load current will be significantly higher than the natural rate of fall (see Section 12.5).

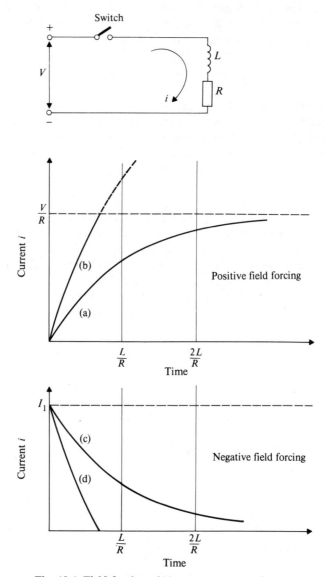

Fig. 12.1 Field forcing of high-inductance loads

In some applications, reversal of the load current may be necessary, for example, to reverse the direction of a d.c. motor or to reverse the output voltage of a Ward–Leonard generator. If this is to be provided statically, then two supply convertors in opposite polarity will be required to achieve it. Antiparallel-connected naturally commutated circuits are most frequently used when this is required. Special arrangements are needed to achieve this when d.c.-to-d.c. chopper controllers are being used (see Section 12.5).

12.2 Voltage Transients

The energy stored in an inductance, when current is flowing through it, will be used to maintain the flow of current. If an attempt is made to interrupt this flow, very high voltages can be generated in the inductance coil and these can damage the coil insulation and any components and circuitry connected to it. Thyristors used to supply the coil are particularly affected by such overvoltages, which will always be in such a direction to try to maintain the current flow.

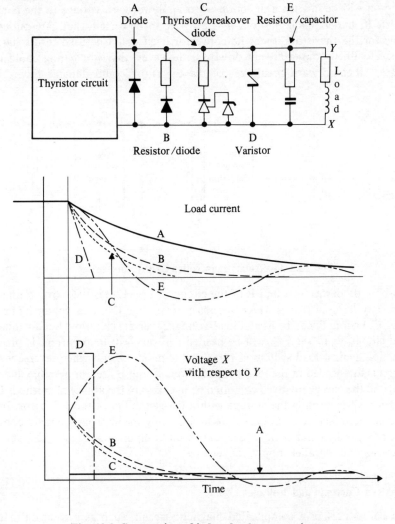

Fig. 12.2 Suppression of induced voltage transients

Whenever the supply to an inductance load is to be cut off, for any reason, some alternative discharge path for the inductive energy is needed. A number of the practical methods of doing this are discussed in Chapter 6 and are shown in Fig. 12.2. The simplest approach (alternative A) will allow the load current to die away naturally,

233

the energy being dissipated in the load resistance. A long discharge time may be involved. The other alternatives discharge the energy faster by inserting resistance into the current flow path. The use of a capacitor/resistance circuit will allow the load energy to oscillate between the load and the capacitor while its energy is being discharged in the circuit resistance. Figure 12.2 indicates the comparative results of these methods when the supply is removed while load current is flowing.

The maximum voltage produced during the supply interruption and load discharge period must be within the capability of the thyristor controller. If the thyristor controller is a naturally commutated convertor circuit, the induced load voltage on supply interruption will be in such a direction as to apply forward voltage to the convertor thyristors. If, under this condition, it is possible to be certain that gate pulses were available for the thyristors, then the convertor itself could be used to discharge the load energy, albeit comparatively slowly. If, however, thyristor gating could not be guaranteed, then forward breakover of the thyristors could damage them beyond repair.

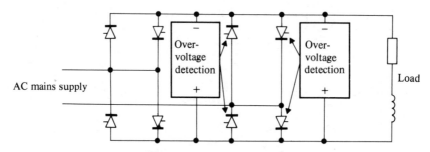

Fig. 12.3 Overvoltage protection by thyristor firing

The use of diodes as in A and B of the circuit in Fig. 12.2 is the most common but this can only be used if it is never necessary to reverse the load voltage. The other methods, C, D, and E, can be used if load-voltage reversal is required but an additional reversed circuit, as method C, will be needed if reversal of load current is provided.

Protection against load switch-off transients is most difficult when reverse voltages and currents are needed in the load coil. Methods A and B are not possible due to the reversal, and the energy involved can often be in excess of the ability of methods D and E to absorb while keeping the voltage within the capability of the convertor. In such cases, some manufacturers have used method C using the appropriate main convertor thyristors as the flywheel path to economize on components. Figure 12.3 shows an example using antiparallel supply convertors.

12.3 Induced Currents and Voltages

When a coil is part of a complicated magnetic circuit, such as a rotating machine, which will be exposed to other magnetic effects, the coil may have currents and voltages induced in it by the action of the other circuit m.m.f.s. Any thyristors connected to the coil will have to be capable of accepting these without damage.

Induced currents are usually caused by change in the current flowing in the other windings of the machine. The magnetic circuit will not immediately allow the flux change which would result; and it tries to produce current flow in any coils associated with it to compensate. Sudden change in armature current in a machine will induce a transient field current; Fig. 12.4 shows the case of a sudden short-circuit on the machine armature terminals.

It is only possible to generalize here as the value of induced current will depend on many factors. The presence of eddy current in the iron will affect it, and a laminated-core machine will generally have higher induced field currents than one with a solid core.

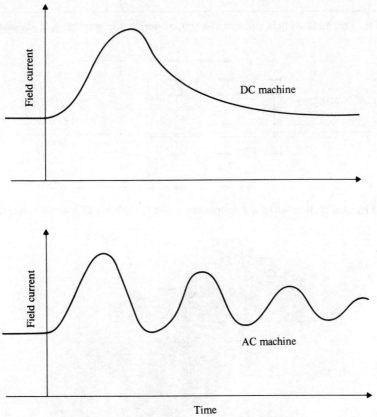

Fig. 12.4 Induced currents in machine field windings

The induced effects are not always in such a direction as to increase the field current; they may attempt to reduce it and even to reverse it. If there is a path for the induced field currents, then the reverse current will automatically flow. If, however, the thyristor convertor supplying the field cannot pass the induced current, then an induced voltage will occur. The most common case of this is pole slipping or asynchronous running of a synchronous machine. This mode of operation tries to induce a.c. into the field coil. The supply convertor may only be unidirectional and hence the reverse current cannot flow and a high reverse voltage results; Fig. 12.5 demonstrates this effect.

In some circumstances, if this mode of operation, i.e., induced a.c., is one of the normal conditions, it may be necessary to provide a reverse current flow path to avoid the high voltage which can result.

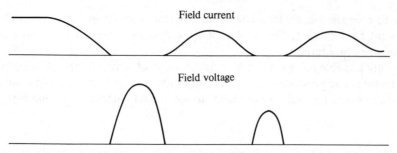

Fig. 12.5 Induced field currents and voltage during a.c. machine pole slipping

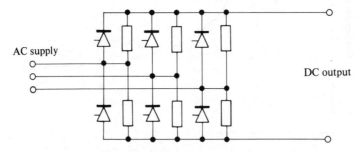

Fig. 12.6 Voltage-sharing resistors can assist the sharing of induced voltages

Fig. 12.7 An alternator field control unit that will provide 16 A d.c. at up to 80 V. It is complete with voltage control and current compounding and can be used in direct excitation, self-excitation, and brushless schemes (GEC Industrial Controls Ltd)

It is worth noting here that if a high reverse voltage is applied to a bridge-connected convertor from the load, then resistors across the thyristor can cause it to be shared by the two series thyristors (see Fig. 12.6). This can in some cases increase the withstand capability of the convertor. However, it can only work if the thyristors are not gated (see Chapter 7) and if the a.c. supply voltage is small compared to the induced reverse voltage.

12.4 Thyristor Latching Currents

In Chapter 1, it was explained that the anode-to-cathode current of a thyristor must reach a specific latching level if the thyristor is to remain in the ON-state when the gate pulse is removed. With a long load-time constant, the current may take a long time to reach this level. The most satisfactory arrangement with high-inductance loads is therefore to pass gate current through the thyristor during the whole of its likely conducting period.

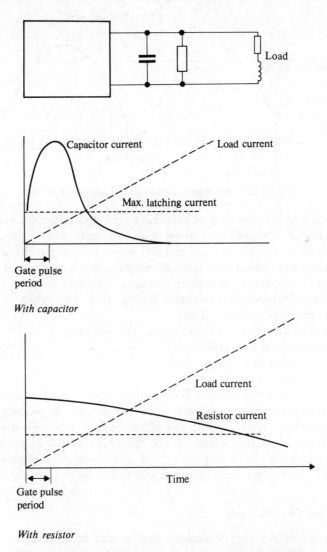

Fig. 12.8 Additional load components to assist thyristor latching

In practical applications, however, this is not often done due to the high gate power needed and the difficulty of achieving a fast pulse rise time for a long gate pulse. A pulse train or a single pulse are the more common gating methods. In these cases, latching current becomes an important factor because if the thyristor has not switched

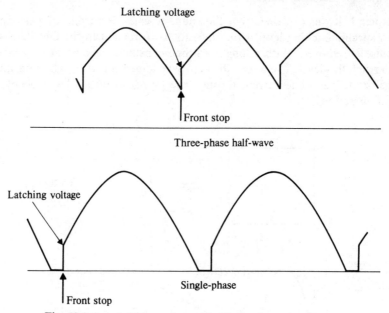

Fig. 12.9 Low latching voltages on single-phase circuits

to the ON-state by the time the gate pulse has ended, no significant level of load current will ever flow; just a small load current pulse will occur at every gate pulse.

The most usual way to overcome this difficulty is to alter the character of the load by fitting a parallel capacitor or resistor (or both) to it so that when the thyristor is switched on the capacitor or resistor current is sufficient to allow the thyristor to remain in the ON-state. This is shown in Fig. 12.8. The values of the additional components required will depend on:

(a) the convertor voltage available during the gate pulse;
(b) the length of the gate pulse;
(c) the level of latching current; and
(d) the load time constant.

The most satisfactory latching will occur if the thyristors are fired when the maximum instantaneous voltage is available from the convertor. In practice, when latching is needed the control system will usually phase the convertor to its lowest delay angle α. In three-phase convertors, nearly the full voltage is available at this point. In single-phase convertors, the front stop point will correspond to a relatively low output voltage and a much larger capacitor or resistor will be needed (see Fig. 12.9).

12.5 Thyristor Circuits Used

One advantage of the high-inductance load is that as the current cannot change quickly the amount of load-current ripple will be small even with a large applied voltage harmonic. The result is that the circuit used can be of lower pulse number with a lower operating frequency than would be the case with other loads. It is not, therefore, unusual to find field thyristor supplies using very simple circuits which would be unacceptable with, say, motor loads.

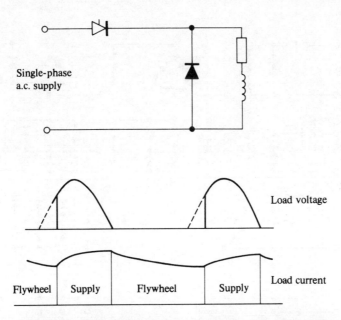

Fig. 12.10 Single-phase, half-wave supply for inductance load

Fig. 12.11 A thyristor automatic voltage regulator for an alternator that uses a single thyristor and can provide an output of up to 85 A d.c. at 180 V. The complete voltage control and firing systems are contained on the single printed circuit card (GEC Industrial Controls Ltd)

For example, the single-phase, half-wave, phase-controlled circuit of Fig. 12.10 will give a sufficiently smooth load current for many generator fields and as the power is often low, the passage of a d.c. current through the a.c. supply may well be acceptable.

The three-phase, half-wave circuit may also be used but it is more common in half-controlled bridge form as it ensures a.c. currents in the supply system.

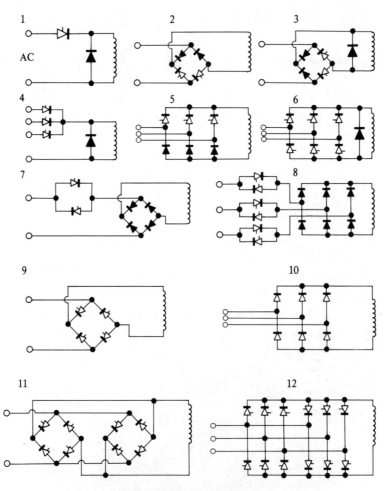

Fig. 12.12 Circuits for high-inductance loads

Figure 12.12 shows the wide variety of naturally commutated thyristor circuits used to supply high-inductance loads. Circuits 1 to 8 all have an effective flywheel diode across the load and so none of these are able to apply reverse voltage to the load, and hence no negative voltage forcing to reduce field current is available. Circuits 9 and 10 are used when negative forcing is required with a unidirectional current load. When current reversal is required with comparatively fast control, then an antiparallel connected arrangement as in circuits 11 and 12 would be used.

The design of antiparallel circuits, particularly single-phase, with high-inductance loads has to be done carefully so that the current in one bridge is definitely zero before the reverse polarity bridge is allowed to fire. This is caused by the comparatively slow rate of current reduction even under field forcing and the fact that in the single-phase case, zero current cannot be reached while the convertor is controlled with firing pulses on. The need for a firing circuit backstop means that two pulses of current per cycle will continue to occur in the load. In addition, the presence of latching capacitors (Section 12.4) may affect the point when the thyristor reverts to the OFF-state. Most antiparallel systems will usually allow a longer delay time between switching the pulses off one bridge to switching them on, on the other. Also, in single-phase cases the zero-current measurement has effectively to be a discontinuous current-measuring device.

These problems have led to the use of circuits where both bridges can be operated together either temporarily or permanently. Circuits 11 and 12 of Fig. 12.12, with series resistors in each bridge, are suitable for temporary operation of both bridges but they cause additional losses. In the circulating-current antiparallel circuit, both bridges are continuously fired, one bridge being fired for the required forward load voltage and the other for the same voltage in the opposite direction to balance the convertor loop. The loop cannot be balanced instantaneously and inductances are included to limit the flow of circulating harmonic currents between the bridges. This system allows instantaneous response to voltage and current reversal with none of the time delays needed with a switched antiparallel arrangement.

Forced-commutated d.c.-to-d.c. 'choppers' are used when only a d.c. supply is available and any of the designs discussed in Chapter 5 are applicable. These circuits of necessity require a flywheel diode across the load inductance, to allow the commutation capacitors to work correctly, and so their use has to date been limited to uni-directional load current without negative forcing. If the equivalent of an antiparallel system was needed, two choppers and two flywheel thyristors would be used, the appropriate flywheel being gated on when needed.

12.6 Field Supplies for D.C. Generators

In recent years, the use of d.c. generators has reduced considerably owing to the economic availability of silicon diode and thyristor static d.c. supplies. The main application which has persisted longer than others has been the *rotating Ward–*

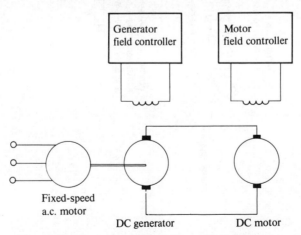

Fig. 12.13 The rotating Ward–Leonard system

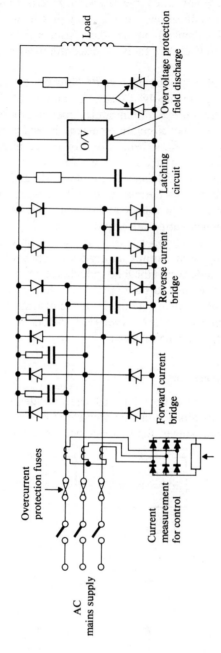

Fig. 12.14 A Ward–Leonard generator field controller

Leonard system for speed control of d.c. motor drives, although this is gradually being displaced by the static convertor equivalent.

As shown in Fig. 12.13, the rotating Ward–Leonard scheme uses a constant-speed d.c. generator to provide the controlled power for the motor load. The motor speed is varied by altering the d.c. generator output voltage by field control. The type of field control required is dependent on the speed and voltage range of the load motor. More often than not, a reversing field is needed, calling for an antiparallel thyristor supply.

Although field forcing is frequently included to minimize the generator time constant, the speed of field change is dictated only by compensating for load changes and the desired rate of load motor reversal, etc. Inversion of load motor power is achieved by current reversal in the d.c. link and it does not significantly involve the field supply system.

With this Ward–Leonard scheme, zero speed of the load motor is achieved by bringing the d.c. generator voltage to zero. Not all thyristor circuits are able to do this due to the need for a back stop in the firing circuit. Reference to Chapter 4 will

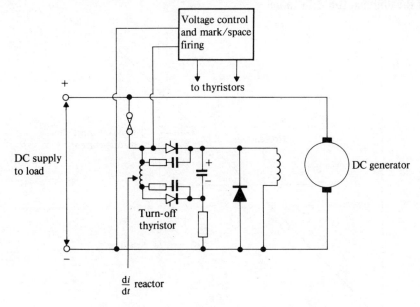

Fig. 12.15 A field chopper for a d.c. generator

show that the single-phase circuits and the three-phase, half-controlled circuits have this difficulty. With these, the back stop has to be set about 15 degrees from the 180° point, i.e., $\alpha = 165°$. Small voltage pulses will occur 2 or 3 times per cycle and a field current will flow. Three-phase, fully controlled circuits are most suitable for this duty.

Figure 12.14 shows a typical example of a thyristor field supply for a Ward–Leonard generator demonstrating the design features referred to in the previous sections of this chapter.

1. A high forcing factor is required, making a very positive current limit necessary.
2. As the circuit is antiparallel, a bidirectional switched field discharge circuit is needed, operated by high d.c. voltage to prevent high transient voltages when the a.c. supply circuit is opened.

3. To minimize normal power loss, a resistor/capacitor thyristor latching circuit is used.

D.C. generators are usually shunt-excited using the armature voltage to provide the field current. The inclusion of a chopper unit can enable the level of excitation to be controlled more readily, and Fig. 12.15 shows such a practical system.

12.7 Field Supplies for D.C. Motors

The speed of a d.c. motor can be varied by altering its field current, and its direction of rotation and torque can be changed by reversal of the field current. Widespread use of field control is, however, limited by the loss of torque resulting from reducing the field current. In addition, the inherent motor stability is affected by the level of excitation and this limits the minimum value which can be used (see Fig. 12.16).

The use of field control therefore tends to be restricted to those applications where the load torque requirement at high speed is comparatively low. When it is used, the minimum value of excitation will usually be restricted to no less than, say, 25–30 per cent of the nominal full field value.

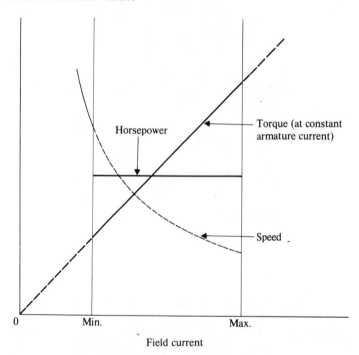

Fig. 12.16 Field control of a d.c. motor

Two other factors are of importance to the design of d.c. motor excitation supplies:
(a) The induced voltage of the armature winding is directly proportional to excitation flux. If, while a motor is running fast in the field-weakening range, the field is quickly strengthened, a high armature voltage can be produced which can damage the insulation.
(b) Loss of field current can cause loss of motor control, high overspeed, and in extreme circumstances complete mechanical destruction of the motor.

Most field-controlled motors will have separately supplied field circuits and all the naturally commutated thyristor circuits shown in Fig. 12.12 are used as necessary. Non-regenerating circuits will be used where fast field reduction is not required, and antiparallel systems will be used if high-speed reversal of field current is needed, say, to achieve quick motor torque reversal (see Section 10.2).

Figure 12.17 shows a typical unidirectional thyristor field supply unit capable of providing positive and negative field forcing. This shows:

1. A direct field current-measuring field-loss protection relay.
2. Overvoltage protection to short-circuit the field by firing the two series thyristors whenever excessive voltage occurs.
3. A control system incorporating direct control of field current and including a maximum current limit to prevent overloading (as the unit can have a positive field-forcing capability) and a minimum current limit to avoid overspeeding or loss of motor stability.

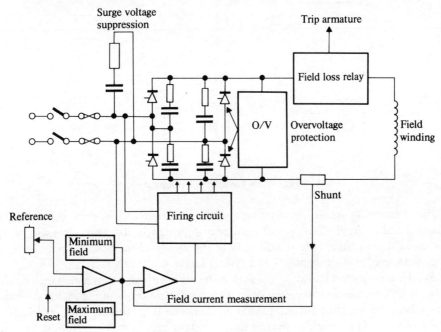

Fig. 12.17 D.C. motor field controller

4. The protection fuses for the thyristors are included in the a.c. lines so that they do not attempt to interrupt the field current when they blow, as very high voltages can then result.

Figure 10.18 shows an example of a reversing field supply for a large motor drive.

12.8 Field Supplies for A.C. Generators

A.C. synchronous generators or alternators are the backbone of all our present-day electricity generation and transmission systems. Thyristor excitation is widely applied and shows considerable advantages in economics and in overall power-system stability.

There are two basic ways of using thyristors for generator excitation:

(a) Direct excitation of the generator field coils from a thyristor power supply.

(b) The use of a rotating a.c. exciter generator with diodes to rectify its output to feed the main generator field, using thyristors to supply the exciter generator field current. This is the basis of the increasingly used brushless generator system.

These methods are illustrated in Fig. 12.18. The a.c. supply for the thyristor unit can be taken either directly from the main alternator output (self-excitation) or from a separate source of power (separate excitation). From the thyristor circuit design point of view, the main principles of Sections 12.1 to 12.5 are universally applicable. These different methods of excitation, however, introduce additional considerations.

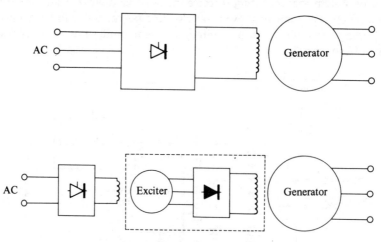

Fig. 12.18 Generator excitation

Direct excitation means the thyristors are closely related to the main alternator field winding and induced effects are of particular importance. Response time will be very fast and this can contribute significantly to the ability of the power supply system to cope with sudden load demands and system faults.

Brushless excitation has many attractions to the user from the maintenance point of view. It reduces the thyristor excitation requirements to those of the exciter alternator and this alternator then becomes the significant one from the thyristor circuit design point of view. The increased overall time constant caused by the additional rotating machine may lead to a higher degree of field forcing being needed on the exciter alternator.

Self-excitation with the thyristor circuit a.c. input connected directly to the alternator terminals has a major influence on the thyristor circuit design:

(a) The output voltage of the alternator is directly dependent on the excitation and the excitation is derived from the alternator output voltage. Special arrangements may be needed to ensure initial build-up of alternator voltage.

(b) In the case of short-circuit faults on the power system which the alternator is supplying, the alternator voltage will reduce. The thyristor convertor therefore has to be capable of coping with a wide range of a.c. input voltage.

(c) As a consequence of (b), a self-excitation scheme may be limited in its ability to provide short-circuit fault current to hasten the operation of protective circuits.

Where this is of particular importance, the thyristor unit may have some of its input power provided from current transformers in the alternator output. This is sometimes known as *short-circuit maintenance*.

Separate excitation where the power for the thyristor unit is from another source means the design can follow the normal principles explained elsewhere.

Fig. 12.19 A unit which controls the field current of an a.c. rotating exciter, which itself provides the field current for a turbo-alternator via a diode rectifier. It is complete with firing, regulating and protective apparatus for the whole turbo-generator (NEI Electronics Ltd)

Control Methods

The aim of the majority of alternator excitation schemes is to control the field current so as to maintain a constant alternator output voltage irrespective of load changes. The high reactance of alternators due to armature reaction effects means that current-measurement feedback circuits from the alternator output are almost always required. If alternators are to be connected directly in parallel and are expected to share a total load, then a current feedback is also needed to provide an output voltage drop proportional to reactive kVA; this is often termed *quadrature droop compounding*.

The following two examples typically illustrate the practical methods used for alternator excitation.

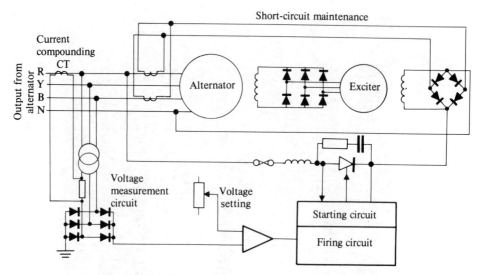

Fig. 12.20 Self-excitation of a low-voltage alternator

Figure 12.20 shows a self-excited system for a brushless alternator which uses a single thyristor for control. The following facilities should be noted:

1. A starting circuit is included which makes the thyristor operate as a diode whenever the alternator output voltage is low. This allows the voltage to build up gradually as long as a small residual magnetism initially exists in the machine.

2. A three-phase voltage measurement is used so as to compensate practically for unbalanced loads.

3. Quadrature droop compounding is performed by one current measurement CT added to the voltage on the a.c. side, working on the principle that at zero power factor the current will be in phase with the voltage measurement and so have maximum effect, whereas at unity power factor it will be in quadrature and hence hardly affect the total measurement.

4. Short-circuit maintenance is provided to ensure a satisfactory alternator output current when a fault occurs.

The second example (Fig. 12.21) shows the circuit for a separately fed direct thyristor excitation scheme for a large turbo-alternator. This uses a fully controlled thyristor bridge to provide both negative and positive field forcing. The control features use operational amplifier techniques and incorporate rotor angle control to boost excitation at high loads as well as current and voltage limiting. In this case, fuses are permitted in the thyristor bridge arms as they are only there to cope with thyristor failure; all other faults are dealt with by the a.c. supply circuit breaker.

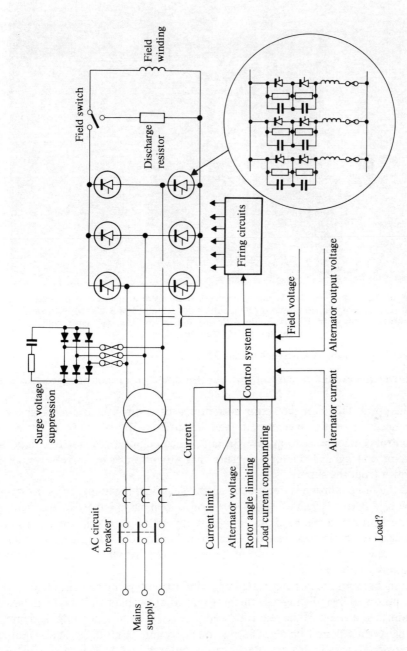

Fig. 12.21 Excitation control of a turbo-alternator

249

Fig. 12.22 A 4500 A, 410 V forced-air cooled thyristor converter to provide a fast-response controlled power supply to the rotor windings of a 400 MW turbine generator. This output is available with any one of the four thyristor cubicles isolated (GEC Rectifiers Ltd)

12.9 Field Supplies for A.C. Synchronous Motors

Control over the excitation current of a synchronous motor can produce two useful effects:

(a) The power factor of the stator current can be controlled to almost any value irrespective of the mechanical load taken from the shaft. In practice, field control is used either to maintain a high or leading power factor to compensate for other lagging loads or to ensure that a constant level of reactive kVA is drawn from the supply.

(b) As the motor torque is dependent on the field flux, the ability to boost quickly the field current when a high torque load is demanded is particularly valuable.

Thyristors provide a means of achieving fast control over the field current and they are often used to obtain these benefits. The normal operation of a synchronous motor, however, needs to be carefully studied before the requirements of such a thyristor power supply can be decided.

Most synchronous motors are started up as induction-type machines in that starting torque is produced by inducing a.c. currents into rotor busbars and maybe the excitation windings as a result of the relative speed between the stator rotating field and the rotor. The starting period involves asynchronous running and if the field winding is kept open-circuit, very high a.c. voltages can be induced in it. It is normal to close the field circuit to allow the a.c. induced currents to circulate and to limit the level of induced voltages generated in the field winding. A resistance is usually added into the field circuit to maximize the torque produced. A.C. induced voltages therefore occur and these may be impressed across the field supply thyristors. The oscillogram of Fig. 12.23 shows the field winding currents induced during a typical start-up period.

Once the motor has reached its maximum asynchronous speed, the application of field excitation will enable it to pull into synchronism. This may involve switching, to connect the field supply and/or to disconnect the starting resistance. The exact time of switching may need to be selected to ensure correct operation.

Figure 12.24 shows a typical circuit diagram for thyristor excitation of a slip-ring synchronous motor, demonstrating the facilities normally required. It shows:

1. As the requirement is only for slow power factor control and field boosting on high load, a non-inverting three-pulse thyristor circuit is adequate.
2. A slip frequency detector is used to initiate field application via the d.c. switch and a timed release of the thyristor gate pulses.

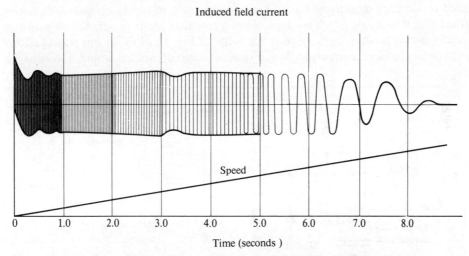

Fig. 12.23 Induced field currents during acceleration of a synchronous motor

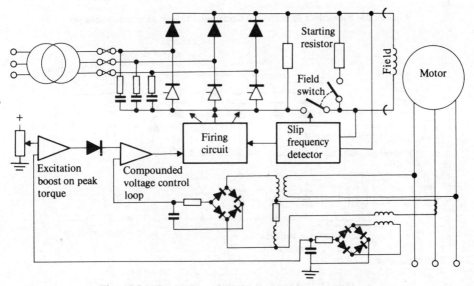

Fig. 12.24 Excitation of a slip-ring synchronous motor

251

3. The field circuit is closed via a resistance during starting, to allow induced currents to flow.
4. Another resistance is connected across the output of the convertor to provide a path for induced currents when the starting resistor is disconnected. This resistance also ensures satisfactory current pick-up when the thyristors are fired by short pulses.
5. Although not essential due to the presence of the load resistance, the fuses are in the a.c. lines so as not to interrupt the discharge path through the thyristor bridge.

Brushless excitation of synchronous motors is now common practice and thyristors are being increasingly used as part of the rotating assembly. They are thus continually exposed to the induced effects in the motor field winding. Thyristors are not normally used for controlling purposes as this would involve a relatively complicated control transfer across the air gap. They are used in a switching mode to help the starting and synchronizing process. For example, the circuit of Fig. 12.25 shows one way of allowing starting induced currents to flow. Forward induced currents would flow through

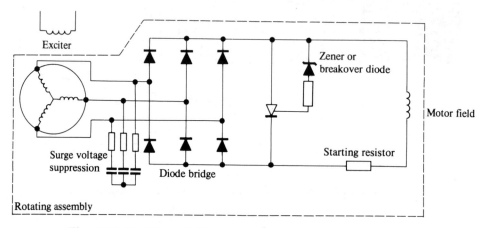

Fig. 12.25 Simplified brushless synchronous motor excitation scheme

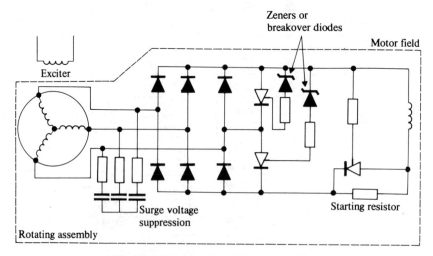

Fig. 12.26 Practical brushless motor scheme

252

the diodes and the thyristor will carry the reverse currents. In this case, the resistance would be permanently in circuit, causing unnecessary dissipation during normal running. This circuit also has the additional limitation that if ever a high induced voltage occurs in the field winding while normal excitation is being applied, the thyristor may be turned on and will not go off. A more practical and useful circuit is shown in Fig. 12.26 and this includes other protective features. Two thyristors are used to allow the reverse current to flow and the central connection to the diodes ensures that they are turned off if they are operated during normal running. The resistance will be in circuit during starting but when the d.c. exciter voltage is applied, the thyristor will turn on, shorting the resistor out to reduce power dissipation.

12.10 Magnet Supplies

Thyristors are used for many forms of electromagnet excitation, from simple lifting magnets for scrap-steel transport to complex bending magnets for cyclotrons and synchrotrons, used in plasma and atomic particle physics.

For lifting magnets, thyristors are only employed where static switching is required or where control over the level of excitation is beneficial to the application. In many instances, a simple contactor-switched diode arrangement is acceptable.

Bending magnets used in research into atomic physics usually require rather sophisticated power supplies, and most of these incorporate thyristors. The usual requirement in these magnets is for a very steady level of excitation, and low current ripple and high stability are needed. Good fast response to changes is also a benefit to the user. Also, a definite programme of excitation current may be required with the current increasing over a specific time period, then being retained at a set level accurately before being reduced linearly to zero again over a specific time. The thyristor power supply for this type of duty may well incorporate the following facilities:

(a) High positive and negative forcing factors to ensure fast response and controlled current rise.
(b) High pulse numbers to limit the load ripple current.
(c) Firing circuits with very accurate phase-displacement between the channels to minimize output ripple.
(d) Firing circuits with inherent compensation for supply-voltage variation to minimize the effects of such variations on the load.
(e) Highly accurate methods of measuring and controlling the current to ensure highly stable operation over long time periods.
(f) High-quality control systems using temperature compensation, high-stability power supplies and amplifiers, and high loop gains.

As far as the thyristor circuit design is concerned, Sections 12.1 to 12.5 will provide sufficient guidance.

12.11 References

1. P. A. B. Wooldridge and A. L. Blythe, 'Considerations affecting the design philosophy of solid-state exciters', *IEEE*, **PAS-87**, 5, 1288–1299, 1968.
2. V. Easton, 'Static rectifier excitation', *GEC Journal*, **30**, 1, 1963.
3. D. C. Gilchrist, 'Thyristor automatic voltage regulators and static exciters', *GEC Journal of Science and Technology*, **35**, 1, 3–13, 1968.

4. J. D. Edwards, A. J. Gilbert, and E. H. Harrison, 'The application of thyristors to the excitation circuits of synchronous motors', *IEE Conference Publication 17*, 158, Nov. 1965.
5. S. H. Dale, N. A. Dugard, and D. Finney, 'Precision controlled thyristor power supplies for synchrotron beam line magnets', *GEC–AEI Journal*, **35**, 2, 48–56, 1968.
6. M. Canay, 'Overvoltages in the field circuit of synchronous machines with rectifier excitation', *Brown Boveri Rev.*, **5**, 217–227, 1974.

13. Fixed-frequency Inverter Systems

A significant and increasing use of thyristors is in static inverters which produce a.c. power from d.c. supplies. These applications come about for two main reasons:
1. There are many instances where batteries are the only source of power and where electrical appliances and instruments are designed to be operated from a.c. mains inputs.
2. Static thyristor inverters are a convenient means of obtaining a.c. at other than normal power frequencies. They are therefore used as frequency changers to power special equipment.

Most of the battery-supported applications are associated with guaranteeing a source of a.c. power to a critical or important load even when the normal source of a.c. power has been disconnected due to supply power-system fault conditions. A few examples will make the point:
1. The lighting of an operating theatre in a hospital will normally be fed from a 50/60 Hz power supply. A fault on the mains supply cannot be allowed to interfere with operations. An alternative source of power from a battery via a static inverter will answer the need.
2. The sophisticated instruments used in an airport control tower, although normally fed by a 50/60 Hz mains power supply, must be able to continue in operation if the mains supply fails, to avoid landing accidents. A battery-supported static inverter can provide an instant source of a.c. power.
3. The increasing power of computers means that more and more calculations are stored within them at any one time. Loss of power to them can cause complete loss of the stored information, interrupting much important work. Even comparatively small changes in the supply voltage or frequency can have a similar effect. A static inverter supported by a battery can provide a very stable source of a.c. power.

Battery-fed inverters are also found in mobile vehicles where the only source of power is d.c. They are often used to supply a.c. power for public-address systems in cars and vans. In submarines, the need to operate under water with very low noise and vibration levels means battery supply is used with static inverters providing the power to drive instrumentation and communication apparatus.

Static inverters have the unique ability of being able to produce a.c. power over a very wide range of voltage and frequency and to control both these parameters accurately and independently. For example, a power supply at 400 Hz can considerably reduce the size of some electrical equipment, and a thyristor inverter can provide the power. Inverters having a frequency accuracy of a very high order can also be used to supply digital clock and timing systems.

In short, static thyristor inverters are used:

(a) Whenever a.c. power is needed from a d.c. source.

(b) Whenever an important load needs a guaranteed a.c. supply.

(c) Whenever an unusual frequency is required.

(d) Whenever an a.c. supply with accurate voltage and frequency control is needed.

This chapter will deal with the techniques used in thyristor inverters for these applications. All of these inverters will use the forced-commutated switching methods explained in Chapter 5; these will only be referred to here if they are relevant to the overall operating factors of the application. The principal techniques used in most fixed-frequency inverter applications will be discussed in the first part of the chapter, the specific applications being covered in the later sections where the examples have been chosen to illustrate the techniques discussed in the early sections.

13.1 Thyristor Inverter Design

Reference back to Chapter 5 will show that switched a.c. voltages can be produced from a d.c. power source using forced-commutated thyristor circuits based on capacitor turn-off methods. Any practical inverter will also involve the use of other equipment as well. Figure 13.1 shows a typical general example of a fixed-frequency inverter unit used for many of the applications already discussed. It will be used to demonstrate the total content of such inverter equipment.

1. *Output filtering* is normally necessary, as many loads require a reasonable sine wave power source and many inverter circuits produce waveforms with a large harmonic content. These will be discussed in more detail in Section 13.2.

2. *Input battery filtering* of some kind is usually needed because of the high currents required by the inverter circuit during commutation and recharging of the commutation capacitors. Even if the battery is capable of providing the high currents, its storage capacity and life will both be reduced by allowing the high currents to flow.

3. *An output transformer* is often needed as economic battery voltages are generally lower than the required output voltage. When placed before the filter, it helps to improve its effectiveness in reducing the harmonics in the output.

4. *A firing circuit* including a firing-pattern generator and pulse amplifiers will be needed to fire the thyristors in their correct sequence (see Chapter 8).

5. *An oscillator* will be used to set the frequency of the inverter. It may be a free-running, voltage-controlled oscillator giving the facility to tune the inverter to the correct frequency or it may be a fixed, highly accurate, crystal-controlled unit. As will be seen later, it may be necessary for the inverter to be synchronized with other a.c. supplies; the oscillator would then be synchronized from the reference source.

6. *Regulation* of the inverter output voltage will be needed to allow for the wide variation of battery voltage during its charge and discharge cycle and the voltage drops in the inverter and filters due to load current variation.

7. *Protection* of the inverter against overcurrents and faults may include the addition of a current-limit circuit to reduce the output voltage whenever an overload current is detected.

In addition, a total equipment will probably include a battery charger (see Chapter 14), auxiliary power packs, measurement, cooling, and protection apparatus.

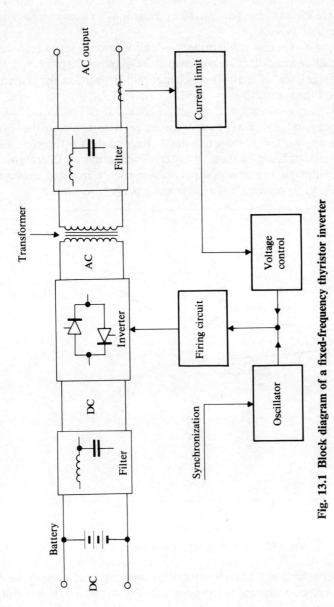

Fig. 13.1 Block diagram of a fixed-frequency thyristor inverter

257

13.2 Voltage Control and Regulation

In most of these applications, the load requirements will be met by a constant output voltage from the equipment. Some means of internal voltage control is, however, required to compensate for the changes caused by variations in load current and to correct for changes in battery voltage.

The input and output filters and transformers will all introduce series impedance into the current flow path, which will cause a change in the output voltage when current change occurs. The magnitude of the voltage change will depend on the particular design of the filters and the transformer.

Economic use of batteries dictates that their output voltage shall be allowed to drop significantly during the period of time allowed for discharge. Also, to charge the battery fully it is necessary to apply a higher-than-nominal voltage to it. It is therefore usual to have to allow for a significant change in battery voltage during operation (see Fig. 13.2). Therefore, although a constant output voltage may be required, a range of control allowing for up to 50 per cent voltage variation is often required.

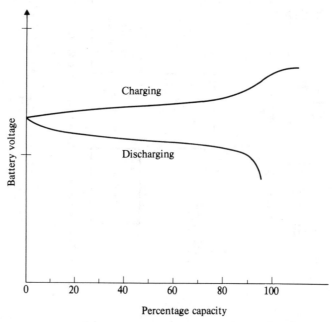

Fig. 13.2 Battery voltage variation

Reference back to Chapter 5 will show that there are many ways of varying the output voltage from a forced-commutated thyristor circuit: Fig. 5.13 shows some of them. They all involve alteration in the time during the cycle when the d.c. supply is connected to the load. The practical methods in use will be explained and compared in the following paragraphs.

Pulse-width control can be used directly if the circuit being used has individual commutation circuits for each main thyristor. For example, if the switches in Fig. 13.3 are completely independent of each other, i.e., either can be opened or closed at any time, then any width of pulse per cycle can be obtained as shown.

This principle can also be used in other single and multiphase circuits but only when each switch is an independent one with its own commutating circuit, i.e., each switch is a 'chopper'. The complementary commutating and auxiliary thyristor circuits described in Sections 5.6 and 5.7 cannot operate in this way as one switch must always be in the ON-state.

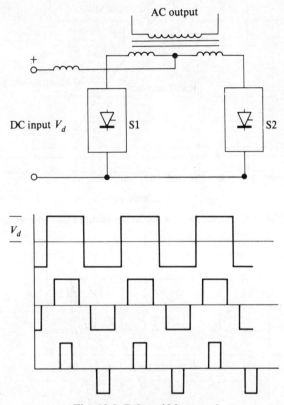

Fig. 13.3 Pulse-width control

As the ON-time of the switches is reduced, the ouput voltage will be reduced according to the curves of Fig. 13.4.

This method of control gives a satisfactory result but it must be appreciated that:

(a) The ON pulses must be centralized on a fixed time, otherwise change in the level of voltage will also produce a phase change.

(b) While the switches are in the OFF-state the current will flow in the feedback diodes and they need to be rated accordingly.

(c) The change in the output waveshape means a change in the amount of harmonics it contains. Figure 13.5 shows the values of the lowest and most significant harmonics over the range of control. As in most practical applications, the aim is to keep the output fundamental voltage constant, these harmonic curves are plotted as percentages of the fundamental at that point of control.

The single-phase bridge with phase displacement is a useful method where single-phase output is required. In Chapter 5 the detailed operation of the complementary

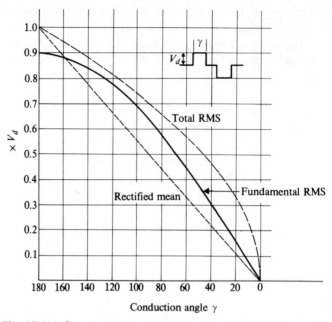

Fig. 13.4 A.C. output voltage variation using pulse-width control

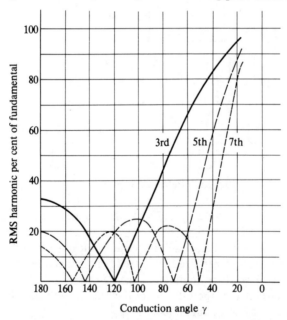

Fig. 13.5 Harmonic content of pulse-width controlled waveform

commutated and auxiliary thyristor half-bridge arrangements was explained, and also the fact that two of these units together form a useful complete single-phase bridge only needing one d.c. supply. This is shown in Fig. 5.21.

If thyristor switches S1 and S4 are switched off together and thyristor switches S2 and S3 switch on at the same time, a full square-wave output results. If the time of transfer from S1 to S2 is different from that of S4 to S3, then it is possible to change the output voltage waveform. Variation in the time between these two switchings makes it possible to alter the level of output voltage. This is shown in Fig. 13.6, which demonstrates that the resultant output voltage waveforms are the same as those obtained in the previous method (pulse-width control). The voltage and harmonic relationships are therefore also shown in Figs 13.4 and 13.5.

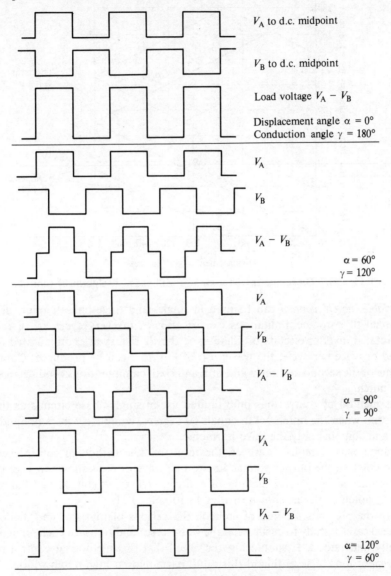

V_A to d.c. midpoint

V_B to d.c. midpoint

Load voltage $V_A - V_B$

Displacement angle $\alpha = 0°$
Conduction angle $\gamma = 180°$

V_A

V_B

$V_A - V_B$

$\alpha = 60°$
$\gamma = 120°$

V_A

V_B

$V_A - V_B$

$\alpha = 90°$
$\gamma = 90°$

V_A

V_B

$V_A - V_B$

$\alpha = 120°$
$\gamma = 60°$

Fig. 13.6 Single-phase bridge voltage control

When this method of control is being used, it should be remembered that:
1. The mean current flowing through the thyristors and diodes varies as the delay angle α between the half-bridges is changed. Figure 13.7 shows that the conduction angle of the diodes and thyristors is different on the two sides of the bridge

and it varies with load power factor also. Specific calculations are needed in each particular case to assess correctly the diode and thyristor ratings.

2. The delay angle α should preferably be achieved by firing one half-bridge $\alpha/2$ early and the other $\alpha/2$ late so that the output voltage does not change in phase angle at the same time.

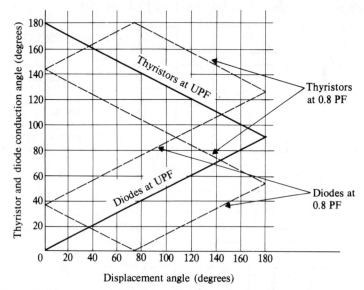

Fig. 13.7 Diode and thyristor ratings with phase-displacement control

Variable 'notch' control can be used in single- and three-phase circuits as long as additional thyristor commutations can be allowed in every cycle. If, in the forced commutated inverter circuits of Chapter 5, the thyristors are commutated six times instead of twice per cycle, the waveform of Fig. 13.8 can be produced. Control over the time of the second and third and fifth and sixth commutations produces a variable-width notch.

This method of control has only limited use in single-phase circuits as the above waveform, when the notch width equals 60 degrees, completely loses its fundamental value and contains only the third harmonic.

In three-phase circuits, however, the result of this method of control becomes a double notch in the output voltage line-to-line waveform, as shown in Fig. 13.9, and this provides a very useful method of control, giving the voltage and harmonics at different notch angles as shown in Figs 13.10 and 13.11.

As in the previous method of control, the periods of thyristor and diode current flow need careful study to ensure that the worst-case conditions for each semiconductor are fully understood. It should also be noted that this method of control produces high proportions of seventh and thirteenth harmonics at high notch widths.

Pulse-width modulation control (PWM) using sinusoidal modulation requires many commutations per cycle of output and produces many high-frequency pulses in each cycle of the output voltage. Control over the width of the pulses allows the magnitude of the output voltage to be controlled. Figure 13.12 shows the principle involved.

The main harmonics in the PWM waveform will be related to the commutation frequency and this is therefore usually of relatively high value compared with the

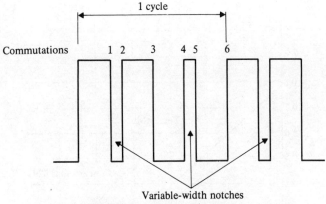

1 cycle

Commutations   1 2   3   4 5   6

Variable-width notches

Fig. 13.8 Variable notch control

fundamental. The change in harmonics as the voltage level is changed is not normally a dominating influence on system design.

Input chopper control. All the methods explained up to now have involved using the inverter thyristors to control the voltage as well as to carry out the d.c./a.c. conversion.

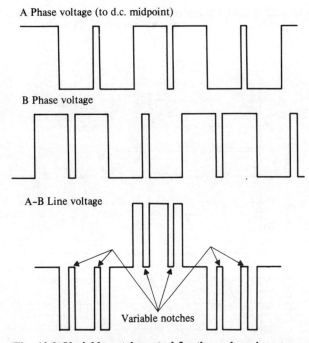

A Phase voltage (to d.c. midpoint)

B Phase voltage

A–B Line voltage

Variable notches

Fig. 13.9 Variable notch control for three-phase inverters

In some circumstances, these methods may impose unwelcome restrictions on the ratings of the thyristors or excessive power losses due to multiple commutations in each cycle. This situation may be aggravated by the fact that these battery-fed inverters often spend most of their life with a high battery voltage and hence the inverter operates at its voltage-reducing extreme.

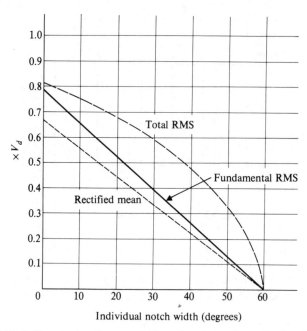

Fig. 13.10 A.C. output voltage variation of a three-phase circuit with variable notch control

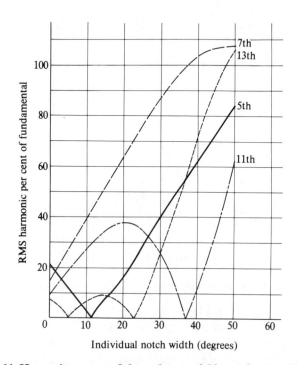

Fig. 13.11 Harmonic content of three-phase variable notch controlled waveform

The use of a d.c./d.c. chopper in the input circuit to the inverter can allow the inverter always to run under optimum voltage and waveform conditions and this may produce a more economic and satisfactory equipment design. Any of the chopper circuits referred to in Chapter 5 can be used in such circumstances and they would invariably be followed by a filter to give a smooth, constant d.c. voltage for the inverter.

Fig. 13.12 Voltage control by pulse-width modulation

13.3 Limited Current Ability

The current which can be drawn from any forced-commutated thyristor circuit is limited by the size of the commutating capacitors and the turn-off time of the thyristors. If this current is exceeded, the thyristors will fail to turn off and a short-circuit will occur. It will be impossible to stop this d.c. current flow except by opening the circuit with a contactor, fuse, or suitably designed static switch.

In most circuits, the level of current which can be successfully commutated is also dependent on the value of input d.c. voltage. Where a wide variation of battery voltage occurs, the maximum current which can be drawn from the circuit will normally be lowest at minimum d.c. voltage, because the energy in the commutating capacitors will be lowest at this point.

Much inverter equipment therefore includes a means of limiting the output current to prevent commutation failure. The current is measured and whenever it reaches a predetermined safe level the output voltage is reduced to ensure the current is not exceeded. The safe level of current limit may be varied as the d.c. input voltage varies, to obtain the maximum safe output from the inverter.

In some applications, particularly no-break power supplies, reduction in the output voltage may not be acceptable to the load, in which case a larger inverter may be required or additional facilities introduced in the load to ensure the fault current is limited.

The most common condition leading to such an overload is a load fault. The protection provided against this must be such as to disconnect the fault before the inverter current has reached its limit value. Subcircuit fusing is normally used and the maximum size of fuse that is acceptable will be related to the peak current capability of the inverter.

13.4 Output Harmonic Filtering

It will be appreciated from the foregoing that all inverter circuits produce significant harmonics in the output voltage, some more than others. Most of the loads which these inverters supply require a reasonable sine wave and an output filter is necessary to remove the unwanted harmonics. It is not intended here to go into the detailed design of filters, but it is worth while to cover some of the principles involved to enable a reasonable degree of understanding of the overall operation of these circuits. Figure 13.13 shows some of the combinations of components used to filter the output of fixed-frequency inverters.

Filter A is the simplest circuit but it will affect all frequencies including the fundamental and as a result it cannot be made very selective. The series inductance will also cause a voltage drop due to the normal load current. The impedance of C2 will decrease as the frequency increases and the impedance of L1 will increase as frequency increases, and hence the filter will attenuate the higher frequencies more easily. The amount of harmonic current drawn from the inverter will be controlled principally by the value of L1. If this is made small to keep the fundamental voltage drop low, then high harmonic currents will be drawn from the inverter and this will mean the commutating current ability of the inverter will need to be increased.

Filter B can be arranged to attenuate selectively one harmonic; if C3 and L3 are chosen to resonate at the selected frequency, the combined impedance of C3 and L3 will be very low at this frequency. Very little output voltage at that frequency will then occur. As all inverters produce many harmonic frequencies, this filter is never used on its own but as part of a more complex circuit.

Filter D is such an arrangement, where L3, C3 and L4, C4 will be chosen to resonate at two selected frequencies, usually the dominating ones. Other frequencies are

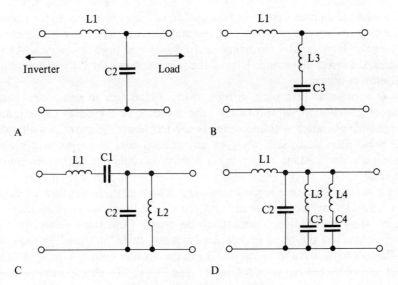

Fig. 13.13 Types of filter circuit

attenuated by the presence of the capacitor C2. Again, the series inductance L1 will cause a voltage drop at the fundamental frequency and, again, its value will control the level of harmonic currents drawn from the inverter. This filter will not attenuate the fundamental voltage quite so much as filter A as the value of C2 would be much lower as the resonant shunt circuits (L3, C3 and L4, C3) will cope with the lowest frequencies.

The problem of the voltage drop in the series inductance has led to the use of:

Filter C in which L1 and C1 are chosen to resonate at the fundamental frequency and this gives zero series impedance under this condition. However, as this is so, any

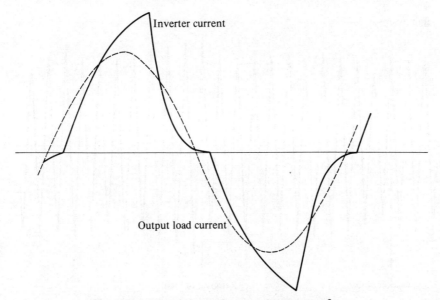

Fig. 13.14 Filter input and output current waveforms

267

parallel-connected circuits have to be arranged to be high-impedance to the fundamental or else they will carry significant fundamental currents, so C2 and L2 are chosen to resonate at the fundamental frequency and hence to be high-impedance. At higher frequencies, the series inductance L1 and the parallel capacitor C2 will dominate and attenuation will occur.

Filter C appears at first sight to offer many advantages in component size and efficiency of attenuation. Unfortunately, the presence of the series capacitance can lead to unstable operation with motor loads and this limits the use of this filter design.

In all these filter designs, it must be appreciated that resistance will always be present in inductances and in capacitor connections, and this will ultimately limit their effectiveness.

That the series inductance is the component which controls the flow of harmonic currents from the inverter has been mentioned already. Effectively, all these filters operate by allowing harmonic currents to be drawn from the inverter, so causing harmonic voltages in the series inductance to cancel those produced by the inverter. Hence, these currents have to be allowed for in the inverter design. Figure 13.14 shows the input and output currents of a filter of type C and this clearly demonstrates the effects and shows that the inverter has to be capable of commutating higher currents than the load receives.

13.5 Transient Response of Output Voltage

Some fixed-frequency applications require close control of the output voltage even for short transient periods of time. If the load current taken from an inverter equipment suddenly changes, then there will be a sudden change in the output voltage due to the presence of series inductance and resistance in the inverter, filter, transformers, etc. The size of the series impedance directly controls the instantaneous level to which the output voltage drops or rises when a load change occurs.

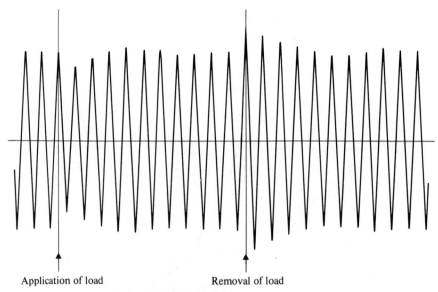

Application of load   Removal of load

Fig. 13.15 Transient response of an inverter

268

Usually it is the filter design which is the dominating influence in this respect; the larger the series impedance the more effective the filter and the lower the harmonic currents drawn, but the bigger is the voltage change which occurs when the load changes. As usual, compromise is required: the inverter is chosen to produce the lowest level of harmonics in its output consistent with acceptable cost. The filter is then chosen to attenuate the harmonics sufficiently and produce the minimum voltage drop on load application.

The overall output voltage will be controlled by a closed-loop system based on a measurement of output voltage. When a sudden change occurs the control system will correct the output voltage as quickly as it can. Hence, in general, a sudden change in output voltage will be followed by a more gradual return to the set voltage level, possibly with some transient overshoot.

Figure 13.15 shows a typical output voltage oscillogram for the sudden application and removal of a load from an inverter. The initial voltage deviation is controlled principally by the size of the load change and the value of the series impedance, and the time to return to the set level is decided by the speed of response of the control system.

13.6 General-purpose A.C. Power Supplies

This section will deal with the applications for inverters which arise simply due to the need for a.c. (where mains supplies are not normally available) and where unusual frequencies are required. Such situations occur with vehicle-mounted equipment where batteries may be the only source of power available. Much of the equipment needed on the vehicle will have been designed for use off normal main a.c. supplies, and rather than convert them for operation from the vehicle batteries (and thus restrict them to use on the vehicle) a more suitable arrangement is to provide a separate a.c.

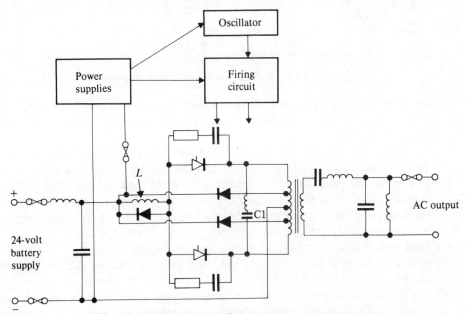

Fig. 13.16 A battery-supplied, fixed-frequency inverter

269

power supply, powered from the batteries to feed the standard apparatus. These supplies therefore usually produce the normal standard voltages and frequencies available from mains distribution systems, e.g., 230 V, 240 V, 50 Hz, and 110 V, 208 V, 60 Hz, etc.

There is usually a need for a transformer to step-up the voltage as battery voltages are generally low, and some degree of output voltage filtering will be required to ensure a reasonably sinusoidal output. The inverter will have to operate at the battery voltage but this will not normally be allowed to drop too low or else it may be unsuitable for its other purposes. Other loads on the battery may, however, cause temporary battery voltage changes.

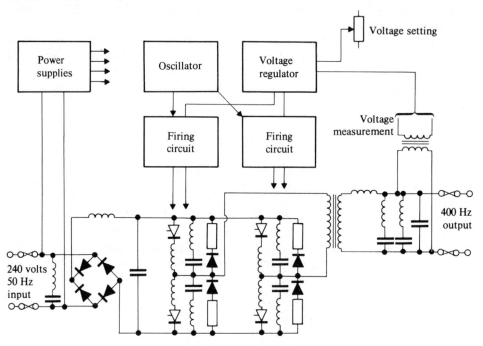

Fig. 13.17 A 50 to 400 Hz frequency changer

Figure 13.16 shows a typical vehicle power supply capable of providing 1000 VA, 208 V, single-phase, 60 Hz from a 24-V battery source. This will be used to illustrate the main design points.

(a) In this case a non-regulated output is sufficient, i.e., no voltage-variation capability, as the battery voltage variation is within the load requirements.
(b) The low battery voltage of 24 V means that a rated input current of 40 to 50 A is needed depending on power factor. (The battery will supply the kW needs of the load plus the circuit losses.) The most economic circuit for these voltages and currents is the parallel inverter, as it uses only two thyristors.
(c) Feedback diodes allow for load power-factor variation.
(d) A d.c. capacitor is needed to provide the high commutating currents needed quickly and to accept the reactive currents carried by the diodes.
(e) The firing circuit provides the two isolated gate pulse outputs for the two thyristors displaced 180 degrees apart. Solid block pulses are used to ensure

270

that gate current is always available whenever current is required to flow in the thyristors.

(f) A resonant output filter is used to give a satisfactory reduction of harmonics while minimizing the voltage drop at 60 Hz.

(g) The electronics need to be powered from the d.c. battery input and this is likely to mean that they are electrically tied to the battery, the point of isolation between the electronics and the thyristors being the firing circuit pulse transformers.

(h) Simple overcurrent protection using input and output fuses is employed for economic reasons.

(i) R/C snubber circuits are included for thyristor $\mathrm{d}v/\mathrm{d}t$ protection, and the choke in series with C1 reduces $\mathrm{d}i/\mathrm{d}t$.

Another frequent thyristor inverter application is as a static frequency changer to provide a supply at a different frequency to that available, e.g., to obtain a 60 Hz supply from a 50 Hz input or vice versa. A wide range of possibilities is available:

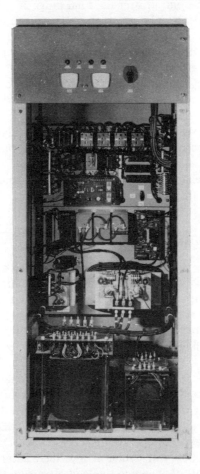

Fig. 13.18 A single-phase 3 kW standby inverter specifically designed for supplying fluorescent lights (GEC Industrial Controls Ltd)

when thyristor inverters are used, almost any voltage at any power frequency can be provided. The example of Fig. 13.17 has been selected to illustrate the important design points. This shows the circuit for a unit capable of providing 400 Hz at 115 V single-phase a.c. from a 240 V, 50 Hz supply. In this case, the output was required to be particularly stable in voltage and frequency, and voltage compensation for load and supply changes is incorporated.

1. The inverter circuit in this case could be operated directly from the rectified a.c. supply, and the bridge inverter is a suitable choice. The complementary commutated circuit is chosen to minimize the number of components. The auxiliary thyristor circuit may be more efficient (i.e., less power losses), but it doubles the number of thyristors.

2. Voltage control can be effected by phase displacement between the two halves of the inverter bridge.

3. The nominal operating point of the inverter bridge is chosen as being with a displacement angle of 65 degrees between the two halves, giving a normal waveform as in Fig. 13.6 with the conduction angle = 115°. This is done to minimize the harmonics in the output over the total range of plus and minus 11 per cent needed to cope with supply and load voltage variations. This means at high supply voltage, low load current, the waveform angle γ will be approximately 95 degrees; and with low supply voltage, high load, it will change to approximately 150 degrees giving maximum harmonics of 24·5 per cent of third and fifth.

4. The output filter, placed after the transformer to take advantage of its leakage reactance, includes resonant shunts to remove the fifth and seventh harmonics.

5. Output voltage measurement works into a closed-loop voltage control which alters the angle between the firing of the two half-bridges.

6. In this case, the electronics can be powered from a mains-supplied transformer rectifier unit.

7. As in the previous example, snubber circuits, block gate pulses, feedback diodes, and an input filter are all included in this equipment.

13.7 Emergency Standby Inverter Power Supplies

Static thyristor inverters can provide a way of obtaining a.c. power from batteries when the mains supply fails. If the load can sustain a short period without a supply during a mains failure, then the provision of a standby inverter not normally supplying the load can produce an acceptable system. When a mains failure occurs, the inverter is switched in to supply the load as soon as possible. This arrangement is very practical and economic for providing power to important lighting, communication equipment, or alarm systems.

In most of these instances, the inverter would not normally be in operation at all; it would be started up and switched on when a failure of the mains occurred and switched off again when the mains supply returned. The load would, in this case, experience a short loss of supply of between 200 and 500 milliseconds while the inverter was being brought into operation.

Equipment for this purpose will include an inverter, a battery, and a battery charger, with some switched means of changing the load over from the mains to the inverter. Figure 13.19 shows a single line block diagram of a suitable system.

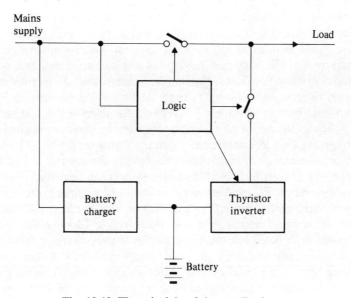

Fig. 13.19 The principle of the standby inverter

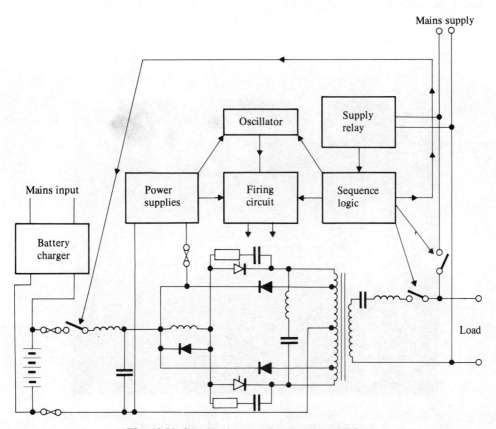

Fig. 13.20 Standby inverter for fluorescent lights

Single- or three-phase arrangements are possible and any of the inverter circuits and principles may be incorporated into them. Regulation of voltage can be achieved by series choppers, pulse-width control, notch control, or PWM methods, and filtering with varying degrees of efficiency in removing harmonics can be included. In practice, however, standby systems tend to use the simpler arrangements as, by implication, the load can always tolerate normal mains supply deviations. More accurate and stable requirements would be met by no-break inverters, discussed in the next section.

Figure 13.20 shows the circuit of a single-phase standby inverter designed to supply a fluorescent lighting load in emergencies when the mains supply fails. You will note the similarity between this circuit and that of the battery-fed inverter of Fig. 13.16, but in the present case a simpler filter is used and the system can be designed with a wider d.c. supply voltage range. This will enable a smaller and cheaper battery to be used and it is possible because fluorescent lamps can cope with the large change in output voltage which will occur. The charger will be dealt with in Chapter 14.

In some designs, it is possible to incorporate the battery-charging facilities within the inverter circuitry using some of the same components in both the inverter and battery-charging circuits, e.g., transformer chokes, rectifiers, etc. This does not, however, change the basic principles involved in either the inverter or the battery charger thyristor circuit design.

The above arrangement, where the inverter is normally switched off while the mains supply is available, gives a significant switchover time on mains failure. This time can

Fig. 13.21 A complete three-phase 150 kVA uninterruptible power supply equipment (Emerson Electric Industrial Controls Ltd)

274

be improved if the inverter is made to run at all times with its output synchronized with the mains supply which is supplying the load. If the mains supply then fails, high-speed switching can be used to give minimum transition time.

13.8 No-break/Uninterruptible Power Supplies

Some loads cannot tolerate loss of supply for any time without malfunctioning and many of them require the a.c. supply to be maintained within close voltage and frequency tolerances. Thyristor inverter systems are able to provide a no-break or uninterruptible a.c. power source to supply such loads and they are fully capable of meeting the requirements of the most critical loads.

Figure 13.22 shows the block diagram of the no-break system in which the inverter always provides the power to the load. While the mains supply is present, the rectifier supplies the inverter and keeps the battery charged to its prime condition. When the mains supply fails, the battery will supply the required power to the inverter at reducing

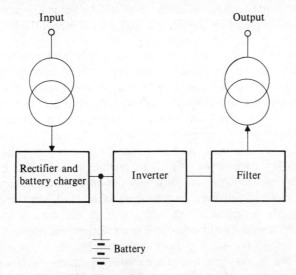

Fig. 13.22 Block diagram of a no-break power supply

d.c. voltage until such time as its voltage is too low for satisfactory output from the inverter. This system has the following important characteristics:

(a) The design can be such that the load will not distinguish any difference whether it is being supplied from the mains or the battery or being changed over.

(b) The size and capacity of the battery only will decide the length of time the system can operate without a mains supply.

(c) Any number of input and output phases are possible.

(d) The input and output frequencies need not be related.

(e) The input and output voltages need not be related.

(f) The output can be designed to meet much more stringent specifications than those normally obtainable from the input power supply, i.e., closer voltage and frequency tolerances and freedom from transient variations.

Because of the wide battery voltage range and the need for accurate output stability, inverters will always include means of voltage variation, probably with one of the methods described in Section 13.2. The method chosen will depend on the transient voltage performance specification required. For example, pulse-width control with a 50 per cent change in battery voltage will from Figs 13.4 and 13.5 lead to inverter output harmonics of about 60 per cent of third harmonic, up to 25 per cent of fifth, and up to 22 per cent of seventh during the majority of its working life. A filter to reduce these to around 5 per cent will be the deciding factor in transient voltage performance. An improved transient performance can be achieved if a high commutating frequency, pulse-width modulation method is used to reduce the harmonics or if multiple-phase displaced-bridge circuits are used with the same objective.

The main design principles involved will be described with reference to Fig. 13.23 which shows the block diagram of a typical uninterruptible power supply equipment to provide the same frequency supply as the mains.

The inverter can be any of the single- or three-phase circuits mentioned previously and it could use multiple circuits to achieve the necessary ratings or harmonic performance. It will include one of the methods of voltage control to allow for a wide input voltage variation from the battery. An input filter will be needed to prevent the high commutating currents required by the inverter being drawn from the battery or rectifier.

The filter will be chosen to reduce the ouput harmonics to be within the load requirements. As mentioned before, its design will depend very much on the method of inverter voltage control employed and the transient response required by the load.

The mains rectifier/charger system shown in the diagram is one of two alternative systems which are used. This arrangement with a separate charger and a battery thyristor switch allows the battery to be charged independently of the d.c. voltage required by the inverter, i.e., if it is beneficial, the battery can be at a higher voltage than that feeding the inverter. It also means that a diode rectifier can be used to provide the mains power for the inverter and that this only has to cope with the inverter load requirements. This method, however, has the drawback that when the mains supply returns after a failure it can cause a high output voltage transient, particularly, if by that time, the battery is near its minimum voltage and the inverter is giving its maximum output. The alternative input system shown in Fig. 13.20 avoids this mains re-application problem by phase control of the convertor but the convertor now has to cope with the full inverter load and the high boost charging current of the battery after a battery discharge during a mains failure. In addition, the inverter has to be able to cope with the maximum input voltage decided by the needs of efficient battery charging.

A static switch bypass circuit is shown in Fig. 13.23. This is there to provide an alternative supply to the load in case of inverter failure. It can also be used to provide a higher-capacity mains supply to the load if a load fault occurs; this may be beneficial in blowing load subcircuit fuses quickly. A fast thyristor static switch (see Chapter 16) is used to enable the transfer to be effected without the load realizing that a fault has occurred. Transfer of the load via the bypass to the mains is effected as soon as any fault condition is detected. The static switch can only be closed quickly (i.e., in a few milliseconds) if the inverter output voltage is maintained in voltage and frequency synchronism with the mains supply, as initially the inverter output and the mains will be paralleled together.

The oscillator and voltage control arrangements included will therefore be normally controlled by a mains voltage measurement, the oscillator being maintained to keep

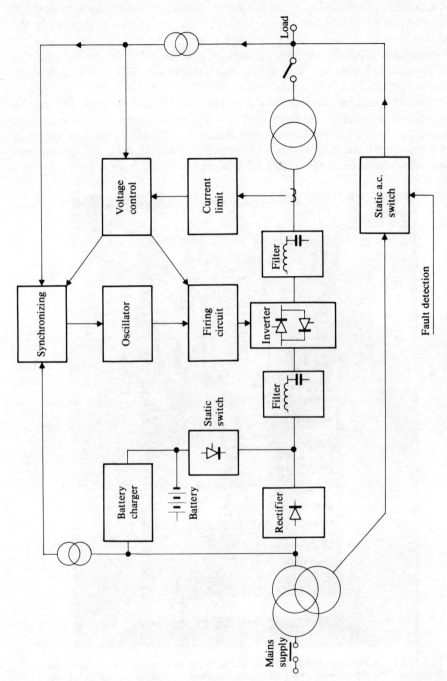

Fig. 13.23 Uninterruptible power supply block diagram

the inverter output correctly in phase with mains, and the voltage control to ensure the same level of voltage from the inverter and the mains. This system is, however, additionally complicated by the requirements that:

1. The oscillator and voltage control systems have to work independently of the synchronizing inputs when the mains supply fails and they still have to keep the inverter performance within the voltage and frequency tolerances required by the load.
2. Synchronism with the mains must only be maintained if the mains supply is within specified tolerance: if it deviates too much the inverter must run correctly and independently of the synchronizing input.

In particularly exacting circumstances, a number of complete no-break sets may be paralleled together to supply the same load so that if one fails the other inverters can continue to feed the load. This is known as a *parallel redundant* arrangement and leads to additional complication to ensure equal sharing of the load current and correct selection and disconnection of a faulty no-break set.

Fig. 13.24 An inverter cubicle of a no-break power supply showing clearly the necessary filter components required to give less than 3% output voltage distortion at power rating of 30 kVA (GEC Industrial Controls Ltd)

13.9 References

1. D. Finney, 'Static inverter system for emergency supplies', *Electronics and Power*, 32–34, Feb. 1973.
2. A. Hansen and H. Havemann, 'Comparison of filters for uninterruptible power supplies', *IEE Conference Publication 154*, 132–135, Sept. 1977.
3. J. Schmitt, 'Uninterruptible power supply systems with static power convertors', *IEE Conference Publication 154*, 136–141, Sept. 1977.
4. D. D. S. Reardon, 'A static power inverter system for a submarine', *IEE Conference Publication 154*, 74–77, Sept. 1977.
5. S. Watabe, 'A 3-phase 250kVA no-break power supply with current limiting filter', *IEE Conference Publication 53*, 216–224, May 1969.

14. Electrochemical Applications

The passage of direct current through liquid chemicals causes a wide variety of electrochemical reactions which are the basis of a large part of the world's chemical industry.

D.C. power can be stored in batteries for later use; they are the only static and long-lasting method of electrical power storage. The life and efficiency of storage batteries depend on the methods used to charge them and maintain them in the charged condition.

Many metals oxidize and corrode if exposed to normal atmospheric conditions. Their life can be extended considerably if they are coated or plated with a more stable material. Highly efficient coating can be applied by electrochemical means whereby the metal is immersed in a liquid electrolyte and a current passed through it between the metal and separate electrodes. Chemical reactions can cause the electrode material to be deposited on the metal in a non-porous, corrosion-resistant finish.

As an alternative to plating, metals can also be painted and a process known as electrophoretic painting enables highly effective paint coatings to be applied electrochemically. The metal is immersed in a tank of water-based paint and a voltage is applied between the metal and the tank. As the paint is non-conductive, while it coats the surface it is self-regulating, and very smooth constant-thickness coatings are possible. Control over the current flow can produce a very high-quality protective finish.

Gases can be obtained by electrolysis. Hydrogen and oxygen can be produced by passing direct current through water, and chlorine from the electrolysis of salt solution. The volume of gases produced depends on the level of current flowing.

Many pure metals are obtained from the ore material by electrolytic reduction or refining. Copper and aluminium are the most significant metals obtained in this way.

These processes must be the largest users of direct current throughout the world's industry and large amounts of d.c. are essential for their operation. Very large manufacturing plants are in existence using these methods, often using hundreds of megawatts of d.c. power in one installation.

Thyristors, with their ability both to convert power from a.c. to d.c. and to control its value, play a very significant part in these applications. In general, the naturally commutated, phase-controlled thyristor circuits are in wide use to produce the necessary controlled d.c. for these applications. The control facilities are used to compensate for load and system variations and to produce a smooth and efficient process.

In the past, this duty of control has been carried out by a variety of methods from variable transformers and induction regulators to controlled d.c. generators. The high efficiency, fast operation, and freedom from maintenance shown by thyristor equipment have now resulted in all of these electrochemical processes being economically controlled by thyristors.

Power supplies for electrochemical loads are somewhat different from those for other applications. In general, high levels of current are involved requiring parallel connection of thyristors and circuits. Very high-power equipment is sometimes needed and special construction methods involving liquid cooling are frequently employed to minimize the physical size. Most of these processes are continuous and the efficiency of the power supply equipment is of prime importance.

In this chapter, the principles of operation relevant to thyristor power supply equipment will be explained and the important design factors associated with thyristor equipment will be discussed.

14.1 Battery Charging

The usable life of all batteries is principally governed by the electrical conditions imposed upon them. The charging conditions are particularly important in this respect. Experience over the years has established the most suitable ways of ensuring a long battery life. As far as charging is concerned this means:

Fig. 14.1 A thyristor battery charger designed for use with an uninterruptible power supply (GEC Industrial Controls Ltd)

(a) Charging at relatively high current can take place initially if the battery is discharged and therefore at a low voltage.

(b) As the charge in the battery and its voltage increases, the charging current should be reduced.

(c) Even when the battery is fully charged, it will still need to be charged at a low level (or occasionally) to maintain it in this state.

(d) If the maintaining charge is at too high a level, gassing will take place and the electrolyte will evaporate and need topping-up too frequently.

(e) If the battery is continuously 'float'-charged, the exact voltage at which it is maintained will have a significant effect on its life.

(f) The ripple current should be kept to as low a value as possible.

A wide variety of battery designs are available employing different materials, e.g., lead acid and nickel cadmium, and different internal constructions. They all have different capabilities and are used for a whole range of requirements, from engine starting to emergency supplies for lighting. The detailed charging needs of each type

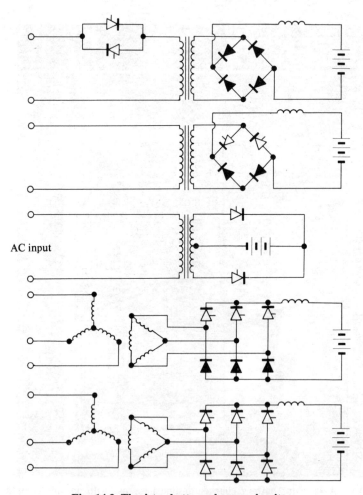

Fig. 14.2 Thyristor battery-charger circuits

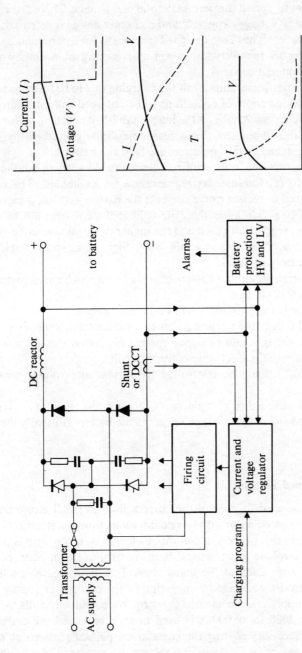

Fig. 14.3 A single-phase battery charger

Labels visible in figure:

Current (I)

Voltage (V)

V

I

V

T

I

to battery

+

−

Alarms

Battery protection HV and LV

DC reactor

Shunt or DCCT

Firing circuit

Current and voltage regulator

Charging program

Transformer

AC supply

need to be fully understood before the charger power supply unit can be properly specified.

Most individual battery cells operate at d.c. voltages between 1 and 2 V and many cells are connected in series to obtain the necessary total d.c. voltage. There is therefore a very wide choice of battery voltages available and a charger design is often arranged to suit a range of voltages unless it has been designed specifically for a particular battery. In general, battery chargers are relatively low-power units as they are normally only a fraction of the battery's nominal capacity.

Naturally commutated thyristor circuits allow the charging rate to be fully controlled at all times and enable a wide variety of conditions to be obtained without changes in the power circuitry of the charger. Although the long-established constant-voltage and taper-charging methods can still be used, the increased flexibility offered by thyristors enables a charger to be matched to the optimum needs of the battery.

Any of the naturally commutated or a.c. controller circuits can be used, but the half-controlled systems tend to predominate as regeneration is not needed. The circuit choice is affected by the need to reduce ripple current; the battery acts like a capacitor and current ripple would be much larger than the voltage if steps were not taken to reduce it. In practice, series reactors are used and the higher pulse number circuits may be employed to keep the size of reactors to a minimum. Figure 14.2 shows a selection of the circuits used for battery chargers.

Figure 14.3 shows a typical circuit of a battery charger and it will be used to demonstrate the main design factors.

1. A single-phase bridge is used and only half control is necessary.
2. The d.c. reactor will reduce the ripple current to an acceptable level.
3. A variety of output voltages and charging current characteristics are available purely by suitably setting the electronic control circuits.
4. The electronics would usually be controlled by current and voltage measurements.
5. Battery protection is included to give alarm if charger faults result in the battery being operated outside its design voltage range, as the battery is usually the high capital cost item.

14.2 Electrolytic Plating and Tinning

Although thyristors can be used to control the current flow to small electroplating facilities, their main use is in association with large continuous-flow metal strip coating, plating, and tinning lines. In this process, a continuous length of metal strip is passed through a sequence of electrolytic and chemical baths in turn to clean, plate, reflow, and chemically treat the strip. Each of the many electrolytic baths contains a liquid electrolyte and fixed electrodes connected to one side of the d.c. power supply. The other side of the power supply is connected to the strip via conducting rolls. A high current of anything from 2000 to 10 000 A is used in each bath and the current is regulated to produce the necessary coating thickness at the particular speed at which the line is working; this may be in excess of 700 metres per minute. The d.c. voltage required is usually relatively low at up to 36 V.

The design of thyristor equipment necessary for this duty is affected mainly by:

(a) The high currents and low voltages needed.

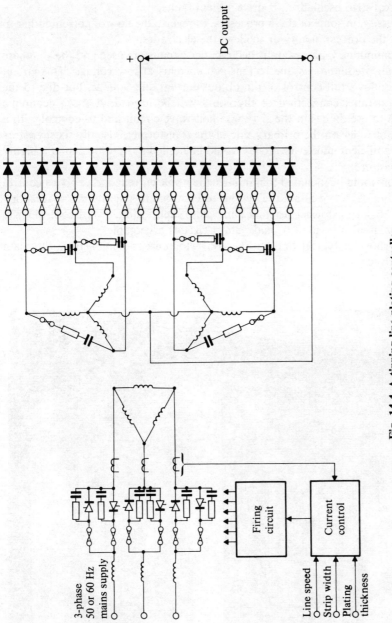

DC output

+

3-phase
50 or 60 Hz
mains supply

Firing
circuit

Current
control

Line speed
Strip width
Plating
thickness

Fig. 14.4 A tinning line plating controller

(b) The need for reasonably smooth d.c. current as the quality of the finished plating may be influenced by d.c. current ripple.

(c) The possibility of short-circuits between the strip and the electrodes caused by mechanical strip oscillation or drive system faults.

(d) The necessity, in some of these processes, to reverse the flow of current either to improve the process quality or to clean the electrodes.

Naturally commutated, phase-controlled rectifier circuits are used and the six-phase half-wave circuit predominates due to the high currents at low voltage. This circuit with thyristors allows full control of the output current and voltage, but due to the high currents, parallel connection of thyristors will be needed. A more economic arrangement is to use diodes in the six-phase half-wave circuit and to control with a thyristor a.c. controller on the primary side of the transformer. Usually six thyristors would then be sufficient and fewer diodes would be needed as they are run at a higher junction temperature.

A d.c. reactor would be included to minimize the ripple current and to give a control current limit time to act to allow the system to continue to operate if a load short-circuit occurs. High transformer reactance and pulse suppression, or fast control angle delay change, may also be used to make short-circuits acceptable.

Figure 14.4 shows a typical tinning line convertor unit to demonstrate the main principles involved:

Fig. 14.5 A thyristor controller used in association with a diode rectifier to provide control of an electroplating bath (Westinghouse Brake and Signal Co. Ltd)

1. A six-phase half-wave diode rectifier circuit is used and 120 degree conduction is assured by using a suitable transformer core design.
2. Although three parallel diodes are required per arm of the rectifier circuit, only two thyristors in each a.c. phase are required due to the higher supply voltage.
3. The d.c. reactor will reduce the ripple and slow down the rate of rise of fault current.
4. Small a.c. reactors may be needed to protect the a.c. controller if a firing fault occurs to saturate the transformer.
5. A.C., CT current measurement can be employed and gives a satisfactory measure of the load current for control purposes.

14.3 Electrophoretic Painting

Paints can be deposited on bare conducting metal by an electrophoretic process which involves immersing the metal in a bath of ionized water-based paint and applying a d.c. voltage between the tank and the metal to cause a d.c. current flow. This method is used to apply an initial primer coat or a one-coat finish to mass-produced components such as washing machines and refrigerator cabinets and car bodies. The method's main benefit is that a constant-thickness coat of paint can be applied to all surfaces, even edges and internal surfaces (as long as a suitable hole allows paint access). The paint coat consolidates in the bath, paint runs do not occur, and a simpler drying process is possible. The thickness of coat depends on the voltage and metal area being coated. Variation of voltage is required to produce consistent results.

The metal to be coated is usually fully immersed in the paint bath and is carried on a moving mechanical conveyor system as part of a production line. Each component may be treated separately with a separate power supply, or a combined paint bath supply may be used with a number of components in the bath at the same time.

The main characteristics of this application from the d.c. power supply point of view are:

(a) Voltages between 200 and 600 V d.c. are usually used.
(b) Currents from 1000 to 4000 A may be needed during the painting process and the current will vary during the cycle of operation and the condition of the metal being coated.
(c) The surface finish of the paint may be affected by sudden changes in current, including current ripple, and if the power supply is on while the metal is being immersed; a stop in the production line can cause a noticeable line in the finished coat.
(d) Short-circuits are relatively frequent due to mechanical disturbances in the conveyor system and internal electrodes falling off, etc. The system must be capable of accepting the short-circuits and continuing in operation if it is only temporary. The 'burn marks' resulting from a short-circuit should not be too noticeable.

As a result, thyristor power supplies tend to use bridge circuits, phase multiplication to reduce ripple current, and reactors to limit short-circuit currents. Static methods of reducing short-circuit currents may also be used, e.g., pulse suppression, fast delay angle control, or crowbars to minimize the 'burn marks'.

Figure 14.6 shows a typical electrophoretic painting convertor to demonstrate the design principles employed:

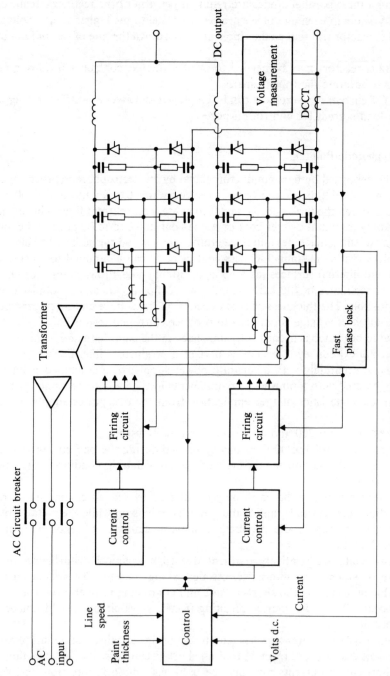

Fig. 14.6 An electrophoretic painting convertor

1. Two thyristor bridges are employed connected in parallel and phase-displaced to give twelve-pulse control to minimize ripple current.
2. The two d.c. reactors limit the circulation of harmonic currents between the two bridges, reduce the level of current ripple, and slow down the rate of rise of short-circuit current.
3. The fully controlled bridges allow inversion to take place to bring the short-circuit current to zero very quickly to minimize 'burn marks'. Fast increase in delay angle is used when a short-circuit is detected.
4. Parallel connection of thyristors is often needed.
5. Individual current control is required on each bridge to balance the load current between them to compensate for small resistance and reactance differences.
6. The overall control is usually programmed in with the conveyor operations, the voltage increased as the painting process proceeds.

Six-pulse systems and series operation of bridges may be used depending on the particular rating and circumstances.

14.4 Electrochemical Machining

The cutting, shaping, and drilling of metals can be carried out by electrochemical removal of the metal. If the space between the metal workpiece and a metal tool is flooded with a suitable electrolyte, and d.c. current is passed between the tool and workpiece, electrochemical action can cause 'deplating' of the metal, the removed material being carried away by the fast-flowing electrolyte.

This process, known as electrochemical machining, can be used to shape even very hard metals, at very fast machining rates while still producing a very good surface finish.

The d.c. supply will be required to provide currents from 1000 to 50 000 A at voltages between 10 and 20 V. The current will need to be regulated along with the speed of tool movement to give the necessary metal removal rate and ensure a constant tool-to-workpiece spacing. Fast protection is required as the tool and workpiece may come into direct contact, causing a short-circuit which may result in damaging burn marks.

Thyristor supply units will use the single-phase half-wave and six-phase half-wave circuits due to the high-current, low-voltage requirements. Thyristor control may be on the primary side of the transformer using an a.c. controller with diodes in the secondary side circuit.

Short-circuit currents will be limited by d.c. or a.c. reactors and pulse suppression or fast phase-back may be incorporated to prevent damage due to short-circuits.

Six-pulse systems and parallel operation of bridges may be used depending on the particular ratings and circumstances.

14.5 Electrolysing of Gases

Many gases, particularly hydrogen, oxygen, and chlorine, are obtained by passing d.c. currents between two electrodes with liquid electrolyte contained in specially designed electrolytic cells. The cells operate at low voltages and are connected in series to form a complete gas-production unit. The amount of gas produced is directly dependent on the d.c. current flow and operation will normally be at a set value of current. The vol-

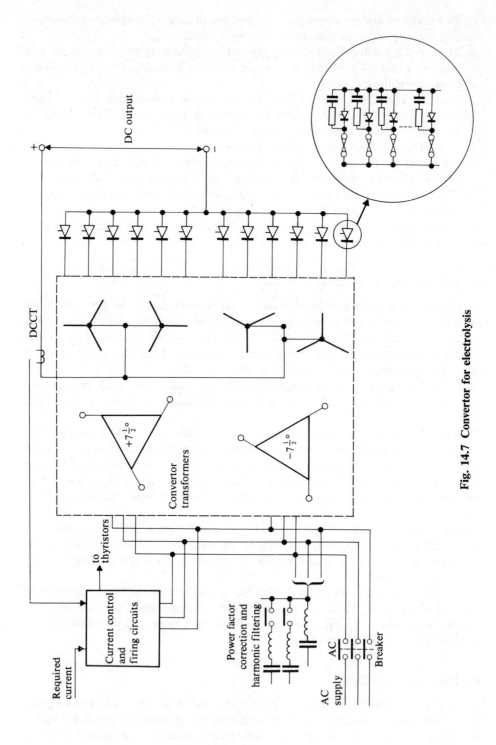

Fig. 14.7 Convertor for electrolysis

tage required to maintain the current flow will alter due to changes in the condition of the electrolyte. A further reason for voltage change is the regular need to take cells out of service for cleaning and electrode replacement. The cells are short-circuited during this operation.

Thyristor power supplies can be used to regulate the level of current flow to obtain optimum gas production. The power ratings of the equipment will vary with the size of the plant and the number of electrolytic cells in series. Voltages from 50 to 300 V are usual, and currents up to 300 000 A are frequently used. With such large plants, the most important factors are power supply efficiency and operating power factor. Thyristors satisfy the first requirement very well but normally voltage control brings with it a reduction in power factor which may be unacceptable. It is, however, possible to add switched power factor correction capacitors to such plants as current and voltage changes occur slowly and infrequently.

At these voltage and current levels, the six-phase half-wave thyristor circuit is invariably the most economic choice. A number of such circuits would be phase-displaced to reduce the mains supply harmonic currents and individual circuit current control will be employed to equalize the currents. Figure 14.7 shows a typical power circuit for such an application.

This heavy current equipment needs particular special constructional design to ensure that the total current is equally shared between the various circuits and parallel-connected thyristors. As explained in Chapter 7, at heavy current the inductance and resistance of the connecting busbars have a significant effect on the degree of parallel sharing. Special busbar arrangements have been developed by some manufacturers to minimize these impedance differences. As, at high currents it becomes difficult, expensive, and inefficient to incorporate current-balancing reactors, special selection of thyristors may be made to obtain a satisfactory degree of balance between the parallel-connected devices.

14.6 Metal Production and Refining

Copper, aluminium, zinc, sodium, and magnesium can all be produced or refined by electrochemical means in cells specially designed for the purpose in preference to other chemical furnace methods. The electrochemical methods allow very high-purity metal to be produced. There are two basic processes: an aqueous electrolyte process (similar to that used for gas production) used for tinning and refining, for example, copper; and a fused electrolyte method used, for example, for aluminium production. In this latter process, the electrolyte has to be fused by electric heat first before the electrolytic process can commence, and as a result very much more power is needed than in the aqueous case.

The electrolytic cells operate at high currents between 10 000 and 100 000 A and low voltages up to approximately 5 V. They are operated in series to produce an overall economic high-power plant requiring many megawatts of d.c. power. Total plant voltages vary from 100 V or so for copper refining to 850 V for an aluminium potline.

The main factors affecting the power supply equipment needed for metal production and refining processes are:
(a) All these processes are expected to operate continuously for very long periods of time without shutdown. Individual cells are taken out of service regularly without shutdown.

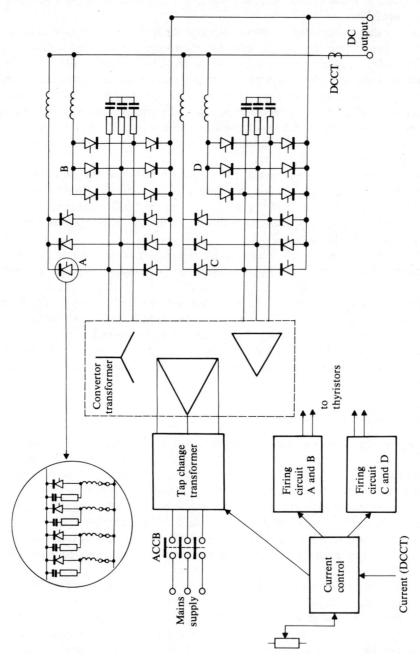

Fig. 14.8 A reversible electrochemical convertor

(b) Electricity is one of the major costs involved and high efficiency of the power supply plant is essential.

(c) The fusion process in particular has to be kept in operation as loss of power for more than a few minutes can result in freezing of the electrolyte, causing damage to the cells and a very expensive recommissioning period.

(d) Sudden changes in the load resistance can occur in individual cells and this can affect the total circuit current. In aluminium potlines, cells regularly jump from 5 V to 40 V suddenly, prior to replenishment of the electrolyte.

(e) Short-circuits can occur, particularly in cells where the electrodes are closely spaced, for example, in copper refining. This will cause a reduction in circuit resistance and an increase in circuit current.

(f) A variety of chemical reactions take place at the electrodes, and in some processes a short time reversal of the cell current can improve the total output of the cells by improving the electrochemical efficiency.

(g) The power supply equipment must be able to work under the corrosive and dirty atmospheric conditions which exist in these large chemical plants.

The high power requirements lead to the use of fully controlled six-phase half-wave or three-phase bridge circuits, naturally commutated, as appropriate to the circuit voltage. Circuits are often used in parallel to increase the pulse number and reduce the level of a.c. power supply harmonic currents. The thyristors may be used as a.c. controllers in the primary circuit of a rectifier transformer, with diodes to convert the power to d.c., or in the rectifier itself to carry out both control and conversion functions.

Fig. 14.9 A forced oil-cooled, current-reversal thyristor convertor installation for a copper-refining plant. The equipment supplies up to 30 kA at 150 V in the forward direction and 20 kA in the reverse direction (GEC Rectifiers Ltd)

As power factor in these large plants is again important, they will be used either with power factor correction capacitors or with tap change transformers; in this latter case, the thyristors would operate with low delay angles, normally with just sufficient in hand to cope with fast cell-resistance variations.

In all these cases, constant current control is normally required to ensure a smooth efficient production of the metal.

Figure 14.8 shows a typical circuit diagram of a reversible thyristor equipment which could be used for a refining process and this can be used to demonstrate some of the design principles considered:

1. Bridge circuits are chosen because of the higher voltage required, say, greater than 300 to 400 V d.c.
2. Parallel circuits are used to produce twelve-pulse operation.
3. The thyristors of the parallel bridges are operated always with 30 degrees angular displacement between them, i.e., bridges A and B 30 degrees from bridges C and D, to ensure maximum cancellation of the low-order harmonics.
4. To enable this to be possible, the transformer reactances must be chosen so that the current will automatically balance between the two bridges.
5. Bridges A and C operate for forward load current and bridges B and C for reverse load current. They are used in antiparallel operation (see Chapter 10) to obtain high-speed switching from forward to reverse and vice versa.
6. The d.c. reactors are to limit the flow of harmonic circulating current.
7. The thyristors are used to obtain high-speed control of the current with the tap changer following up slowly to ensure operation at the highest overall power factor possible.
8. Protection against overall load short-circuits is not normally necessary owing to the location of output busbars and their relatively high resistance, but in this case a control failure could result in the firing of both forward and reverse bridges. The d.c. reactors have therefore been split into the individual bridges to help slow down the rate of change of fault current to allow the a.c. circuit breaker time to clear.

14.7 References

1. B. Turton Smith, 'Thyristor control of traction battery chargers', *IEE Conference Publication 123*, 165–170, Dec. 1974.
2. M. Barak, 'Recent developments in batteries and voltage cells', *Electronics and Power*, 290–296, Sept. 1972.
3. J. Groeneveld and W. Simon, 'New methods and equipment for the power supply of electroplating plants', *Siemens Review*, 38, 2, 1971.
4. H. Schene and S. Berger, 'Thyristorised power supplies for electrocoating plants', *Siemens Review*, **40**, 6, 261–266, 1973.
5. PERA Report No. 145, *Electrochemical Machining*, Sept. 1965.
6. H. Mori, 'DC 200 V 330 KA thyristor rectifier for electrolysis', *IEE Conference Publication 53*, 225–233, May 1969.

15. Furnace Power Supplies

The most important advantages of electric furnaces over other heating methods are their efficiency, accuracy of control, and their freedom from pollution of the heated material. The heat can be directed precisely at the required points and furnaces can be split into separately heated zones. The avoidance of a flue improves the overall operating efficiency. Very fast, accurate, and stable control of furnace temperature can easily be achieved with electric heating, and thyristors enable the full potential in this respect to be achieved. Electric furnaces do not introduce any impurities into the material being heated and they therefore allow the metallurgical properties of the materials to be very closely controlled. Finally, the heating can be arranged to take place in any required environment, for example, in a vacuum or inert-gas atmosphere. All these advantages lead to an increasing use of electric furnaces and thyristors play a significant part in providing the necessary precision of control and conversion of the power into a suitable form.

There are many electric methods of generating heat and three of the most important will be considered in this chapter:

1. Electric current passing through resistance elements is one of the simplest and most used methods. It enables the heat to be located precisely and to be available in any local atmosphere.
2. Heat can be produced by striking an arc between two conducting electrodes. This method allows a high concentration of heat to be obtained and arc furnaces are particularly used for melting metals.
3. If a metal is surrounded by an a.c. induction coil, currents and therefore heat can be induced in the metal. This method means the heat is generated from within the metal and it allows precise control of temperature gradients within the metal.

In this chapter, the thyristor power supplies suitable for these three methods of heat generation will be discussed.

15.1 Resistance Furnace Power Supplies

Furnaces using heating elements made of resistive materials are used for a wide variety of heating purposes in many industries; from paper drying to ceramics and from gas heating to metal annealing. Usually, many heating elements made of molybdenum, tungsten, tantalum, or graphite are connected together in series and in parallel to achieve the required power dissipation and to locate the heat in the required places. A wide variety of power ratings and voltages are therefore employed.

From the thyristor controller point of view, the main factors of importance are:

(a) All the resistance materials used have a wide variation of resistance across the temperature range over which they are used. In some materials, operating temperatures in excess of 1000 °C can result in 10 times the cold material resistance, occurring under rated furnace conditions.

(b) Can the elements be split up into a three-phase arrangement or is it essential that a single load resistance is used?

(c) The life of some heating elements may be significantly lengthened by reducing their rate of temperature change and keeping any repetitive temperature oscillations to a minimum.

In general, the main purpose fulfilled by thyristor control is to compensate for changes in the element resistance so as to ensure a consistent and controlled level of heat dissipation. They are also used to enable the working temperature to be precisely controlled irrespective of environmental, loading, or supply voltage changes. The accuracy of temperature control possible is limited only by the capabilities of the temperature-measuring method.

A.C. thyristor controllers are the most popular for resistance furnaces as, in general, mains-frequency operation is acceptable and the loads can be split up to form three-phase arrangements. For full understanding, reference should first be made to Chapter 3, where the principles of a.c. controllers are fully discussed. Resistance-furnace applications will use all of these principles depending only on the particular requirements of the furnace. Any of the circuits can be used and either phase control or integral cycle control can be employed.

Integral cycle control is more often possible in heating applications due to the comparatively long thermal time constants in the load, and so it is frequently used often in association with thyristor/diode circuits.

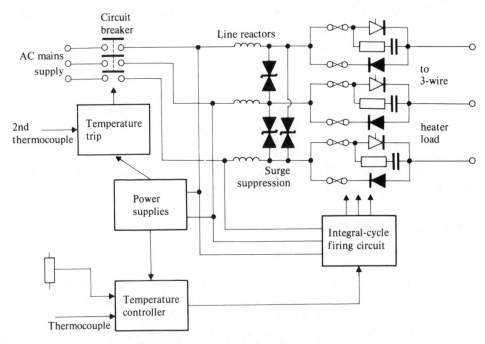

Fig. 15.1 A resistance furnace controller

In cases where the power pulsations of integral cycle control would cause either too great a load-temperature fluctuation or too high a supply-voltage flicker, then phase control would be employed using any of the methods previously discussed depending on the particular circumstances and requirements.

Some resistance materials, notably molybdenum and tungsten, have large temperature resistance coefficients so that when the furnace is cold the resistance elements will be of low resistance. The application of too much current under this condition may cause mechanical damage and so integral cycle control may not be practicable. Even when phase control is used it may still be necessary to apply a current-limiting system to avoid too high an initial starting surge of current and power.

All a.c. controllers alter the power by reducing the amount of the supply voltage used to supply the load. If at any time control is lost, one effect can be the application of full mains supply to the load. In the case of furnaces and heating elements, this can clearly be unacceptable as both the furnace and its contents may be destroyed. This condition may be caused by loss of the temperature-measuring signal or by a failure within the a.c. controller itself. The condition is not easy to detect as the application of full power for a significant time may be a normal part of the operating cycle. The only foolproof method is a furnace temperature measurement arranged to switch off the power completely, using a mains switch, whenever excessive temperature is detected.

A 200 kW A.C. Controlled Resistance Furnace Supply

Figure 15.1 demonstrates the practical application of these principles to control the heating of one zone of a multizone electric furnace with a power of approximately 200 kW.

In this particular circumstance, the load thermal time constant is relatively long and an integral cycle method of control is acceptable. The following points would have been used in deciding the design of the equipment:

1. The combination of integral cycle control and a three-wire load makes it possible to use a thyristor/diode circuit to economize on thyristors and firing circuits. The performance will be just as good as that obtainable using six thyristors.
2. An integral cycle firing circuit using a 50 Hz base for T, varying the number of ON cycles from 0 to 50, provides a suitable method of control giving 50 possible steps of output power which is adequate for the temperature accuracy required.
3. The thyristors are protected against short-circuit by fuses. Putting the fuses in series with each semiconductor rather than in the a.c. line allows a smaller fuse to be used so that it provides faster and better protection. The series inductances are included to reduce the prospective level of short-circuit current to within the fault capacity of the fuses.
4. The series inductances also help the RC snubber circuits across the thyristor to be effective in attenuating supply transient voltages.
5. The temperature controller receives both the required temperature setting and the measurement thermostat signals and provides an amplified signal to drive the firing circuit. The controller would also include a facility so that if the thermocouple measurement was lost it would turn off the thyristors to avoid furnace damage.

6. A further back-up furnace protection is provided by a separate high-set temperature measurement which would trip the a.c. supply switch if its temperature
setting was reached.

A.C.-to-D.C. thyristor convertors may be used to provide d.c. to particularly critical
heating elements where splitting into separate phases may not be possible or where
mains-frequency fluctuations may not be acceptable. In such cases, any of the naturally
commutated convertor circuits of Chapter 4 can be used and the equipment design
would be based on the principles already explained in this section.

15.2 Arc Furnace Supplies

Heat can be produced by drawing an electric arc between two conducting electrodes.
This principle is used in a range of metal-melting furnaces where usually the arc is
struck between the material to be melted and a separate consumable electrode. A.C.
and d.c. arcs can be used and very high currents are needed to generate the necessary
heat as the arc voltage drop is comparatively low (usually below 50 V).

Arc furnaces are used for general bulk melting of metals including scrap where an
efficient and consistent process is required, and for the production of very high-quality
metals; in these latter cases the melt may well take place in vacuum or an inert-gas
atmosphere.

Most arc furnaces are mechanically complicated and may involve a variety of electrically controlled components which may use thyristors. The furnace can usually be
tilted, and a variable-speed motor drive may be used for this purpose. The arc is struck
between the material to be melted and the moving electrode. This is adjusted to maintain the arc at the correct length during the melt; it is usually controlled by a motor
drive which again may use thyristors. Chapters 10 and 11 should be referred to for the
use of thyristors for these purposes.

In this section, the power supplies providing the necessary melting heat will be
considered and the use of thyristors for this purpose will be discussed.

Most large arc furnaces use mains-frequency power supplies and three electrodes
operating into a common pool of metal. The use of three phases ensures that an arc is
always present and can be maintained reasonably consistently although the supplied
currents are alternating and passing through zero twice per cycle. Furnaces using
single moving electrodes are mainly supplied with direct current to ensure a continuous
arc and to spread the power between the mains-supply phases.

The arc is usually struck by bringing the moving electrode into contact with the
metal to be melted. The moving electrode is then withdrawn to extend the arc and
controlled so as to maintain the arc. If the arc goes out, as it does regularly for many
reasons, the moving electrode is again brought into contact with the metal to restrike
the arc. The presence of such high-temperature arcs means that the electrodes melt
during operation and the electrode control system is designed to allow for this.

The arc voltage does not vary very much as its length is changed or the current flow
altered. The power dissipated in the furnace is therefore altered by controlling the level
of current flowing. The overall principles of control are usually: to control the current
flowing to establish the furnace heat and to control the electrodes, and to maintain the
maximum arc length consistent with satisfactory arc stability.

From the power supply point of view, therefore, the important features of arc
furnace loads are:

1. The load is short-circuited to establish an arc and this can occur frequently if arc stability is difficult to maintain.
2. Arc current levels are high and voltages relatively low.

The use of a.c. thyristor controllers in the supply to step-down transformers is therefore the most satisfactory and economical method for arc-furnace supplies.

Three-phase arc furnaces are most suitably supplied this way and Fig. 15.2 shows an appropriate circuit to use. The step-down transformer would be a high-reactance type or separate series reactors would be necessary to limit the initial level of short-circuit current.

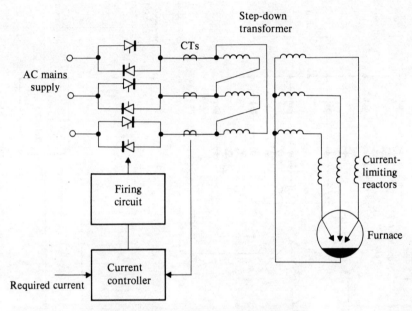

Fig. 15.2 A three-phase arc furnace controller

The thyristor a.c. controller would be phase-controlled and may use series and parallel operation of thyristors. The necessary requirements to feed a transformer would be included (see Section 3.6).

The controller would be current-controlled but this control may be complicated by the effect of load short-circuits and by the fact that the load phases effectively operate independently.

Three-phase furnaces are rarely thyristor controlled: tap change transformers and saturable reactors are more common.

D.C. arc furnace supplies. Arc furnaces supplied from a d.c. power source have a number of advantages over those supplied by a.c.:
1. A d.c. arc is more stable than an a.c. arc.
2. The single arc load can be equally shared between the a.c. supply phases under all loading conditions, whereas in a three-phase a.c. furnace the unstable arc can lead to temporary load imbalance between phases.
3. The total system can operate at a higher power factor as the circuit limiting reactance has no influence during steady operation. In the a.c. case, the reactance is a direct series a.c. one reducing the power factor at all times.

299

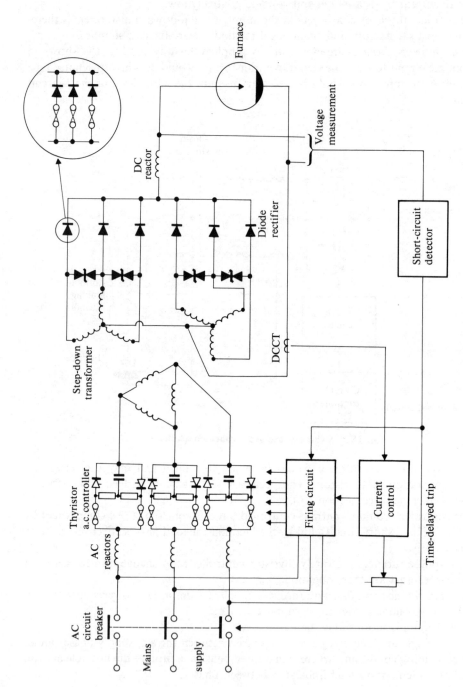

Fig. 15.3 A d.c. arc furnace controller

Furnace

Voltage measurement

DC reactor

Diode rectifier

Short-circuit detector

Step-down transformer

DCCT

Thyristor a.c. controller

AC reactors

Firing circuit

Current control

Time-delayed trip

AC circuit breaker

Mains

supply

Again, the arc will operate at low voltage with a high current and hence a step-down transformer with a rectifier on the high-current, low-voltage side is required. Thyristor control can be incorporated in two ways:

(a) A.C. controllers can be used in the primary circuit with diode rectifiers in the secondary.

(b) A secondary thyristor naturally commutated convertor can be used to carry out both control and rectification functions.

In most practical applications, either of these circuit arrangements can be used; the second, however, has the added advantage that inversion of energy from the d.c. side to the a.c. side can take place whereas with the a.c. controller, load energy can only flywheel through the diode rectifier.

In either case, a d.c. reactor is included to limit the rate of rise of current when a short-circuit occurs in the furnace so that the current control has time to prevent significant overcurrent occurring.

Fig. 15.4 A 20 000 A, 40 V forced air-cooled thyristor convertor for a vacuum arc remelting furnace for refining special alloy steels, in the final stages of test (GEC Rectifiers Ltd)

301

The practical design of d.c. arc furnace power supplies is illustrated by the example shown in Fig. 15.3, which shows a unit to supply a vacuum arc melting furnace with 15 000 A at an arc voltage of 25 V.

Whereas the diode rectifiers need to have a number of parallel diodes in each arm of the circuit to meet the load current requirement, the primary current is such that a single thyristor in each direct primary phase is all that is required.

The following points should be noted:

1. The d.c. air-cored reactor is included to keep the rate of rise of short-circuit current down.
2. The transformer uses a diametric star circuit and probably a five-limb core to give 120 degree diode conduction.
3. A.C. line reactors are included to limit the fault current if a misfire occurs in the a.c. controller.
4. Voltage protection is included in both a.c. controller and diode rectifier.
5. The short-circuit detector is included to trip the equipment out if prolonged operation on short-circuit occurs.

Fig. 15.5 A 1800 kW, 250 Hz induction furnace power supply using a 12-pulse input convertor on the left and the double inverter for the load on the right (Radyne Ltd)

15.3 Induction Furnace Supplies

If metal is surrounded by an a.c. electric coil, it will act like a transformer and current will circulate in the metal. Heat will be generated due to this current flowing through the resistance of the metal. The amount of heat generated will depend on the efficiency of flux coupling between the primary winding coil, the characteristics of the metal, and the frequency of the power supplied. The heat is generated within the metal being affected by the coil flux.

The principle is employed in a wide variety of furnaces for melting metals or heating them to consistent temperatures quickly. For melting furnaces, the coil will surround the crucible or a part of it; for component heating, the components may pass through or near to the heating coil.

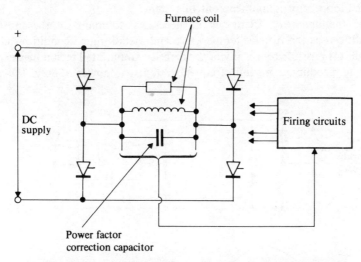

Fig. 15.6 A naturally commutated induction furnace supply

Again, the main concern in this section is the power supply to the heating coil rather than the other furnace auxiliary supplies or drives, which are considered elsewhere.

Load power factor. The furnace coil when transferring heat operates like a short-circuited transformer and it will hence operate at a low power factor. The inductance and resistance of the load may change during the heating process and so the circuit power factor may change. It is therefore normal to connect capacitors with the coil and these may be variable to maintain a high power factor load on the power supply equipment, as the inductance of the load coil changes.

Single-phase load. A single load coil is normally employed and this requires a single-phase a.c. supply.

Coil frequency. The optimum operating frequency depends on many factors. The effective metal resistance will increase with frequency, the depth of penetration of the flux, and therefore the heat will reduce with frequency; when melting metals, the degree of automatic stirring will depend on the frequency of operation. Although there are many mains-frequency furnaces in operation, due to the convenience of power supplies, there is an increasing move towards higher operating frequencies. Furnaces operating at up to 500 kHz are in operation but the more regular range is between 500 Hz and 50 kHz.

Mains-frequency induction furnace supplies normally use conventional contactor and variable transformer methods of control, thyristors do not seem to have been used up to the present. Perhaps this is an area where thyristors have yet to make an impact.

Medium-frequency induction furnace power supplies operating in the range from 500 Hz to 10 kHz are now a very significant area of application for thyristors. A static thyristor power supply is able to:

(a) Convert the three-phase mains supply into single-phase while maintaining balanced currents in the mains supply.
(b) Provide the most suitable frequency to enable the furnace to be designed for operation under optimum metallurgical and efficiency conditions.
(c) Vary the level of power fed to the furnace at will. It can be incorporated in any closed loop or programmed control system.
(d) Alter the operating frequency as necessary to maintain the most suitable conditions as the furnace temperature and metallurgical conditions change.

Although it is possible to use any of the forced-commutated techniques explained in Chapter 5 to produce a medium-frequency thyristor power supply, the particular

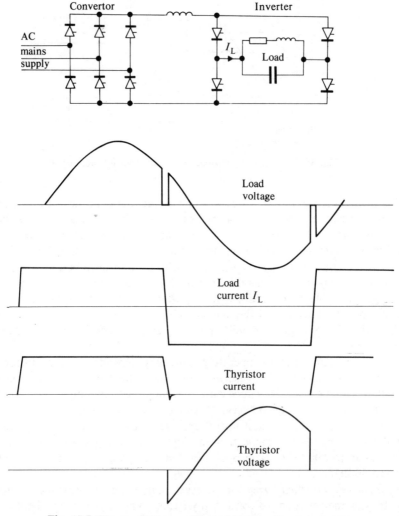

Fig. 15.7 The parallel-compensated induction furnace circuit

304

conditions of induction furnaces enable a simpler and less costly inverter method to be used. Any power-factor-corrected induction furnace load will have a particular natural resonant frequency, and an ability to store energy temporarily. These facts make it possible to use a naturally commutated inverter circuit using the load itself to assist in the commutation process. For example, the arrangement of Fig. 15.6 will operate very successfully at or near to the resonant frequency of the load as long as the thyristor firing points are made dependent on the load voltage waveform. No additional commutating components are needed.

In practical applications, two different thyristor circuit arrangements are in use for induction furnaces.

The current-fed inverter circuit of Fig. 15.7 is used when the load coil is power-factor compensated with a parallel-connected capacitor. The series d.c. reactor maintains the d.c. current constant. The power is altered by controlling the input convertor to vary the d.c. voltage and hence the output voltage. The inverter thyristors are each fired for 180 degrees of the output cycle and the output frequency is dictated by the resonant frequency of the load itself.

In this circuit, the load voltage will be sinusoidal and the inverter current will be a square wave due to the effect of the d.c. choke. A large resonant sinusoidal current will circulate between the capacitor and the load coil. To ensure satisfactory commutation between the thyristors, the firing point must be sufficiently before the load voltage zero

Fig. 15.8 A 1000 kW, 250 Hz induction furnace power supply for a parallel-compensated load showing the liquid-cooled inverter on the right and the d.c. reactor next to it (Radyne Ltd)

at all times. This can be guaranteed as long as the load-operating frequency does not change quickly. If the thyristors are fired too late, commutation will not occur and a short-circuit fault will be produced through the inverter. Protection will be needed to cut off this fault current (see the paragraphs on inversion failure in Section 6.5).

As can be seen from the waveforms in Fig. 15.7, the thyristors are not exposed to high dv/dt conditions or excessive peak voltages. The current level is controlled and ripple is minimized by the d.c. choke. The initial switch-on di/dt can be controlled by small inductances and the main part of the current-rise period is controlled by the commutating inductance in the output cables, etc. As these circuits are often operated at high frequency, turn-off times may be very short and circuit stray inductances can have a considerable effect. The mechanical design has to be very carefully considered to ensure all conditions are within the thyristor capabilities.

The voltage-fed inverter of Fig. 15.9 is an alternative arrangement used when the load power factor is compensated by series capacitors. In this case, the d.c. capacitor keeps the d.c. voltage constant and the current into the inverter is allowed to change at will. The d.c. reactor is now much smaller than in the previous case and is used to prevent the high output current ripple from flowing in the input rectifier. The load current now flows through the inverter and the load voltage across the furnace depends on the operating frequency compared with the resonant frequency. Slight change in the operating frequency will cause a large change in furnace voltage and therefore furnace current and power.

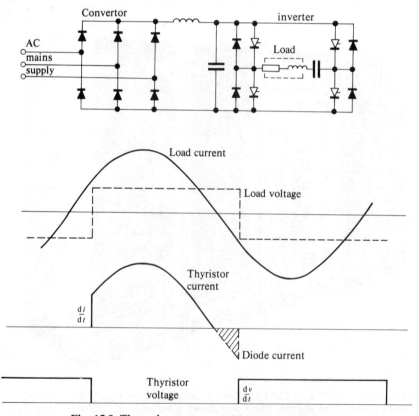

Fig. 15.9 The series-compensated induction furnace inverter

306

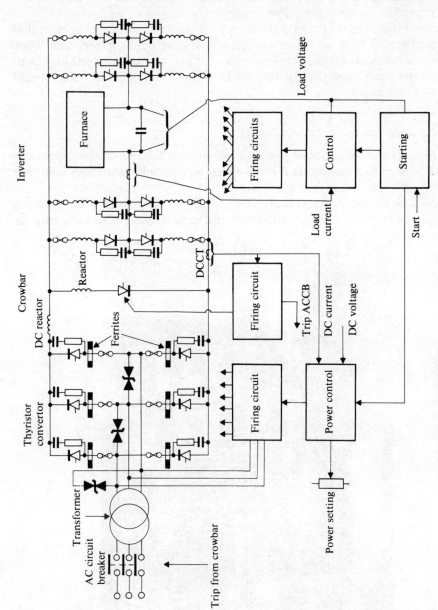

Fig. 15.10 A medium-frequency induction furnace inverter

There is consequently no need to control the d.c. voltage in this case and a diode input rectifier is adequate. The feedback diodes across the inverter thyristors allow the circuit to operate at other than unity power factor, feeding the reactive load current back into the d.c. capacitor. The furnace voltage can be many times the level of the d.c. voltage depending on the degree of resonance.

This circuit is less critical from the thyristor firing point of view: it can be controlled by the current zero point to ensure operation at leading power factor at all times. However, the thyristor conditions are more onerous as both high di/dt and high dv/dt conditions can occur. Also the thyristor has to turn off with only the diode forward voltage as a reverse bias.

A Practical Induction Furnace Power Supply

Figure 15.10 shows the complete power circuit suitable for a parallel-compensated induction furnace to demonstrate the overall design principles used. The following points should be particularly noted:

1. Protection against inversion failure is provided by a crowbar thyristor or thyristors. If an inversion failure is detected from a current measurement, the crowbar

Fig. 15.11 A 600 kW water-cooled rectifier/inverter power supply for induction heating and melting using a series-compensated load circuit (GEC Rectifiers Ltd)

is fired (to remove the fault current from the inverter thyristors) and the supply circuit-breaker tripped. The d.c. reactor limits the fault current while the breaker is tripping. In this way, the blowing of any of the circuit fuses can be prevented when inversion failure occurs.

2. Although a single thyristor per arm is sufficient for the input convertor, the inverter thyristor arms carry more current and two thyristors in parallel are needed in this case. Reactors are included in series with each thyristor to assist the sharing of the current.

3. Input convertor voltage protection is provided by varistors across the a.c. lines and RC snubber circuits. Series ferrite cores limit the level of dv/dt applied to the thyristors.

4. A starting circuit is required to 'kick' the load into resonance initially and ensure a gradual build-up of current.

15.4 References

1. P. Richardson, 'Thyristors for vacuum arc melting', *Electrical Review*, Aug. 1964.
2. N. Bardahl, 'Power supplies for vacuum arc melting plants', *Siemens Review*, **40**, 5, 233–237, 1973.
3. *Brown Boveri Review*, **53**, Baden, Oct. 1966.
4. K. Thorborg, 'A three-phase inverter with reactive power control', *IEEE*, **1A-9**, 4, 473–481, July 1973.
5. J. P. Cordier, 'Medium-frequency inverters for induction heating', *IEE Conference Publication 154*, 62–65, Sept. 1977.
6. E. J. Davies and P. G. Simpson, *Induction Heating Handbook*, McGraw-Hill, London, 1979.

16. Miscellaneous Applications

Having decided to group like applications together in the preceding chapters, we are left with a variety of thyristor uses which do not easily fit into the chosen groups. These are therefore dealt with briefly in this chapter so as to complete the present-day picture.

16.1 Static Switching by Thyristors

All thyristors are static switches and all the applications previously dealt with use them as such. This section is intended to deal with those cases where the thyristors are used for relatively long periods in either the fully ON or the fully OFF states, to carry out those duties done by electromagnetic devices such as relays, contactors, and circuit breakers.

Compared with mechanical switches thyristors have many advantages, namely:
(a) They are fully static with no moving parts.
(b) No arc is produced when they are opened.
(c) They are very fast in operation.
(d) They are silent and produce no mechanical vibrations or shock when being operated. They are also unaffected by vibration or shock applied from elsewhere.
(e) They can withstand an infinite number of operations and have an unlimited life.
(f) The local environment does not directly affect their ability to switch the power; they can be used in dangerous and explosive situations safely.
(g) Their speed and control accuracy makes it possible to switch them at precise times, e.g., point-on-wave switching can be used to limit asymmetrical current flow.

The only limitations to their use as static switches are:
1. There is no mechanical gap when they are opened and protective circuits across the thyristors may still allow small leakage currents to flow.
2. The voltage drop across the contacts when the switch is closed will be significantly higher than that of a mechanical contact. The switch losses are therefore higher and extra cooling will be required.
3. They can be relatively expensive compared to the cheap, mass-produced electro-mechanical equivalent.

A.C. switches using natural commutation can use a variety of circuit arrangements, as shown in Fig. 16.1. The thyristors are always used in either the fully ON or fully OFF state and they turn off at the natural circuit current zeros when the gate signals are removed. If required, the point of turn-on can be precisely chosen to optimize the switching performance.

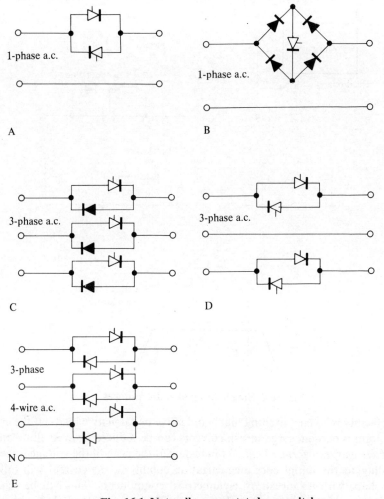

A

B

C

D

E

Fig. 16.1 Naturally commutated a.c. switches

Single-phase switches will usually use circuit A of Fig. 16.1; B can be useful as only one thyristor is involved but the current always has to pass through three semiconductors. Three-phase, three-wire equipment may use circuits C, D, or E but a four-wire supply must use circuit E in order to cut off the circuit current completely.

Although the principles explained in Chapter 8 can be used to fire static switch thyristors, simple arrangements as shown in Fig. 16.2 are possible. Reed relays can be used to obtain the necessary isolation and switching to avoid pulse transformers, and the a.c. anode supply can be used to provide the gate power to avoid additional circuits. The use of the main anode voltage is convenient, but the circuit components have to be carefully chosen to ensure early firing in each half-cycle as well as to limit the peak gate current; it is also difficult to obtain a sufficient initial gate pulse to produce good thyristor di/dt performance. The figure indicates some possible circuits with the gate current waveforms achievable.

Accurate control of the point of turn-on can be achieved, if required, so that the current can commence at any point in the mains-frequency cycle. The most frequent

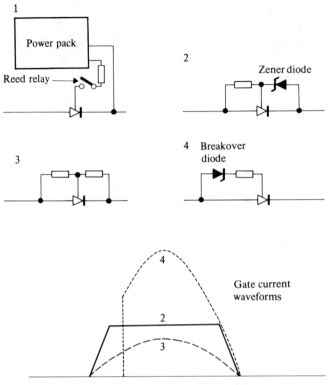

Fig. 16.2 Simple firing of static switches

use of this facility is when switching highly inductive or capacitive loads; if the correct switch-on point is chosen, surge inrush currents can be reduced or even eliminated.

If an *inductive* or *transformer load* is switched on at the peak of the voltage waveform corresponding to the initial core magnetization condition, the current will follow a sinusoidal shape with no inrush or asymmetrical components. This can be achieved satisfactorily with single-phase or with three-phase, four-wire loads but with three-phase, three-wire applications it is not possible to switch all phases at their optimum points and some compromise is necessary.

Two methods can be used to switch *capacitor loads*; phase control can be employed to allow the current to rise smoothly over an initial starting period; or instantaneous switching without inrush or asymmetry can be achieved if the switches are closed when the supply voltage equals the initial capacitor charge voltage. With this latter method, switch-on and switch-off need to be co-ordinated to ensure correct polarities.

These naturally commutated switches will always revert to the OFF-state at the thyristor current zero, and once current flow has been initiated the magnitude of the current is decided by the remainder of the power circuit. When switch-off is required before the current zero, forced commutation may be applied and this is referred to later in this section.

D.C. load switching using natural commutation. D.C. loads can be switched on and off using simple thyristor rectifying circuits as long as the power supply comes from the a.c. mains. Any of the rectifying circuits explained in Chapter 4 can be used with or without the phase control facility.

Fig. 16.3 A pulsed power supply using thyristor switches to discharge large capacitors into a load circuit to provide 50 kA for 160 microseconds, four times per second (NEI Electronics Limited)

D.C. switches using forced commutation. Current zeros do not occur naturally in d.c. circuits and circuit opening can only be achieved by forced commutation. Any of the chopper power circuits explained in Chapter 5 can be used for this purpose with a simpler gating system dictated by the required speed and frequency of switching. As with all forced-commutated circuits, the switch will have a definite limit on the maximum current which can be turned off and this will have been decided at the design stage.

It will be noted from Chapter 5 that all of these circuits include flywheel diodes to allow the load energy to be removed slowly on switch-off. If either polarity of d.c. current is required to be switched statically, then two antiparallel switches will be needed with thyristors to carry out the flywheeling duty.

A.C. switches can be forced-commutated to achieve fast and precise switch-off but special consideration has to be given to the dissipation of the stored energy in the load or else very high voltages will occur across the switches. The methods referred to in Section 12.2 can be employed.

16.2 Static Compensators for Power Systems

The increased use, in recent years, of electric arc furnaces and other loads which disturb power-system voltages has led to the development of static voltage compensating devices capable of quickly controlling the power system reactive kVA to maintain reasonably constant power-system voltages. These are based on the use of switched capacitors and variable reactors.

The principle in all of these static compensators is to allow a varying compensator current to flow so that the sum of load current and compensator current remains constant at all times, i.e., the supply current to the load and its parallel-connected compensator will remain sensibly constant. The compensator therefore usually has to take a leading (capacitive) current and it varies this by having more capacitance in parallel with a variable reactor.

Thyristors are used for this application in one of three ways:

(a) As a.c. static switches to quickly switch capacitors on and off the power system.

(b) As phase-controlled a.c. controllers to regulate the current in the large reactors, to compensate for load reactive kVA swings.

(c) As rectifying units to control the excitation current to saturable reactors and transductors connected to the power system.

As mentioned already, when *thyristors are used to switch capacitors*, the surge inrush current on switching can be minimized if at the point of switching the instantaneous

Fig. 16.4 A thyristor switch used to control two 6-MVAR capacitor banks (ASEA Ltd)

supply voltage equals the initial charge voltage on the capacitors. It is essential to provide means of achieving this to avoid the very large surge currents which could occur, damaging the thyristors. Arrangements must be made either to precharge the capacitors to a predetermined voltage from a separate source or to maintain their charge while they are not connected to the power supply. Obviously, the protection of the thyristors against surge currents, di/dt, transient voltages, and dv/dt needs to be very carefully selected for this application and reference should be made to Chapter 6.

A.C. reactor current control by thyristors using a.c. controllers, phase-controlled, provides a convenient way of achieving fast, controllable reactive current. The operating principles have already been established in Chapter 3, and Figs 3.6 and 3.7 show the performance achievable from such an arrangement. Reduction in reactor current will bring an increase in its harmonic components and these will need to be filtered out by the compensator.

In both capacitor switching and reactor control, the thyristors will be directly connected to the power system, maybe at a relatively high voltage. Series connection of thyristors is very likely and the principles described in Chapter 7 would then apply.

In some compensator designs, variable reactors use saturable reactor or transductor principles in which the effective impedance of the reactor varies as the current in a d.c. control winding is changed. Thyristors are used to provide and control such d.c. excitation and their design will be fully based on the principles outlined in Chapter 12, which should be referred to.

16.3 High-voltage D.C. Power Transmission (HVDC)

In recent years, it has been found to be economic to transmit large amounts of power over long distances or across water by means of high-voltage d.c. rather than multi-phase a.c. The savings in cable costs can pay for the necessary conversion equipment required to connect the transmission system into the a.c. power systems at either end. Many hundreds of megawatts of power are now transmitted by this method, across the English Channel, between the two islands of New Zealand, and across the vast continents of America and Russia, and at many other locations. This method also has additional very important operational benefits in that the two interconnected systems can be at different frequencies and voltages, they do not need to be synchronized together, and the d.c. interconnection does not increase the maximum fault currents in either a.c. system.

All of the initial HVDC installations used mercury arc valves in the conversion equipment, but now, with their improved capabilities and lower prices, all new designs incorporate thyristor convertors.

The a.c. power is converted into high-voltage d.c. at one end, transmitted along the d.c. cables, and then converted back to a.c. at the receiving end. Both conversion stations use naturally commutated convertors, one station operating in the rectifying mode and the other in inversion. The power can usually be transmitted either way and so both stations can operate in the rectification or inversion modes. Very high powers (over 100 megawatts per installation) at very high voltages (between 100 and 200 kV) are used and the convertors have to work at these levels. As they are part of the large national and international electricity generation and supply networks, extremely high reliability is expected of the d.c. transmission schemes and of the convertor stations; they have to be capable of accepting major system fault conditions and must be able to operate continuously for many years.

Three-phase bridge circuits are universally used in combination to produce 12- or 24-pulse conversion. Large a.c. filters are used to minimize the flow of harmonic currents into the a.c. networks. Figure 16.5 shows a typical total system, showing fault limitation by d.c. reactors and including bypass switches to allow convertor maintenance. Each of the thyristor switches shown in this diagram consists of a very large number of thyristors in series and probably a few strings of thyristors connected in parallel.

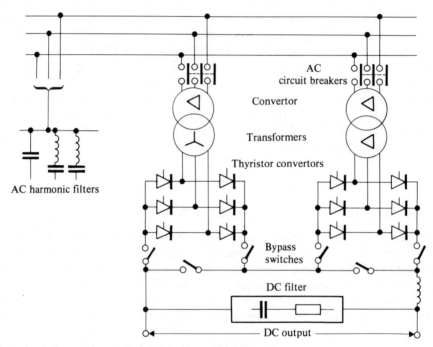

Fig. 16.5 An HVDC thyristor convertor

Series operation of thyristors. Often, with more than 100 thyristors connected in series, this application poses the ultimate in series operation. The principles explained in Chapter 7 are followed but the use of so many thyristors at such high voltages means that the design of voltage-sharing circuits needs extremely careful consideration to ensure that each and every thyristor is always used within its rating capabilities. Firing so many series-connected thyristors, all at different potentials to earth, is particularly difficult and many methods have been tried. High-voltage isolation is required on every thyristor gating circuit and all the thyristors in a string need to be fired simultaneously. The use of fibre-optic light guides seems to be gaining preference for this purpose but the amount of firing power transmitted by these is limited and individual power amplifiers requiring isolated power supplies are needed with every thyristor. With so many thyristors and firing and protection components, it is inevitable that some will fail and cause thyristor failure and so strings always include a percentage of spare series

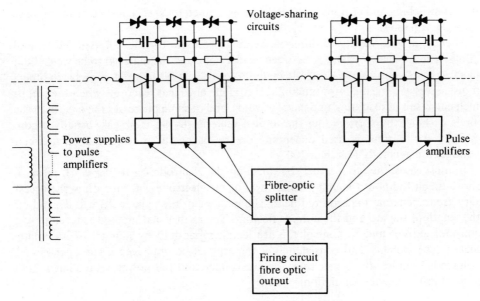

Fig. 16.6 A typical HVDC series thyristor string

thyristors and the system is designed to operate with these failed, i.e., short-circuit. Figure 16.6 shows the circuit of a typical thyristor valve suitable for HVDC use.

Parallel operation of thyristor strings is often needed and the principle described in Chapter 7 can be used. They have to be designed to take into account the possibility of failed thyristors in the strings. In some cases, it may be found more practical to use pairs of selected thyristors in parallel using the same voltage-sharing networks for both.

Overcurrent protection against inversion failure and system faults has to be carried out using phase control and a.c. circuit breakers: fuses on such large installations are completely impractical and unacceptable. Hence transformer and d.c. circuit reactance is included to limit the value and rate of rise of fault current and the two convertor stations may be employed together to remove the fault.

The construction of thyristor valves and equipment is very special due to the influence of stray capacitances on the series voltage sharing and firing of such large series thyristor strings. The necessity for large clearances also affects the constructional design. Forced-air cooling, piped oil cooling, and oil immersion have all been used to date. It is fair to say that the constructional design of HVDC thyristor valves will only stabilize when significant operational experience has been obtained.

16.4 Arc Welding

Electric arc welding of metals is another area where control plays a big part in ensuring a high-quality result. Although welding experts may disagree about the precise chemical reactions which take place during welding, they are unanimous in their belief that the most satisfactory welds are produced by controlling the physical and electrical conditions precisely. Thyristors are playing an increasing part in improving welding processes in both manual and automatic equipment. They provide a means of switching the current on and off, or maintaining a specific level of current, as well as enabling

317

on–off switching and current levels to be programmed to a set sequence or in response to other variables.

There is a wide variety of different welding processes for the different metals and alloys. The arc is always struck between an electrode and the material to be welded but in some cases consumable electrode material forms part of the weld, whereas in others it just serves as a means of producing the arc. The chemical reactions when the metals melt can result in oxidation and gaseous voids, and in some processes the oxygen in the air is excluded by surrounding the molten material by an inert gas, usually argon. A.C. or d.c. current is used depending on the particular process and open-circuit voltages are generally less than 100 V.

In most cases, the arc is struck by touching the electrode on to the work piece to short-circuit the power source; withdrawal of the electrode will then draw the necessary arc to generate the required heat. The amount of heat produced will depend on the length of the arc and the current flowing. The most usual method is to employ a constant current and to control the arc length separately by manual or automatic means. The stability and consistency of the arc can be improved if the open-circuit voltage is significantly higher than the arc voltage and the power source has a high natural instantaneous regulation.

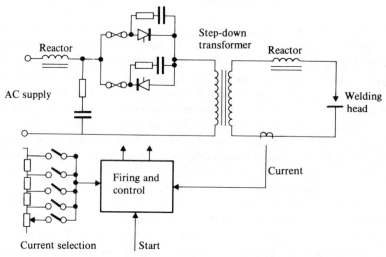

Fig. 16.7 A primary controlled a.c. welding unit

Seam welding requires a significant period of arc operation as the welder traverses the necessary distance with the current being switched on and off and controlled during the weld. Spot welding requires repetitive switching of the current. Argon arc welding of aluminium particularly benefits by the current being increased and reduced gradually at the start and finish of the weld. Some methods use repetitive changes from one level of current to another.

Except for very special circumstances, naturally commutated thyristor arrangements are employed, using either a.c. controllers or rectifying circuits. The thyristors may be used in a purely switching mode, with other means of selecting the level of current or, alternatively, phase control of the thyristors enables them to control as well as switch

318

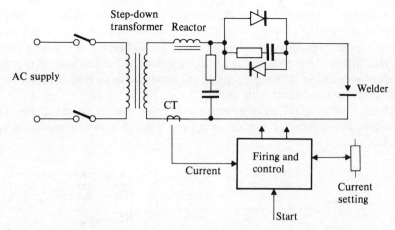

Fig. 16.8 An a.c. welder with secondary side control

the current. The following are a few examples of electrical circuits used for thyristor-controlled welding equipments.

Figure 16.7 shows an a.c. arc welder using control of the primary side of the step-down transformer. The secondary iron-cored reactor is used to limit the level of short-circuit current and to help stabilize the arc. The unit is started by releasing the inhibit on the firing pulses and stopped by re-imposing the inhibit signal. Closed-loop current control is used based on an actual measurement of arc current. Individual thyristor fuses are required to protect against misfiring and the resulting transformer saturation (see Section 3.6) and the firing circuit will have to include arrangements to avoid inrush current by initial point-on-wave pulsing or by phase control to gradually increase the voltage applied to the transformer.

For the reasons explained in Sections 3.6 and 16.1, primary switching is more difficult than the secondary control method shown in Fig. 16.8 which is equally effective. In this case, the reactor is included for the same reason as in Fig. 16.7 but now it can also be used to limit the thyristor current under fault conditions and to assist in

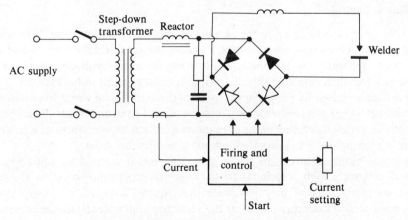

Fig. 16.9 A single-phase d.c. welder

319

surge-voltage suppression. As a result, thyristor fuses are unnecessary, an inverse time overcurrent trip on the supply switch being adequate. In both of these a.c. controller examples, closed-loop current control has been shown because at constant delay angle the current will vary due to both the arc voltage level and the effective power factor of the load circuit (see Fig. 3.7). A d.c. arc can be produced from both the above diagrams just by rectifying the output with diodes.

However, a more usual arrangement would be to use the circuit of Fig. 16.9, the single-phase, half-controlled bridge giving full control with the minimum of semi-conductors.

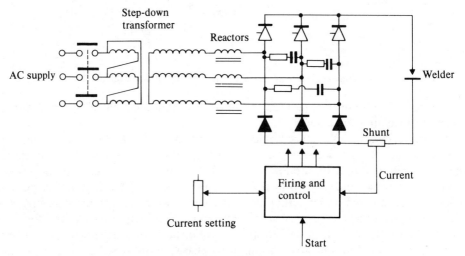

Fig. 16.10 A three-phase d.c. welder

A higher-powered d.c. arc welder may use a three-phase, half-controlled bridge, as in Fig. 16.10. The a.c. reactors are used to limit the fault current and help in thyristor protection. As a.c. current is not now a true guide to arc current, a d.c. shunt is shown as the means of measuring current.

16.5 Ripple Control

This is the term used to describe the process of control communication between two distant points via the mains power cables. It is possible to control the operation of items of electrical apparatus by temporarily distorting the mains voltage waveform in a specific way and then detecting this distortion at another point in the network.

The principle is used by many supply utilities throughout the world to switch street lights and heating appliances remotely from the central control stations. It can be used selectively to switch individual items of plant or to switch all appliances of a particular type or in a particular area – numerous control possibilities exist.

The name 'ripple control' originates from the initial method of achieving this. Bursts of relatively high sinusoidal frequencies are superimposed on to the mains voltage waveform so that they penetrate the required area of the power system. Frequency-selective detectors placed at the receiving appliance detect the presence of the high-frequency distortion and this is used to initiate a control or switching function.

320

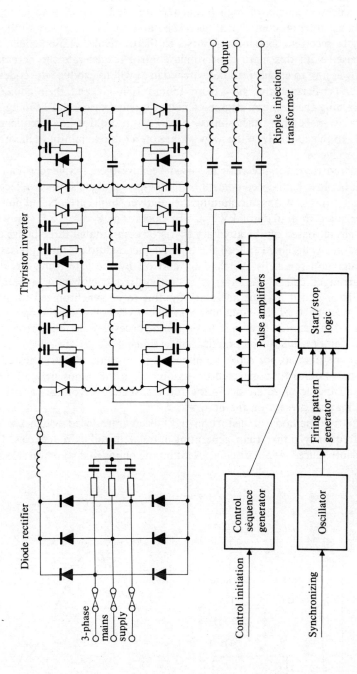

Fig. 16.11 High-frequency ripple control generator

321

Programmed sequences of bursts of high frequency are used according to complex codes to enable many different control actions to be initiated. The receivers would be programmed only to receive a sequence of bursts to the particular chosen code.

Thyristors are used with this method of ripple control to generate the necessary high-frequency power and to enable it to be switched in at will to produce the codes of high-frequency bursts. Frequencies vary from 150 to 1000 Hz and their choice is dependent on obtaining the required degree of network penetration and keeping the level of interference signals from other sources below a threshold value. Frequencies not related directly to the 50/60 Hz of the network are preferable to minimize incorrect detection by the receivers.

Forced-commutated thyristor inverters are used because their frequencies can be chosen at will and because high-speed control from low-power signals can be effected. They also provide a suitable means of obtaining the relatively high currents and powers required; units of many hundreds of kVA are in operation. Figure 16.11 shows a suitable thyristor circuit based on the auxiliary thyristor-commutated three-phase d.c. link inverter. This unit is designed to feed the high frequency into all three phases of the network simultaneously and is switched on and off by the gate firing circuitry according to prearranged codes. The inverter operating frequency would be decided by the static oscillator and it may be necessary for this to be synchronized to other inverters feeding other parts of the same network. The inverter circuit, the operation of which is described in detail in Section 5.6, shows the necessary auxiliary protective snubber and di/dt components for its practical operation.

The choice of thyristors and protective components is, in this instance, affected by the fact that the unit is directly connected on its output to the mains network. The inverter has to be capable of safely accepting the transient overvoltages and fault conditions which may be present on the network.

Recently, alternative methods of distortion have been introduced which use the 50/60 Hz mains frequency rather than generating unrelated audio frequencies. If a small distortion is introduced, at a particular point on the mains sine wave, on selected

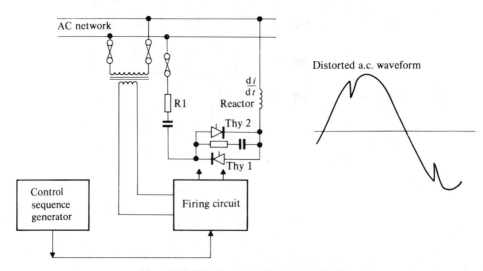

Fig. 16.12 Ripple control by waveform distortion

322

cycles, a multiplicity of code patterns can be produced. Static detectors can detect these patterns without being affected by normal mains variation and distortion.

Figure 16.12 shows one method of using thyristors to generate the required distortion. The firing of thyristor 1 will cause a large current flow from the network to charge the capacitor; this will depress the network voltage. As the capacitor charges, the current will reduce and when it reaches the holding current the thyristor will go OFF, leaving the capacitor with a positive charge. The firing of thyristor 2 half a cycle later will reverse the charge as required. The firing circuit has a mains supply reference input to decide the point in the cycle to fire the thyristors. The control sequence code generation decides which cycles of the mains should receive or not receive a distortion pulse.

There are many alternative ways of using thyristors for this purpose, some using natural commutation and others forced-commutation switches. It should be noted that in the circuit shown the peak current will be controlled by R1, the crest working voltage across the thyristors will be twice the peak of the mains supply (due to the capacitor), and a di/dt reactor will be required to protect the thyristors on switch-on.

Fig. 16.13 A unit designed to replace mercury arc rectifiers in large convertor installations. It is a direct replacement for the tank and it contains all the necessary firing, protective, and cooling apparatus for the thyristors (GEC Industrial Controls Ltd)

16.6 Lamp Dimming

Reduction in the light output from lamps can be done by reducing the voltage applied to them. Thyristor control provides an efficient and fast method of controlling the voltage level from a very small initiating signal. These facilities are particularly important for stage and television studio lighting where fast switching between lighting levels may be required and many lamps may be sequentially controlled from a central programmer. In such instances, lighting powers of many kilowatts per lamp may be involved and thyristors, with their ability to alter the voltage level without significant power loss, are ideally suited.

Controllers for lamps are invariably single-phase a.c. controller units employing phase control to give smooth, flicker-free, variable light output. Although it is possible to control the lighting level from discharge lamps by this method, the need for starting and heater circuits means that it is rarely done. Most controlled lamp sources are filament lamps.

The dimming of small domestic lamps is usually achieved using triacs which are able to carry out the simple requirements in the most economic way at these sizes. Thyristor controllers could be used but they involve more components and are therefore restricted to the more powerful installations.

16.7 Regulating Transformers and Tap Changers

Conventional regulating transformers use electromechanical contacts and switches to alter the voltage ratio and these cause arcing, and contacts require routine replacement. Thyristors can be used to replace these contacts or to reduce their arcing and wear by carrying out the necessary switching action. In addition, they can be used with conventional tap changers as a smooth intertap control feature using phase control. However, perhaps due to the general reliability and economy of the electromechanical methods, thyristor use in this area has been restricted to a few special applications which are referred to in the references at the end of this chapter.

16.8 General A.C.-to-D.C. Supplies

Controllable d.c. supplies for any purpose can be obtained from fixed voltage and frequency a.c. supplies by using any of the naturally commutated arrangements described in Chapter 4. The maximum d.c. voltage will be fixed by the value of the a.c. voltage as given in Table 4.1; using phase control, the d.c. voltage can be controlled at any value up to this level. Input transformers are often included in such equipment to provide isolation between the d.c. and a.c. sides and to allow the optimum choice of voltages and normal operating power factor. It is usually sensible for generous voltage and current safety margins to be allowed unless the precise loading and supply conditions are known (see Chapters 2 and 6).

Applications of this type not already covered in previous chapters are:
1. *Ship degaussing*. Metal ships are normally magnetic and cause a change in the earth's magnetic field in the immediate locality. This change has been used during wartime to set off undersea mines. The most satisfactory method of combating this is to neutralize the ship by passing electric cables, carrying d.c. current, around the ship. The level of currents needs to be controlled to compensate

correctly for the ship's speed, direction, and position. Naturally commutated thyristor rectifiers can be used to provide and control the neutralizing current.

2. *Laboratory power supplies.* Where controlled and/or variable d.c. power supplies are required, naturally commutated thyristor units enable high powers to be obtained.

16.9 General D.C.-to-D.C. Supplies

Controllable d.c. supplies for any purpose can be obtained from fixed-voltage d.c. supplies by using the forced-commutated chopper circuits explained in Chapter 5. The maximum output d.c. voltage will be slightly less than the input d.c. voltage and full control up to this level is usually achieved by mark-space control at a relatively high operating frequency.

These convertors will usually have input filter components to provide a low-impedance path for the necessary high commutating currents, and output filters to give a smooth d.c. output voltage. Such units are used for isolated regulated laboratory power supplies and as efficient d.c. transformers on mobile installations in military vehicles, trains, and ships.

Fig. 16.14 Thyristors are used in this oil-immersed radio transmitter power supply, as an a.c. controller on the primary side of the transformer, four thyristors are connected directly in series (NEI Electronics Ltd)

16.10 References

1. B. Feltbower, 'Thyristor contactors', *IEE Conference Publication 53*, 448–464, May 1969.
2. T. H. Lee, H. N. Schneider, and C. H. Titus, 'Static switches for use in power systems and thermonuclear fusion research systems', *IEE Conference Publication 123*, 234–240, Dec. 1974.
3. H. Frank and B. Landstrom, 'Power factor correction with thyristor controlled capacitors', *ASEA Journal*, **44**, 6, 180–184, 1971.
4. J. J. Weaver, A. M. Eccles, and W. O. Kelham, 'Development of a thyristor valve for HVDC transmission', *IEE Conference Publication 53*, 339–346, May 1969.
5. J. A. Dorrat, 'Arc welding', *Proc. IEE*, **113**, 2, 302–314, Feb. 1966.
6. G. A. Smith and M. J. Brown, 'An inverter power source for welding', *IEE Conference Publication 154*, 58–61, Sept. 1977.
7. W. C. Kidd, 'Development, design and use of ripple control', *Proc. IEE*, **122**, 10R, 993–1008, 1975.
8. A. J. Baggott, 'The use of thyristors to modify power system waveshapes for tele-control purposes', *IEE Conference Publication 53*, 488–497, May 1969.
9. M. E. Roberts and W. G. Ashman, 'A thyristor-assisted mechanical on-load tapchanger', *IEE Conference Publication 53*, 185–192, May 1969.

PART III

Measurement and Testing with Thyristors

In this final part, a practical approach to measuring, testing, and fault finding in thyristor equipments is explained. It is based on many years of successful experiences in this field. The thyristor is a static non-linear switching device and as such it produces special problems in this area. This part should be of particular interest to all those engineers engaged in installing, commissioning, or operating thyristor equipment.

17. Measuring Electrical Parameters in Thyristor Equipment

Electrical measurements on thyristor circuits are difficult to make accurately and great care is needed if worthwhile results are to be obtained. This is partly due to the unusual voltage and current waveforms which contain relatively large amounts of harmonics. This makes accurate measurement of even the simplest parameters difficult.

In addition, the sensitivity of thyristors to high-speed effects leads to very precise measurement being necessary. Transient voltages even of nanosecond duration can be damaging and rate of change of current and voltage need to be confirmed if reliable thyristor operation is to be guaranteed. Measurement of these fast-changing parameters is particularly challenging and it requires the most capable of oscilloscopes or the use of specially designed testing installations.

To make matters even more complicated, thyristor circuits are usually controllable and there are many conditions of operation, each with different magnitudes and waveforms of the important parameters. Often the worst-case condition needs to be selected for measurement and this may not be a simple choice.

A large part of the problem is caused by the complex waveforms which exist, and incorrect measurements can be the result of a number of factors:

1. *Calibration* of most instruments is carried out under specific conditions, for example, a.c. instruments are calibrated with sinusoidal waveforms and d.c. ones with smooth direct current flowing. These ideal conditions rarely exist in thyristor circuits.
2. *The type of instrument* being used will have an important effect on the measurement. Some will ignore the harmonics while others will respond to them by differing degrees. Some will take full account of all the harmonic content.
3. *The quality of measurement transducers* such as shunts, current or voltage transformers will affect the accuracy. Their effect will be particularly important where high-speed oscillographic measurements are required. The output waveform from the transducer may differ from that of the parameter being measured.
4. *Electronic-fed instruments* will usually be designed to accept conventional waveforms and their input circuit may saturate if a high peak value occurs in the waveform of the measured parameter.

It is the purpose of this chapter to help in making the correct choice of measuring instrument for use with all thyristor circuits.

17.1 Current Measurements

Figure 17.1 shows a selection of the current waveforms occurring in practical thyristor circuits, ignoring high-speed transient effects. These demonstrate the very wide variety of possible waveshapes and show the relatively high values of harmonics present.

The measurements most often needed are the *RMS values* of the circuit currents to assess the thermal conditions of busbars, cables, fuses, and resistive elements of the circuit, and *mean values* to confirm the ratings of semiconductor components and batteries. The temperature of all resistive circuit components will be directly dependent on the RMS current flowing through them and this value will take full account of the harmonics present. Although the forward voltage drop of semiconductor devices will contain a resistive component, the dominating influence on power losses is the mean value of the current flowing through them and this is a useful parameter to measure in order to confirm the ratings of such devices against manufacturers' stated information.

A.C. Current – RMS Measurements

Distorted a.c. currents can only be satisfactorily measured using thermal or dynamo-meter-type instruments or meters based on these principles. *Moving-iron ammeters* may not give accurate or consistent results due to the varying eddy-current effects in the iron caused by the harmonic components. In addition, they are calibrated assuming a sinusoidal waveform of current with a form factor of 1·11.

Rectifier-type moving-coil indicators which are widely used in multimeters are also unable to give satisfactory measurements of the RMS values of distorted current waveforms. They usually indicate the mean value of the rectified current multiplied by the assumed form factor of 1·11. However, they do give this specific and consistent measurement, which can be useful for comparison of theoretical and measured values of mean current.

The most satisfactory and economic meters for RMS a.c. current measurements are those based on thermal effects. The *hot-wire ammeter* uses the expansion of a taut wire to provide the deflection and this is a true indication of the heating effect or RMS value of the current irrespective of waveform. Other *thermal ammeters* use a thermo-couple, measuring the temperature of a resistance shunt, to again give a true indication of the RMS value. The rather more expensive and delicate dynamometer-type am-meters, designed mainly for laboratory use, use no iron in their moving parts and the current is passed through both a fixed and moving coil. The deflection is proportional to the true RMS value of the current, even with severe waveform distortion.

Shunts and current transformers can be used satisfactorily for a.c. current measure-ments to extend the range of the instruments. If the current has a d.c. component, i.e., the positive and negative half-cycles do not enclose equal areas, current transformers may saturate and give inaccurate and misleading results.

An increasing number of instruments now use electronic measurement circuitry coupled to either a moving-coil meter or digital readout. When using these to measure a.c. currents, their specifications must be studied carefully. Most of them rectify a.c. measurements and display a mean value of the result, possibly multiplied by a 1·11 form factor. If the measured signal has a high peak-to-mean ratio, the instrument must be capable of measuring the peak value, without saturating the electronic circuits.

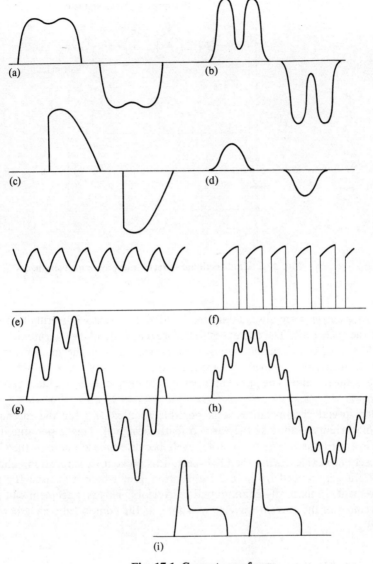

Fig. 17.1 Current waveforms

If there is any doubt about the accuracy of current measurements then an oscilloscope should be used to plot the waveform; RMS and mean values can then be worked out from this.

D.C. Current – Mean Measurements

These measurements can be accurately made by using moving-coil meters or instruments which give the average value of the signal being measured. These will normally take the harmonics fully into account. If an electronic instrument is being used, it must be capable of accepting and reading the peak value of the signal. Correctly chosen transducer-type d.c. current transformers can be used in d.c. current measurements and their outputs will be suitable for normal measurement purposes.

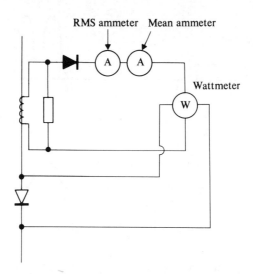

RMS ammeter   Mean ammeter

Wattmeter

Fig. 17.2 Unidirectional current and power measurements

Thyristor currents are always unidirectional and current will normally only flow for part of the cycle time. The current is therefore d.c. with a large harmonic component. The RMS value of the current can only be measured using thermal or dynamometer-type instruments (see above) and moving-coil instruments can be used to find the average or mean value. The peak value can be obtained only by oscillographic measurement.

Under special circumstances it is possible to use CT's for the measurement of thyristor currents as long as they are correctly designed. This is possible if the OFF-period is a substantial part of the total cycle because the iron core of the CT must be fully reset each cycle during the OFF-period to prevent its saturation. The circuit of Fig. 17.2 is reproduced from IEC Publication 146, where it is used for power-loss measurements in naturally commutated convertors. This arrangement can give a true measurement of the current waveform as long as the components have been correctly selected.

17.2 Voltage Measurements

Figure 17.3 gives a sample of the many voltage waveforms (excluding transient effects) which occur regularly in thyristor circuits.

As with current, RMS and mean measurements can only be made satisfactorily with thermal or dynamometer instruments, and moving-coil meters respectively. Usually it is the mean value or the value of the fundamental components of an a.c. wave which will be required. In this latter case, a filter to remove the harmonics from the measurement can be used so that sinusoidally calibrated instruments can be used. Such a filter is unnecessary for d.c. mean measurements as the meter mechanical movement will only respond to the average value.

In practice, however, the most important voltage measurement required in thyristor circuits is the peak value of the voltage. Figure 2.10 shows a practical voltage waveform including its transient components. Accurate measurement of the peak values can only be obtained by oscillographic measurements.

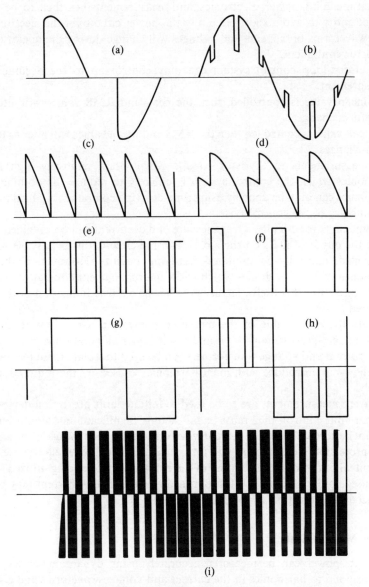

Fig. 17.3 Voltage waveforms

17.3 Measurements for Control Feedback Signals

Most thyristor circuits will include some current or voltage measurements to use in the closed-loop control scheme for overall equipment control. This usually means output currents and voltages and the measurement circuits may need to be isolated from the power circuit to avoid high-voltage connections to the electronics. The following points need to be considered in respect of these measurements:

1. If isolating components are not used, then the electronics will be directly connected to the power circuit via the measurement circuit. The complete electrical circuit including power, electronics, and measurements has then to be designed as one entity to avoid short-circuiting the power circuit via the electronics.
2. The waveforms of currents and voltages will change during the operation of the thyristor equipment.
3. The closed-loop control system can only control up to the accuracy of the measurement.
4. If a mean value is controlled, then the peak and RMS values will alter as the waveform changes.
5. If a peak value is controlled then the RMS and mean values will alter as the waveform changes.
6. All measurements in thyristor circuits will contain relatively high levels of harmonics which the control system is unlikely to require. Smoothing out the harmonics can only be done by using time-delaying components which may upset the stability of the control system.
7. In some thyristor circuits, a true measure of d.c. current can be obtained by rectifying the ouput of CT's on the a.c. side of the circuit; this is possible with fully controlled, naturally commutated rectifying circuits. However, if the circuit contains any flywheel diodes which allow internal current circulation within the thyristor circuit, this useful facility does *not* give a true indication of the current required.
8. Usually the exact value of the measured parameter is not important but the measurement must be consistent and stable under all conditions of operation.
9. D.C. current and voltage transformers can be used to isolate these measurements but they may introduce additional harmonics caused by the required auxiliary supply.
10. If current measurements are to be used to initiate fault protection devices or for current limit control, they must be fast-acting. Significant smoothing time delay will not be acceptable. If the current waveform varies, then the use of mean current as a protection measurement will introduce a time delay, while the use of peak current will prevent the full rating of the equipment from being utilized – a compromise is often necessary. CT's to measure rate of rise of current may be useful to speed up protection tripping arrangements.

17.4 Power Measurements

A.C. and d.c. power can be measured accurately using dynamometer wattmeters; these will respond to harmonics in the current and voltage waveforms and give a true measurement of power. The harmonics in current and voltage waveforms will in general increase the power dissipation in the circuits and it is essential that the harmonic power should be included in the measurement. For example, it is a popular misconception that the power in a d.c. circuit is the product of mean voltage and mean current; if the current and voltage waveforms contain a ripple component, then the true power will be higher than this product. D.C. power is only equal to $I_{mean} \times V_{mean}$ when these are both smooth d.c. with no ripple components.

To simplify instruments, a recent trend has been to use static transducers to calculate power from the current and voltage signals and then drive a simple and economic moving-coil meter. The specification for these must be carefully studied when distorted waveforms are present to ensure they take full account of the harmonics.

17.5 Power Factor

The concept of power factor being the cosine of the angle of displacement between the current and voltage waveforms can only be used freely in sinusoidal circuits. When the waveforms are distorted, the concept is not valid except when considering the fundamental components of the current and voltage.

As a result, two definitions have been used with reference to convertor circuits.

The displacement factor is the cosine of the angle of displacement between the fundamental components of the current and voltage waveforms, i.e., with all the harmonics removed.

The total power factor is the effective power factor resulting from the total of the distorted waveforms. It is normally measured or estimated from the total power in the circuit and the true RMS kVA value, i.e.,

$$\text{Total power factor} = \frac{\text{kilowatts}}{\text{kVA}} = \frac{\text{kilowatts}}{V_{\text{RMS}} \times I_{\text{RMS}}}$$

The values of these two factors will usually be significantly different from each other. The picture is further complicated by the fact that the displacement factor can be calculated but not easily measured, whereas the total power factor can be measured but not easily calculated. It is therefore difficult truly to compare the two. The total power factor will vary dependent on the degree of harmonics, and different types of load will alter its value (all other things being equal). Hence total power factor measurements have to be related to specific loading conditions.

In practice, the displacement factor is the most useful comparative value as it can be estimated fairly accurately and it can be measured satisfactorily by using an oscillographic display of both the current and voltage waveforms. Most power factor meters can only be used to give a general guide to the phase displacement; their readings should not be considered as accurate where distorted waveforms are present. The position on power factor is made additionally difficult by the fact that most thyristor phase-control methods alter the circuit input or output power factor and hence it is continually changing during operation.

17.6 Harmonic Measurements

The harmonic content of any current or voltage waveform can be obtained either by using computer Fourier analysis of the waveform directly, or by measurement using normal harmonic analysers.

The first method is the simplest and cheapest at the present time, its accuracy only being limited by the quality of the original oscillographic measurement. It has the additional advantage that all the harmonics which are occurring at a specific instant can be measured.

All harmonic analysers work on the principle of extracting the harmonic component to be measured by selective filtering and then individually measuring it. This is a comparatively long time process probably taking several seconds to complete for each harmonic. They therefore cannot measure all the harmonics at one instant and cannot

Fig. 17.4 A mains harmonic analyser which can measure harmonic currents and voltages automatically and print out the results required (Robinson Electronic Instruments Ltd)

usually record harmonics which are changing significantly during the measurement period.

In most thyristor circuits, the parameters of the circuit are being continuously controlled by waveform variation. The harmonic content can change dramatically even for a relatively minor alteration in the working point of the thyristors.

In response to these difficulties, the instrument shown in Fig. 17.4 has been developed to enable the harmonic components of any waveform to be continually measured in a wide variety of programmable sequences. This complex instrument will continuously print out the magnitude and phase of the selected harmonics automatically.

17.7 Oscilloscope Measurements

The cathode-ray oscilloscope is the most useful tool for making accurate measurements on thyristor circuits. Its ability to capture the complete waveform of any voltage or current, including transient phenomena, makes it essential for the thorough knowledge of thyristor circuit operation and the correct choice of component ratings. Many important parameters can only be measured using oscilloscopes, for example:

1. The peak voltages occurring across thyristors can only be accurately measured this way.
2. Thyristor power losses can only be accurately estimated from a detailed plot of the current waveform (see Section 2.5).
3. The gate current pulses used to fire thyristors can only be studied properly from oscilloscope measurements.
4. The correct time of firing can only be established from waveform study.
5. The dv/dt applied to a thyristor must be measured using oscillography, preferably by using expanded time-base methods.
6. Measurement of the maximum rate of change of current (di/dt) is difficult even using the very capable oscilloscopes of today.

7. The turn-on, turn-off commutation conditions of thyristors can only be measured by detailed study of the current and voltage waveforms together on the same oscilloscope.

A good knowledge of the use of oscilloscopes is a prerequisite to the satisfactory understanding of thyristor circuits.

It is not intended here to explain the detailed use of oscilloscopes for thyristor circuit measurement or to advise on the most suitable type to use. However, some of the important points to be remembered when carrying out oscilloscope measurements are given here:

(a) When power-circuit measurements are being made directly (i.e., without interposing current or voltage transformers), the oscilloscope itself will usually be at the same voltage as the circuit – extreme care should be taken by the user. If high-voltage circuits are being measured, the oscilloscope input transformer may be damaged; an additional isolating transformer with high-voltage insulation should be used to feed the oscilloscope power.

(b) The oscilloscope must be of a suitable quality for the measurement being made, i.e., its frequency response must be sufficient to register the speed of change occurring in the waveform.

(c) Measurement transducers such as current and voltage transformers, shunts, inverter-type d.c. isolators, opto-isolators, etc, may alter the waveform being measured. For example, shunt inductance will alter a current waveform having fast rates of change.

(d) Where the measured waveform is continually changing, storage oscilloscopes are particularly useful but their writing speed is sometimes limited so that fast changes may not be sufficiently recorded. They are also indispensable for transient measurements which are only occasionally present.

(e) When using multiple input signals to multichannel oscilloscopes, they must all be related to the same ground point or the various signals must be individually isolated.

(f) The power-supply earth on an oscilloscope may need to be disconnected to avoid capacitive leakage to earth.

(g) The connection of an oscilloscope to a thyristor gate circuit can introduce interference and cause misfiring. This connection should never be made while the power circuit is live and a path for current flow exists, or an overcurrent fault may be induced due to the transient change in circuit voltage which can occur.

17.8 Special Instruments for Thyristor Circuits

In recent years, a number of special instruments have been developed particularly for use with thyristor equipments. A few of these are detailed below.

Thyristor Tester

The unit shown in Fig. 17.5 has been designed specifically to enable the voltage capabilities of thyristors to be proved. In addition, it can establish that a thyristor will fire at the correct gate current level. It measures the forward and reverse leakage current at the appropriate voltage level.

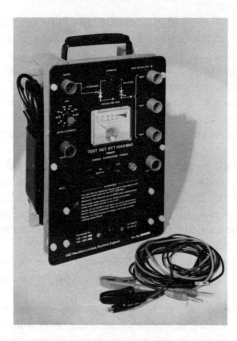

**Fig. 17.5 A portable tester specifically for measuring power diodes and thyristors
(GEC Rectifiers Ltd)**

The leakage voltage–current characteristics of thyristors make it very difficult to check them except by using an appreciable applied voltage. Resistance measurements with portable multimeters can only give a guide to the low-voltage portion of the leakage characteristics and this gives no indication of the thyristor condition except where the device is completely internally short-circuited in one or both directions.

Firing Circuit Pulse Monitor

The unit shown in Fig. 17.6 was developed specifically to enable firing circuits for naturally commutated three-phase rectifier circuits to be checked simply, without the use of oscilloscopes. In general, firing circuits are difficult to check because of the fast-rising current pulses and the fact that most equipment involves many channels of pulses all operating together (see Chapter 8). This pulse-monitor unit is able to check the outputs from six channels of pulse amplifiers simultaneously, using digital electronic circuits. It is able to check:
  (a) the correct presence of all the pulses;
  (b) that no extra pulses exist;
  (c) that the channels of pulses are correctly spaced from each other;
all under any phase-controlled condition. In addition, it can confirm the smooth phase movement of the pulses in response to a changing input signal to the firing circuit.

Thyristor Current Detector

The conventional way of checking whether current is flowing in a thyristor has been to measure the millivolt drop across the fuses or busbars in series with the thyristor. This

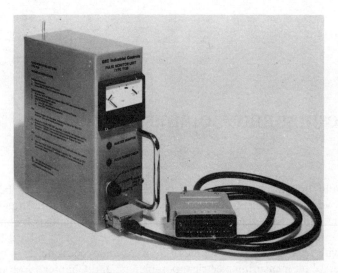

Fig. 17.6 A firing-circuit pulse monitor unit (GEC Industrial Controls Ltd)

is a hazardous and dangerous practice, particularly on high-voltage equipment. The unit shown in Fig. 17.7 has been produced to enable current flow to be confirmed safely. The flux-measuring, double-insulated current probe when placed near the thyristor or its associated busbars will give a positive indication of current flow on the hand-held, battery-powered electronic meter.

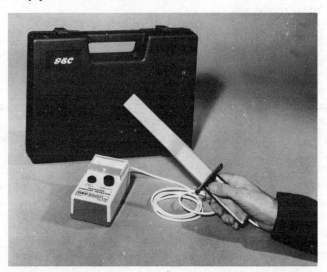

Fig. 17.7 A thyristor current detector (GEC Industrial Controls Ltd)

17.9 References

1. B. W. Lingard and R. E. Colyer, 'Measurements and observations on thyristor equipment', *IEE Conference Publication 123*, 26–31, Dec. 1974.
2. A. J. Baggot, 'The effect of waveshape distortions on the measurement of energy by tariff meters', *IEE Conference Publication 110*, 261–267, April 1974.
3. W. C. Downing, 'Watthour meter accuracy on SCR controlled resistance loads', *IEEE Trans.*, **PAS-93**, 4, 1083–1089, 1974.

18. Testing and Commissioning

Thyristors and thyristor equipment, once manufactured, all need to be thoroughly tested to prove that they meet the specified quality and performance required. In this chapter, brief guidance is given on the tests necessary to obtain such confirmation of performance. It is only intended as an initial introduction to this subject to help those unfamiliar with testing to appreciate the principles employed. It needs to be read along with Chapter 17 on measuring electrical parameters, and Chapter 19 on fault finding; it assumes that the measuring techniques are understood and that any faults found would be located before completion of testing.

There are three main objectives to the testing of electrical equipment:

1. To prove the *design* of the component or equipment. The only sure proof that any design is correct or suitable is practical operation under actual conditions. Testing is used prior to full operation to find any flaws in the design early enough for them to be corrected easily.

2. To prove the component or equipment has been *manufactured* to the design specifications correctly. To show that the mechanical tolerances, the electrical connections and the manufacturing quality are all satisfactory.

3. To prove that the actual *safety margins* are sufficient to give long and reliable operation of the equipment. It is particularly necessary to expose the component or equipment to the extremes of its operating range to ensure that sufficient allowance has been made for these limiting conditions.

With all equipment, tests are carried out at each stage of manufacture, i.e., components are tested to their specifications probably by the maker and maybe by the user; the equipment containing these components is then tested thoroughly; followed by proving tests to satisfy the buyer of the equipment. It is then likely that long and satisfactory service will be obtained. This chapter is written in this sequence, dealing first with thyristors, followed by equipment testing, and finally commissioning.

18.1 Testing Thyristors

There are two different aspects to the testing of thyristors:

(a) The manufacturer must test them to ensure they withstand fully the specification against which he is offering them for sale.

(b) The user's object in testing them is usually to ensure he still has a satisfactory thyristor.

These two very different approaches have grown up due to the very extensive and complicated test facilities needed to test fully thyristors. Users cannot afford to install these testing facilities in their own works and they rely on the thyristor manufacturers whenever further proving is necessary. In practice, the thyristor user is limited to fairly simple checks followed by operation of the thyristor in his equipment as final confirmation of the thyristor's capability.

The key to the thyristor's capability is the manufacturer's code number which identifies the particular specification to which the thyristor has been tested. This specification should always be used as the reference guide as measurements on individual thyristors are always misleading (see Section 1.10).

All thyristor specifications include many parameters which must be confirmed on all devices if reliable and satisfactory performance is to be guaranteed. Also, each parameter has to be judged in the correct way; with some it is the maximum value which is important, while with others it is the minimum; in other cases it may be the spread of the value of the parameter which may be the decisive factor.

Manufacturer Tests

A number of national and international standards set down the testing conditions in detail, for example, BS 9300 (Thyristors of Assessed Quality) and IEC Publication 146 (Semiconductor Convertors). However, a typical manufacturer is likely to test his devices to the following testing schedule. Some of these tests may be repeated a number of times during the manufacturing period.

1. *The OFF-state forward voltage ratings* would be confirmed by measuring the leakage current at voltages up to the maximum level. The current must normally be below a limit figure both hot and cold and the shape of the voltage/current characteristic should be stable.

2. *The reverse voltage ratings* would be decided in a similar way, probably at the same time as the forward voltage ratings.

3. *The forward voltage drop* would normally only be measured at one value of ON-state current. The thyristors would be classified into a number of current rating grades and into forward voltage drop grades, each with a specified narrow band of voltage.

4. *The surge ON-state current capability* would be confirmed by passing the chosen I_{TSM} value through the thyristor while operating at its normal junction temperature. In some arrangements, the current surge would be followed by the application of a high OFF-state voltage. The forward and reverse OFF-state leakage-current measurements after this test would be used to judge whether the thyristor had been damaged.

5. *The critical rate of rise of OFF-state voltage* (dv/dt) would be measured under hot conditions to confirm that the thyristor will not fire when a specified forward voltage is applied at the limiting rate of rise.

6. *The critical rate of rise of ON-state* (di/dt) would be confirmed with the thyristor hot. It would be triggered into the ON-state with a specified gate pulse and it would discharge a capacitor (previously charged to the specified forward voltage). The circuit components would be chosen to give the correct di/dt conditions. Subsequent OFF-state leakage-current measurements would be used to confirm the thyristor was undamaged by the test.

7. *The circuit commutated turn-off time* would normally only be measured as a routine test with inverter grade thyristors. A test commutation circuit would be arranged to turn the thyristor off under specified conditions. Oscilloscopes would

be used to measure the turn-off time directly from current and voltage waveforms. The thyristor must be capable of accepting the critical rate of rise of OFF-state voltage at the end of the turn-off time without switching into the conducting state.

8. *The thermal resistance* would be confirmed, and this is particularly important with compression-bonded thyristors. The thyristor would be mounted correctly on a specially chosen cooling structure. The rated current would be passed through it and an estimate of the junction temperature would be made from leakage-current measurements, so that the thermal resistance could be calculated.

9. *The gate current to fire* the thyristor would be measured to ensure that it will fire satisfactorily within the range of firing current specified over the full operating temperature range.

Other parameters such as holding current, stored charge, etc., would not normally be measured on all thyristors and the data sheet information will usually allow a wide variation of these parameters. Sample tests on some thyristors will be used to check the data sheet information.

In addition, the parameters measured above would only be measured under specific conditions; their values under other conditions may vary significantly and these variations would only be confirmed by sample tests if necessary.

User Tests

It is rarely possible for the thyristor user to carry out comprehensive tests under the necessary controlled operating conditions. The wide variation in thyristor parameters makes uncontrolled testing misleading. The user's approach should be restricted to proving sufficient forward and reverse blocking capability for his application and to proving the thyristor can be fired. In the case of subsequent unsatisfactory performance, he should measure the operating conditions of the thyristor in his application in order to decide if the thyristor is at fault. If the thyristor is in doubt, it should be returned to the manufacturer for proper testing.

The forward and reverse blocking ability can only be proved by applying a high voltage and measuring the leakage current; the shape of the leakage current/voltage curves makes it impossible to deduce anything useful from low-voltage measurements. The use of a thyristor tester such as that described in Section 17.8 is recommended.

The firing ability can also be checked using such an instrument or by firing from a battery via a resistance while a forward voltage is being applied across the thyristor.

Simple forward and reverse resistance measurement of a thyristor using a multimeter can only show if the thyristor has failed completely, i.e., become a short-circuit.

18.2 Testing Naturally Commutated Convertors

All thyristor equipment needs to be thoroughly proved prior to operation to establish that the design specification has been met and to ensure that the correct safety margins exist in all component ratings. Again, detailed guidance on such tests is given in national and international standards, in this case, in IEC 146.

When testing equipment, the principle has been established that some tests are carried out on every piece of equipment manufactured. In addition, further design-proving tests are done on the first equipment of any new design.

The following tests are likely to be done on all equipment:

1. *Auxiliary and control circuit tests* would be carried out first to prove that cooling fans and pumps, thermostats, fuse failure indication circuits, etc., are all operating correctly.

2. *The electronic control circuits* would be thoroughly tested without the power circuits being energized. All amplifier and logic circuits would be checked with simulated measurement signals, and firing circuits would be proved to ensure the correct shape of gate current pulses, that the various channels of pulses are correctly spaced, and that phase control if included operates smoothly with the necessary front and back limits.

3. *An insulation flash test* would be carried out to stress the insulation of all components and the power connections at an a.c. voltage level of approximately twice working voltage plus 1000 or 2000 V. This test is usually done by connecting all electrical power circuits together with fuse wire and applying the test voltage between this wire and the earthed framework. It will prove the insulation level of the gate pulse transformer if their primary circuits are earthed for the test. Great care is needed during this test to avoid the high voltage being applied across any components and all fuse wire has to be fully removed after the test.

4. *A short-circuit test* would be carried out at low voltage of around 10 V at high current, the output of the equipment being short-circuited, probably through an inductance, to establish continuous current flow. The test would eventually be done at the full rated current of the equipment.

   At the start of the test the correct *phasing* of the firing circuits would be checked by studying gate current and anode-to-cathode voltage waveforms of each thyristor in turn to confirm that they are being fired at the correct point of the cycle.

   During the test, all cable and busbar joints would be checked (by mV measurements), the sharing of current between parallel-connected thyristors would be confirmed (by measuring the mV drop across circuit fuses, cable, or busbar), and the outputs from current-measuring devices and instruments would be recorded.

   It should be remembered that the current waveforms occurring during such a low-voltage test will probably be much different to those which would exist in normal operation, due to the relatively high commutating inductance causing large overlap angles. Appropriate corrections have to be made to obtain the test current equivalent to the normal rated conditions.

5. *A light-load test* would be done at rated voltage with only a low current load, connected to ensure satisfactory latching of the thyristors. This test would be used to prove the normal voltage capability of the equipment and its components and to confirm the correct voltage limitation by the snubber circuits and other voltage-protection circuitry. If thyristors are used in series, the correct sharing of the voltage would be confirmed during this test. It would also be used to prove correct firing, satisfactory gate pulse transformer insulation, accurate voltage measurements, etc.

Any new design would have to pass further tests, some examples of which are given below:

6. *A temperature-rise test* is needed to prove the thermal capabilities of all cooling devices under rated load current conditions. This test would be carried out under low-voltage output, short-circuit conditions, probably immediately following

test 4. The current would be applied for a time period sufficient for all components to reach steady temperatures, and all significant component temperatures would be measured. The settings of all thermostats would be confirmed during this test.

7. *Power-loss measurements* may be made to enable the total equipment efficiency to be calculated. In cases where a full-load test is possible, the measurements of input and output power can be used but due to the relatively low losses and instrument inaccuracies, the power-loss measurement done this way cannot be very accurate.

A more accurate method is to measure the losses due to current during the short-circuit test and those due to voltage during the light-load test by input power measurements. The losses can be found by allowing for the load losses during the test.

8. *A full-load test* may be carried out on smaller equipment, where the correct power supply and loads are available, in preference to the short-circuit test. This will prove the equipment under as near to actual load conditions as possible.

9. *Overcurrent-protection tests* may be done on smaller equipment by applying simulated faults. However, it is often impractical to prove fuses and circuits unless the supply system is capable of providing the high level of fault currents which may be found in the actual application.

18.3 Testing Forced-commutated Convertors

Due to their increased circuit complexity, most forced-commutated thyristor systems require a lengthy testing schedule compared with naturally commutated equipments. Many more components need to be checked, often under a wider range of circuit conditions, to confirm that the equipment is operating according to its design expectations and within the rating capabilities of all its components.

As, in most cases, the operation of the turn-off commutating circuitry depends on the unit working at a significant voltage level, tests at low voltage on short-circuit are not possible. The two basic test conditions used for such equipment are light-load testing and full-load testing, both being carried out with the normal range of circuit-voltage variation.

All forced-commutated thyristor equipments should be tested to the following schedule:

1. *Auxiliary and control circuit tests* would be carried out to prove that cooling fans and pumps, power supply units, contactors, relays and indicating lamps, etc., all operate correctly.

2. *Electronic control circuits* would be thoroughly tested without the power circuits being energized. An extensive series of checks, including setting up, would be done to ensure that all amplifiers, logic circuits, firing circuits, etc., operate correctly from simulated input and measurement signals. Meter and oscillographic measurements would be made and waveforms studied to ensure that oscillators worked at the correct frequencies, that all signals were of the correct magnitude and shape, that the correct time delays existed between the firing of all thyristors, that logic controlling the initial start-up sequence was correct, etc.

3. *Insulation flash and megger tests* would be done to confirm all insulation to earth.

Particular care would be taken to make sure that components were not damaged by the high voltages applied (see Section 18.2).

4. *A light-load proving test* would initially be used to confirm the operation of the complete circuit. The unit would be run over its full supply voltage range, and its output would be controlled to prove all operating conditions. The voltage waveforms across all thyristors would be studied under a variety of operating conditions to confirm the circuit turn-off time allowed and the correct operation of snubber and other voltage-protection circuits. The voltage conditions of commutating capacitors would be checked and series voltage-sharing circuits would be confirmed to be working correctly where series thyristors are employed. The correct relative firing timing between all thyristors would be confirmed. Any voltage- and frequency-measuring circuits will be checked and calibrated as necessary.

5. *A full-load proving test* would be used to check again all the parameters checked in the light-load proving test. In addition, thyristor and circuit current waveforms would be studied over the specified range of output current. Any current-measuring circuits would be confirmed and calibrated.

6. *Overcurrent protection tests* would be done. Reduction in load impedance would be used to prove the operation of current-limit circuits. A thyristor may be temporarily short-circuited, its firing signal removed, or its commutation circuit disconnected to cause a commutation failure. An output short-circuit may be suddenly applied to the unit. In all cases, the correct operation of protective devices would be confirmed by oscillographic measurements.

In addition, depending on the type of equipment and the specification to which it has to conform, further tests will be done to prove specific capabilities. Most of these take place under the set-up conditions needed for either the light-load proving test or the full-load proving test as above. The following are examples of likely additional tests; some would be carried out on all equipment as routine tests and others would only be done on the first unit of a particular design as type tests:

7. *Voltage tolerance test.* The output voltage would be measured accurately over the full range of supply voltage variation and output load current to confirm the steady-state accuracy of the voltage-regulating circuitry. If the output is multiphase a.c., all output phases would be measured and their phase angles would be checked under unbalanced load conditions.

8. *The harmonic content* of the output voltage would be measured over the full range of supply voltage and load variation.

9. *The frequency tolerance* would be measured over the complete operating range of the equipment. Where the inverter has to be synchronized with other power supplies as in a no-break set (see Section 13.8), the accuracy and performance of the synchronizing system would be thoroughly confirmed.

10. *A temperature-rise test* under full load with worst-case supply voltage and frequency conditions would be carried out to confirm the thermal ratings of all components, heatsinks, cables, etc. The test would be continued until all temperatures had reached a steady level.

11. *Power losses* in the circuit under all load and supply conditions would be found by measuring the input and output power of the equipment simultaneously.

12. *Transient changes in output* frequency and voltage would be oscillographically

measured during sudden changes of load, i.e., application and removal to establish the full performance capabilities.

13. *Loss-of-supply tests* are needed on battery-supported systems to confirm the performance of the equipment by oscillographically measuring the output voltage during the loss and reapplication of the supply. It may also be necessary to allow the battery to discharge to its limit to confirm that the equipment can continue to give its full output during this period.

18.4 On-site Commissioning of Thyristor Equipment

Many pieces of equipment can be proved to operate satisfactorily over their full working range during the works testing period. In such cases, the initial testing on site, the commissioning, will be to confirm that the operation and settings have not changed during transportation and to prove the equipment under the actual supply and load conditions.

The most important first step is to carry out a detailed physical inspection to ensure no damage has occurred, that all components are firmly fixed, that all cables and connections are still tight, that all potentiometer settings are correct, and that all moving parts will move freely.

Once this has been confirmed, then simplified versions of the basic tests referred to in Sections 18.2 and 18.3 will be sufficient to show up any faults, i.e.:
1. Checking of auxiliary and control circuits.
2. Checking of electronic control circuits.
3. Light-load proving tests.
4. Full-load proving tests.

Where full testing has not been possible in the manufacturer's works, then more extensive tests may be needed on site to prove the performance capabilities. These will probably include tests similar to those detailed in Sections 18.2 and 18.3. Also, it is likely that some setting up of the unit may be required.

18.5 References

1. IEC Publication 146, *Semiconductor Convertors*, 1973, amended 1975.
2. British Standard 9300: 1969, *Semiconductor Devices of Assessed Quality: Generic Data and Methods of Test*.

19. Fault Finding in Thyristor Equipment

There is no doubt that one of the big advantages of static control equipment is that it continues to work for long periods of time without maintenance. It is also true that its biggest problem is finding the fault when the equipment stops working. The long periods of satisfactory operation mean that those entrusted with the job of keeping it running have little opportunity of learning to understand it. Fault finding often provides one of the few chances of finding out how equipment works, but it usually has to take place urgently so that the equipment can be put back into operation as quickly as possible. It is not therefore surprising that some users resort to exchange of subassemblies as a means of reducing downtime, nor that an increasing number of static equipment designs are based on removable, interchangeable functional assemblies.

However, this does not pinpoint the specific fault, and the only sure method of doing this is to understand the basic principles of operation of the particular equipment. It is a main aim of this book to help the users understand their equipment so that they may readily be able to find those faults which occasionally occur.

In this chapter, the most common faults which occur in thyristor equipment will be explained along with the fault symptoms which can be observed or measured. The content has been restricted to considering those faults which occur either in the thyristor power circuit (with its auxiliary and protective components), or in the gate firing system (as defined in Chapter 8). Electronic control-system faults are not included in any detail except where they have a specific bearing on the thyristor circuit fault or its symptoms. In the following section, the 'golden rules' of fault finding are stated and although these are basically common sense, and hardly touch on the technical operation of the equipment, they are fundamental to quick fault-location in all electrical equipment. This chapter has been written to follow on from those dealing with measurement and testing of thyristor equipment. It is assumed that these have already been read and understood.

The most difficult fault finding occurs during the testing period in the manufacturer's works because the tester has to assume initially that anything could be wrong. Fortunately, he will usually have more sophisticated measuring and testing facilities available to him to check all parameters under a variety of operating conditions. Faults which occur after the equipment has operated correctly are relatively easier to assess as it is reasonable to assume that only one fault has occurred and it is possible to compare operating conditions with those which occurred during normal, correct operation. In practice, however, the lack of measuring and loading facilities on site make even simple faults hard to find.

If components just failed completely, fault location would be much easier as the fault would be obvious after only a few simple tests. Unfortunately, components also deteriorate and initially fail only under extreme operating conditions which may be difficult to reproduce. This chapter should help in the location of most faults and does explain the methods which can produce the quickest results. However, there will always be faults which are very difficult to find and no amount of written information will overcome this. Intermittent faults are in this category and these can usually be found over a relatively long period of time by systematic substitution. In these difficult cases, the solution will only be found by observation of symptoms and simple tests, and, most important, technical deduction.

19.1 The Important Principles of Fault Finding

In general, the process of fault location is the application of common sense to a technical understanding of the principles of operation. It is the method of approaching the problem which is all-important.

The following points define the common-sense method which gives quick and efficient results:

1. *Understand the operation of the equipment* and then fault finding will be considerably simplified. Most reputable manufacturers provide instruction books explaining the operation and circuitry of the equipment, they may even include some fault-location advice. Study these and particularly refer to them when a fault occurs. Any time spent working out how the unit works will be amply recovered when a fault occurs.

2. *Do not hurry – think*. Whenever an important or expensive piece of equipment fails to work it is invariably necessary to repair it as quickly as possible. The quickest way is always to observe and think: action can follow later. No problem will be solved by furious action; this usually results in more damage which may be much more difficult to repair.

3. *Record the symptoms*. Fault finding is a technical form of detective work. The clues to the fault are often there to see. Make full use of any fault-indication alarms and lamps. Find out when the fault occurred and under what equipment conditions. Note the location of any obviously failed items.

4. *Prove any potential fault explanation* before accepting it as a true statement of what occurred. Having decided what may have happened, find a way of proving that it is correct. Only the true explanation of the fault will fully satisfy *all* the symptoms.

5. *Study any recent changes first*. Faults often show up when some change in operational conditions has been made or after a routine maintenance check, etc. Always study the recent history; it may be a clue to the fault and it may even be the change which has caused the fault to occur. For example, a change in the load process may result in additional current loading on the control equipment.

6. *Failed components may be the result* of the fault rather than its cause. Many faulty conditions following a failed or incorrectly working component will result in excessive stresses being placed on other components. The original fault may not be obvious until these stressed components fail. When failed components are located, it is essential to investigate the possible cause of their failure before operating the equipment further, to avoid repeated failures.

7. *Check the electrical parameters* of the circuit under a safe operating condition to obtain more clues to the fault. Often auxiliary circuits, e.g., power supplies, electronics, fans, relays, etc., can be measured without the main power circuit being in operation.

8. *Try to reproduce the faulty condition* if the cause of the fault cannot be readily located. This should be done under as safe an operating condition as possible, preferably by temporarily disconnecting the load system from the equipment.

9. *Locate the area of the fault* by studying the equipment in sections. Most systems will naturally split themselves into electrical functions, each having a simply defined role and relatively few input and output connections. The initial aim should be to locate the faulty function.

10. *Faults do not go away*. If the fault has not been found and corrected it will return some time.

19.2 Naturally Commutated Equipment

Any of the following faults can occur in a thyristor power circuit and each will result in different symptoms:

(a) A thyristor short-circuit.
(b) Thyristor forward breakover.
(c) A non-conducting thyristor.
(d) Diode or thyristor reverse blocking failure.
(e) Snubber circuit failure.
(f) Surge suppression circuit failure.

A short-circuit thyristor will invariably result in a high fault current and the protection fuses or circuit breaker will operate. These fault currents can flow even if the load circuit is disconnected.

A thyristor or diode reverse blocking failure will have a similar effect.

Thyristor forward breakover will cause the maximum circuit voltage to be applied to the load. If the load is a low-impedance one, such as a motor, this can cause high fault currents which will blow fuses or trip protective circuit breakers. In an antiparallel circuit, it will cause internal fault currents within the equipment which will probably blow circuit fuses. If it happens while an equipment is inverting, it will initiate an inversion failure, again causing fault currents to flow.

It may be caused by thyristor deterioration, the application of excessive voltage or rate of change of voltage (dv/dt), overtemperature, or it can result from misfiring. Any of these faults will produce the same result as above. If a single thyristor in a parallel set breaks over, then the full circuit current will flow through the faulty thyristor. If it is one of a series string, then its share of the circuit voltage will have to be accepted by the other thyristors. If thyristor breakover occurs in a circuit with a high-impedance load, then it will show up only as instability or lack of control.

A non-conducting thyristor will only result in a reduced output if the circuit is rectifying. If, however, it is inverting, the result will be an inversion failure and a high fault current which will operate protective fuses or circuit breakers. The condition can be due to an internal fault in the thyristor, a lack of firing pulses, or failure of the thyristor to pick up current.

A non-conducting thyristor in a parallel set will cause its current to be shared among the remaining healthy thyristors in that arm of the circuit. If it is one of a series string, it will probably break over when the others are fired and it would eventually fail.

An open-circuit snubber circuit will cause high peak voltages and dv/dt to be applied to the appropriate thyristor, causing it to break over. A short-circuit in the snubber will often be followed by an open circuit due to the high current which would temporarily flow through it.

Surge suppression circuit failure resulting in loss of overvoltage protection will be followed by thyristor breakover or failure.

Similar symptoms can also result from faults within the firing circuit.

Complete loss of pulses will result in no output from the thyristor circuit; if it occurs during rectifying operation, no fault currents will be produced, but if the circuit was inverting, a short-circuit inversion failure will occur, causing operation of overcurrent protection devices.

Loss of pulses to one arm of the circuit will produce exactly the same symptoms as a non-conducting thyristor arm.

Extra firing pulses occurring during normally non-conducting periods will usually have the same effect as thyristor or thyristor arm breakover.

Pulses of insufficient magnitude may not fire the thyristors. If they do manage to fire them, there is a possibility of di/dt failure of the thyristors.

If a sudden jump in the firing pulse phase position occurs, it will cause a rise or fall in the output voltage. Depending on its severity, it may cause an overcurrent fault and operation of the protection or it may cause control-system instability if the current control is able to prevent excessive current rise.

Incorrect setting of the front stops in the firing circuit, for any reason, will only cause a problem with short firing pulses. If the firing pulse occurs before the forward voltage, the thyristor will not fire; if it occurs when the forward voltage is too low, the thyristor may not pick up.

Incorrect setting of back stops in the firing circuit can have more significant consequences. If the firing pulses occur too early, it may not be possible to maintain satisfactory control; if they are too late, inversion failure may occur.

Incorrect phase rotation of the firing-circuit reference voltage waveforms will result in completely erratic firing of the thyristors and closed-loop control circuits will complicate the symptoms even further. The usual results will be lack of control and high overcurrent faults, causing operation of fuses or circuit breakers.

Fault-finding Procedure

When faced with a fault situation on thyristor equipment which is normally working, the basic symptoms are likely to be that no output is available (possibly due to the supply switches having tripped), the control of the output is erratic, or full output is continuously available. This latter case is only likely on a high-impedance load as with others, for example a motor load, high output will normally cause the overcurrent protection devices to trip.

In all cases, the sensible initial procedure is to check all available alarms, indicating lamps, fuses, and protective relays, etc. If this does not enable the fault to be identified, then the equipment should be operated in such a way that high fault load currents cannot flow by:

(a) Disconnecting low-impedance loads.

(b) Removing the interconnection between antiparallel circuits or removing the firing pulses from one of the circuits.

(c) Connecting a low current resistance load to the equipment to enable good thyristor pick-up to occur (say 10 per cent rated load at full voltage).

Table 19.1 Fault finding

Symptom	Possible fault	Action recommended
No output although control signal to the firing circuit is sufficient	No power supply No firing pulses	Check main power supply, fuses, circuit breakers, etc. 1. Check firing pulses. If none: 2. Check any inhibit or pulse suppression system 3. Check power supply to firing circuit 4. Check reference waveforms are present
Equipment trips out due to overcurrent or fuse blowing although the low-impedance load has been disconnected	Thyristor or diode reverse voltage failure	1. Check thyristor associated with blown fuses, if any doubt replace them 2. Check overvoltage protection circuits before switching on again
Erratic control at low output	Erratic firing pulses	1. Check firing pulses with a constant input signal to the firing circuit 2. Check reference waveforms 3. Check inhibit signals
	Thyristor forward breakover	1. Output should still be erratic even with firing pulses disconnected or inhibited 2. Study output voltage waveforms to decide faulty thyristor 3. Check overvoltage protection circuits and snubbers
Erratic control at a specific point in the control range	Firing circuit maloperation	1. Check firing pulses 2. Check reference waveforms
Erratic control near to full output	With short pulse firing circuits this may be caused by incorrect front stop settings	1. Check firing pulses 2. Check front stop settings
Insufficient output although control signal is sufficient	Thyristor(s) not being fired Open-circuit thyristor	1. Check firing pulses 2. Check reference waveforms Study output voltage waveforms to find which arm is not conducting

If these tests do not reveal the cause of the fault, the next stage is to try to reproduce the faulty condition. The fault may exhibit one of the above symptoms, perhaps after running under load conditions, in which case the guidance of table 19.1 should be followed.

If the fault conditions result in immediate blowing of fuses or the operation of overcurrent protection circuit breakers, then Table 19.2 will be of assistance.

Study of the operation of the equipment under these test conditions, with the help of Table 19.1, should enable the fault to be located and corrected. It is often a help to be able to set the level of input control signal directly to the firing circuits during these tests.

Table 19.2 Overcurrent fault conditions

Condition under which fuses or circuit breakers operate	Possible faults
While feeding power to the load at low output	1. Thyristor breakover 2. Erratic firing pulses
During acceleration or high load current	Current-limit failure
During regeneration of power from the load	1. Thyristor breakover 2. Erratic or lost firing pulses
During regeneration at high load current	Incorrect firing circuit backstop settings
On antiparallel changeover to the opposite polarity	1. Antiparallel changeover logic fault 2. Zero-current detection fault
At low output in half-controlled bridge circuit	Incorrect firing circuit backstop settings

19.3 Forced-commutated Equipment

Fault finding in forced-commutated thyristor circuits is dominated by one very important factor: all significant faults will result in a failure to commutate, a short-circuit, and usually operation of the overcurrent protective fuses, circuit breakers, or static switches.

Excessive currents. All forced-commutated circuits have a definite limit to the level of current which can be switched: if this level is exceeded, a commutation failure will occur. In all inverter circuits this will cause a short-circuit current to flow as soon as another thyristor is turned on. This current will quickly increase the thyristor junction temperatures above the controllable limit and they will remain in the ON-state.

The situation is nearly as bad in chopper circuits in that commutation failure will result in the unit giving full output voltage, which, with low-impedance loads, will result in uncontrollable high currents.

Thyristor breakover or misfiring will have the same result and this can be directly caused by many faults in the thyristor circuit and the firing system. Snubber or voltage protection circuit failures, excessive thyristor temperature, faulty firing pulses (for any of the many possible reasons), as well as thyristor deterioration itself all come within this category resulting in commutation failure.

Loss of supply. In addition, most circuits depend on the presence of the input power supply for correct operation. Even temporary loss of the input supply can lead to insufficient commutating ability because the commutating capacitors may not fully charge. Supply difficulties can therefore also be a reason for commutation failure and the equipment consequently tripping out.

Control faults. In some designs it is also possible for failures within the control system, which is instructing the firing circuit, to have the same consequence of incorrectly firing the thyristors or causing excessive currents. The better designs, however, contain electronic circuitry to prevent incorrect firing of the thyristors by control system changes or faults. In addition, a fast and accurate current-limiting control can prevent overcurrents being caused by the load, the supply system, or the control electronics.

The majority of faults will therefore result in the same overall effect and some further investigation will always be necessary to locate the prime cause.

Fault-finding Procedure

When approaching a fault it is first necessary to accept the fact that the cause of the unit having blown its fuses or tripped its protection switches may be:
  (a) A load fault causing excessive current.
  (b) An input power supply failure.
  (c) An internal fault in the thyristor equipment.
It is most unwise to delve into the complicated thyristor and control circuitry until some initial external checks have been made:
  1. Study the load system to find out if any load faults have occurred, i.e., fuses blown, circuit breakers tripped, overloading, etc.
  2. Investigate the power supply system to make sure, as far as possible, that a fault has not occurred causing temporary or permanent loss of supply to the equipment. Check line fuses and circuit breaker trip relays, etc.

If no fault has been located then:

  3. Disconnect the load from the equipment and try to operate the equipment under this condition.

If the unit is unable to operate under this no-load condition either because it gives no output or because it results in a commutation failure, then the following detailed investigations will be necessary:

  4. Note the condition of all alarms, indicating lamps, protective relays and switches, the operation of cooling fans and pumps.
  5. Switch off and visually inspect all significant components, particularly looking for:
  (a) Blown fuses.
  (b) Wire, cables, or busbars disconnected.
  (c) Mechanical damage.
  (d) Failed commutating capacitors (usually observed by their leaking, bulging, or exploding).
  (e) Overheated resistors.
  6. Switch on the auxiliary power supplies, preferably without the main power thyristor circuit being energized. Operate the electronic controls and firing circuits, etc. under this condition and check all possible auxiliary circuits including:
  (a) Auxiliary power packs.
  (b) The firing pulses to the thyristors.
  (c) The frequency of the firing pulses.

(d) The correct timing between the firing of the various thyristors.

(e) The end stop limits of the control range.

7. Inhibit or disconnect firing pulses to the thyristors and switch on the main power supply. All thyristors should remain in the OFF-state and all snubber and voltage protection circuits should be working. If any fault occurs under this condition, it can only be a component in the power circuit, e.g., a thyristor.

If the unit will work, apparently satisfactorily, on no load but not when load is applied, it is recommended that tests 6 and 7 above are carried out, followed by:

8. A light-load test as detailed in Section 18.3 so that circuit turn-off times and thyristor firing could be positively confirmed.

If the unit still fails on load, the following points may help:

9. If the unit fails on starting or stopping, the necessary logic circuitry which controls the sequence of starting or stopping should be checked.

10. If the unit fails after a period of time, then those components which significantly heat up should be suspected. This will include power semiconductors in the firing circuits as well as the main power thyristors.

11. If the unit fails only at high load, then either the current limit system is not holding the current low enough or a thyristor turn-off time is too high.

In the unlikely event of the fault still not being found, then selective replacement of specific subassemblies and components will usually solve the problem in the quickest way. Replacement of the thyristors, which are difficult to test and prove, should be followed by full testing of them by the manufacturer, particularly if there is doubt as to which one is faulty.

Index

When an entry has more than one reference, the principal references are given first.

Forward breakover, 8
Forward voltage drop, 9, 10, 341
Frequency changer, 270
Front stops, 160
Fuses, 130

Gate characteristics, 12
Gate current, 6
Gate firing, 13, 151
Gate isolation, 153
Gate pulse control, 128
Gate pulse monitor, 338

Harmonic currents and voltages:
 in a.c. controllers, 41
 in natural commutation circuits, 61, 62
Harmonic filtering, 266
Harmonic measurements, 335
Heat pipes, 174
Heat sinks, 168
High voltage d.c. transmission, 315
Holding current, 11

Induced currents and voltage, 234
Inhibiting, 157
Injection braking of induction motors, 228
Instruments, 337
Integral cycle control, 38, 47, 162
Interference, 153
Inverse time overload protection, 134
Inversion, 54
Inversion failure, 127
Inverter circuits:
 bridge, 110
 complementary commutated, 101
 harmonic content of, 260, 264
Inverter commutation, 100
Inverters:
 current fed, 100
 standby, 272
 voltage control of, 99, 258
 voltage fed, 100

Junction, 3
Junction temperature, 13, 22, 26, 27

Kramer scheme, 216
kVAR reduction, 148

Lamp dimming, 224
Latching current, 11, 237
Leakage current, 8, 139
Lightning, 114
Line commutation, 50
Load switching, 115
Load time constant, 231

Mark space ratio control, 160
Metrosil, 118
Minimum pulse width, 100, 165, 90
Motors:
 a.c., 206
 d.c., 183
 induction, 208
 series, 184
 synchronous, 206
  excitation, 250
Multichannel firing circuits, 160

Non-linear resistors, 118
Non-repetitive peak off-state voltage rating
 (V_{DSM}), 9
Non-repetitive peak reverse voltage rating
 (V_{RSM}), 8
Notches, 55

Off-state, 6
On-state, 4
Oscilloscope measurements, 336
Overlap, 53
Overlap angle, 53, 59
Overloads, 123, 28
Overvoltage protection devices, 116
Overvoltages, 114

Parallel operation, 135, 143
Parallel redundant operation, 278
Parallel sharing reactors, 136
Phase control, 40, 158
Phase shift range, 160, 61
Phasing, 343
P-N junction, 3
Power factor:
 integral cycle control, 48
 measurement, 335
Power measurements, 334
Power supplies:
 arc furnace, 298
 induction furnace, 302
 laboratory, 325
 magnet, 253
 no-break, 275
  synchronization, 256, 277
 resistance furnace, 295
 uninterruptable, 275
Pulse amplifiers, 154
Pulse application, 129
Pulse inhibit, 157
Pulse magnitude and shape, 152
Pulse multiplication, 144
Pulse number, 60
Pulse suppression, 129
Pulse switching, 129